# Science In Your World

**SENIOR AUTHORS**
**Dr. Jay K. Hackett**
University of Northern Colorado

**Dr. Richard H. Moyer**
University of Michigan-Dearborn

**CONTRIBUTING AUTHORS**
**Stephen C. Blume**
Elementary Science Curriculum Specialist
St. Tammany Public School System
Slidell, Louisiana

**Ralph M. Feather, Jr.**
Teacher of Geology, Astronomy, and Earth Science
Derry Area School District
Derry, Pennsylvania

**Edward Paul Ortleb**
Science Supervisor
St. Louis Board of Education
St. Louis, Missouri

**Dr. Barbara Swanson Thomson**
Associate Professor in Science Education
The Ohio State University
Columbus, Ohio

**CONTRIBUTING WRITER**
**Ann H. Sankey**
Science Specialist
Educational Service District 121
Seattle, Washington

**READING CONSULTANT**
**Barbara S. Pettegrew, Ph.D.**
Director of the Reading/Study Center
Assistant Professor of Education
Otterbein College, Westerville, Ohio

**SAFETY CONSULTANT**
**Gary E. Downs, Ed.D.**
Professor
Iowa State University
Ames, Iowa

**GIFTED AND MAINSTREAMING CONSULTANTS**
**George Fichter**
Educational Consultant
Programs for Gifted
Ohio Department of Education
Worthington, Ohio

**Timothy E. Heron, Ph.D.**
Professor
Department of Human Services, Education
The Ohio State University
Columbus, Ohio

**PRIMARY LEVELS CONSULTANT**
**Maureen E. Allen**
Science Resource Specialist
Irvine Unified School District
Irvine, California

**CONTENT CONSULTANTS**
**Robert T. Brown, M.D.**
Associate Professor of Clinical Pediatrics
Director, Section for Adolescent Health
The Ohio State University/Children's Hospital
Columbus, Ohio

**Henry D. Drew, Ph.D.**
Chemist
U.S. FDA, Division of Drug Analysis
St. Louis, Missouri

**Judith L. Doyle, Ph.D.**
Physics Teacher
Newark High School
Newark, Ohio

**Todd F. Holzman, M.D.**
Child Psychiatrist
Harvard Community Health Plan
Wellesley, Massachusetts

**Knut J. Norstog, Ph.D.**
Research Associate
Fairchild Tropical Garden
Miami, Florida

**James B. Phipps, Ph.D.**
Professor, Geology/Oceanography
Grays Harbor College
Aberdeen, Washington

**R. Robert Robbins, Ph.D.**
Associate Professor of Astronomy
Astronomy Department, University of Texas
Austin, Texas

**Sidney E. White, Ph.D.**
Professor
Department of Geology & Mineralogy
The Ohio State University
Columbus, Ohio

**REVIEWERS: Teachers and Administrators**
**Virginia Ceruti,** Cleveland Elementary School, Norwood, MA; **Sister Teresa Fitzgerald,** CSJ, Office of Catholic Education, Brooklyn, NY; **Carmen G. Guerra,** Felipe R. Perez Elementary, Brownsville, TX; **JoAnn Hamm,** Danville Board of Education, Danville, KY; **Donna Jackson,** Hazel Avenue Elementary School, West Orange, NJ; **Norma Jones,** Austin Tracy School, Lucas, KY; **Barbara Kmetz,** Trumbull High School, Trumbull, CT; **Carol D. Massey,** John Glenn Elementary, San Antonio, TX; **Lee Dell McCarty,** United Methodist Publishing House, Nashville, TN; **Corinne Measelle,** Palm Beach County School Board, West Palm Beach, FL; **Waltina Mroczek,** Beachwood Elementary School, Beachwood, OH; **Deanna Owen,** Travis Magnet Elementary, Odessa, TX; **Linda Payne,** Whitesville Elementary School, Whitesville, KY; **Patrice Burns Reitblatt,** Westwood Terrace Elementary, San Antonio, TX; **Rosemary Schmitz,** Galm Elementary, San Antonio, TX; **Peggy Smith,** Special Education Resource Teacher, Fort Worth, TX; **Frank Stone,** Floranada Elementary School, Fort Lauderdale, FL; **Lana Tarlton,** Cook Elementary School, Austin, TX; **Diane Thomas,** Northwest Crossing Elementary, San Antonio, TX; **Vivian Torres,** Leon Valley Elementary, San Antonio, TX; **Dr. Rosa White,** Cutler Ridge Elementary School, Miami, FL

**CREDITS**
Series Editor: Jane Parker,
Design Coordinator: Kip Frankenberry,
Series Production Editor: Helen Mischka,
Teacher Edition Coordinator: Judy Kinney,
Level Editor: Linda A. Montgomery,
Contributing Editors: Patricia S. Haupt, Lisa K. Higgins,
Beverlee Jobrack

Macmillan/McGraw-Hill School Division
866 Third Avenue
New York, New York 10022

Printed in the United States of America

ISBN 0-675-16252-1

9 8 7 6 5 4 3 2

# What's inside...

## Pupil Edition Unit and Chapter Titles

# Science In Your World
## Designed for you <u>and</u> your student.

**Core Components**

- Pupil Edition
- Teacher Edition
- Teacher Resource Book

**Optional Components**

- Activity Book, Pupil Edition
- Activity Book, Teacher Edition
- Transparency Package
- Posters
- Big Book

- Big Book Audiocassettes
- Software Package
- Videotapes
- Activity Center
- Activity Center, Teacher Edition
- Activity Materials Management System Handbook
- Activity Materials Kit
- Safety Kit
- Stickers
- Safety Cards

## We're bringing language arts and science together in a big way.

Children love the big, colorful pictures and readable type of our Big Books for grades 1 and 2. You'll love bringing science to life with stories, poems, and songs the whole class can enjoy. Detailed teaching notes help you plan exciting lessons that combine science with important language arts skills. And a built-in easel makes it easy for you to stand the book on a table or desk, leaving you free to lead the class in discussions or creative activities.

The Shadow-Shaker

If I could shake a shadow
from a shadow-shaker tin,
And sprinkle it like stardust
after Daddy tucks me in,
I would sprinkle mints and chocolates
on my bed and underneath,
For shadow sugar candy
never, ever hurts my teeth!
I would sprinkle out a carnival
across my bedroom walls,
With ferris wheels and colored lights
and swimming ducks and dolls!
I would sprinkle out a pirate's chest
of jewels and sparkling rings;
A million shadow treasures
would not cost me anything!
I could never sprinkle shadows
when the sun is shining bright,
For a shadow-shaker never works
'til Dad turns out the light!

TEACHER EDITION 1

# SCIENCE
## In Your World

Macmillan/McGraw-Hill

# We designed Science In Your World to hold your students' attention and make reading about science fun.

From the literature excerpts that begin every unit, to the carefully developed questions in every unit review, *Science In Your World* makes reading about science fun. A colorful and motivating format entices students to read and keep reading. Before they know it, they're learning something new about science!

Some dinosaurs were as little as birds.
Some were as big as a school bus.
Many were much bigger than you.

d long ago.
now about dinosaurs?

**1** Active voice keeps narrative moving

**2** Questions get students involved

**3** Examples relate science to students

**4** Second person speaks directly to students

# Science In Your World helps you reinforce the work you've done in reading, math, and writing.

**LANGUAGE CONNECTION**

**Writing:** Have students write a story as if they lived during the days when dinosaurs roamed Earth. Tell students that this writing is just to be a first draft and that they should concentrate on getting their ideas down on paper.

**MATH CONNECTION**

Remind students that Earth was warmer long ago. Tell students you are going to write some numbers that represent temperatures on a number line. See if students can tell which number is missing.

Language Arts Connections and Math Connections in your Teacher Edition help you spend more time on these two important subjects *and* science — by using science content to teach and reinforce concepts and skills from mathematics, reading, writing, grammar, spelling, and oral language.

Unit reviews give you plenty of opportunities to integrate science with other subjects…and have fun at the same time! The Writing Connection is a story starter based on chapter content, and your teaching notes include additional ideas for writing assignments. Something To Do suggestions provide a variety of creative language arts and mathematics activities. Also provided is a list of books about science that will help your students build library and reading skills.

SCIENCE FUN ➡

## Something To Do

Draw some faces on eggshell halves.
Fill the shells with soil.
Plant some rye grass seeds.

### ...iting Connection

...our favorite animal.
...ke?

...?

### Would You Believe?

Goldfish may turn white if kept in a dark room.

## Books To Read

**A Snake Is Totally Tail** by Judi Barrett
**This Year's Garden** by Cynthia Rylant
**The Trek** by Ann Jonas

# Hands-on activities are simple and easy to do for both you and your students.

Science is fun when it's done right. These activities bring science to life using only the simplest materials. They don't take much time. They're a snap to organize, simple to perform, and fascinating to observe. Appealing and motivating opportunities build skills such as classifying, measuring, interpreting data, and forming hypotheses. Hands-on and cooperative grouping symbols in every lesson help support your teaching strategy.

ACTIVITY

## Do living things grow?

**What you need**

a lima bean
a cup of soil
3 paper strips
scissors
glue
pencil and paper

**What to do**

1. Plant the seed in a cup of soil.
2. Put the cup in a sunny place.
3. Add water to the soil.
4. How tall is your plant growing?
5. Use paper strips to measure.

14

# Hands-on science

Doing science in the classroom can be fun! Kids love these activities because they bring science to life right before their eyes. You'll love them because they use only the simplest materials. They're a snap to organize.

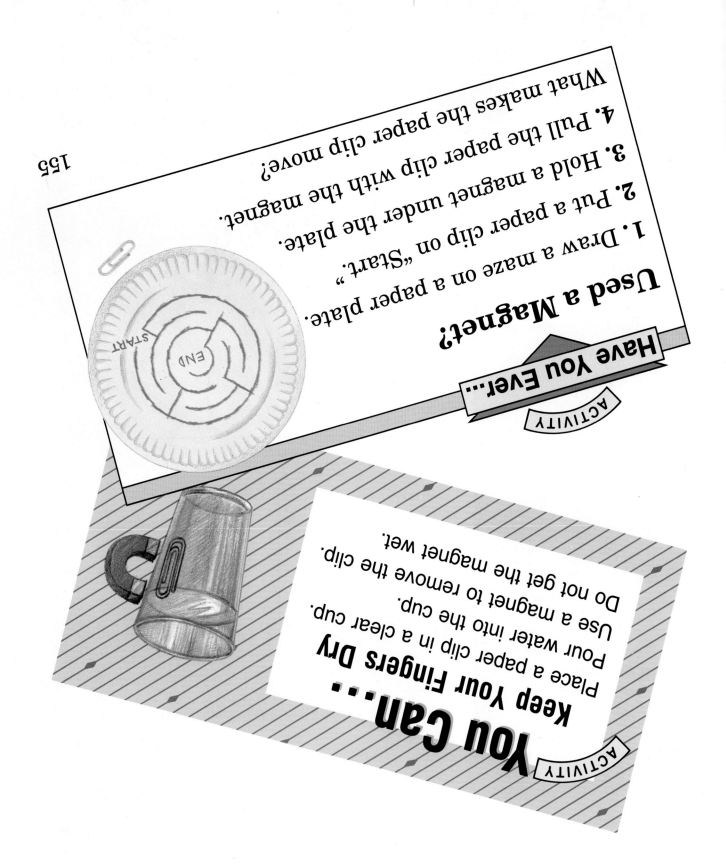

ACTIVITY

## Have You Ever...

### Used a Magnet?

1. Draw a maze on a paper plate.
2. Put a paper clip on "Start."
3. Put a magnet under the plate.
4. Hold a paper clip with the magnet. Pull the paper clip move? What makes the paper clip move?

155

ACTIVITY

## You Can...

### Keep Your Fingers Dry

Place a paper clip in a clear cup.
Pour water into the cup.
Use a magnet to remove the clip.
Do not get the magnet wet.

# Teaching cycles help you shape up lessons quickly.

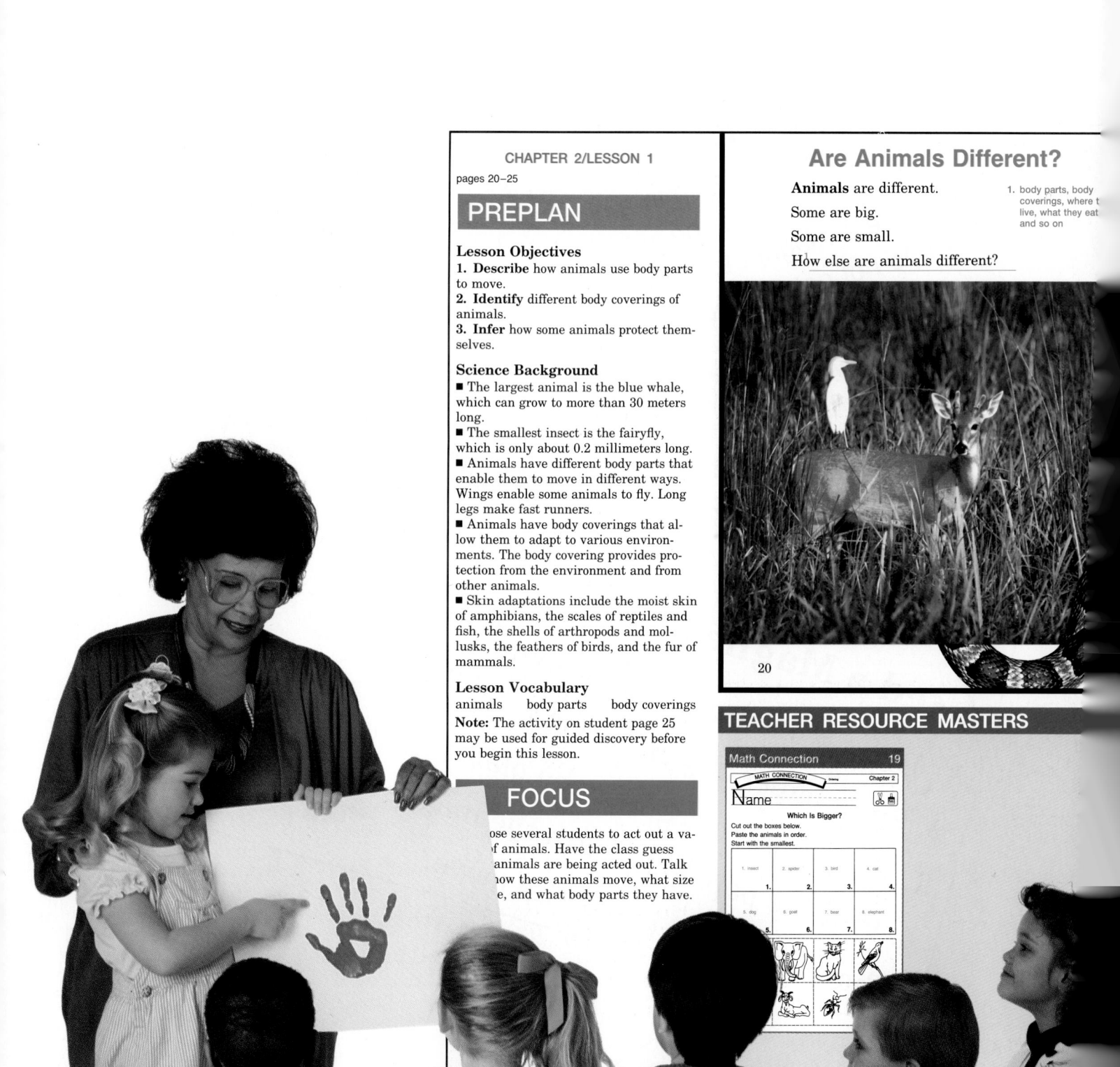

pages 20–25

## PREPLAN

**Lesson Objectives**
1. **Describe** how animals use body parts to move.
2. **Identify** different body coverings of animals.
3. **Infer** how some animals protect themselves.

**Science Background**
■ The largest animal is the blue whale, which can grow to more than 30 meters long.
■ The smallest insect is the fairyfly, which is only about 0.2 millimeters long.
■ Animals have different body parts that enable them to move in different ways. Wings enable some animals to fly. Long legs make fast runners.
■ Animals have body coverings that allow them to adapt to various environments. The body covering provides protection from the environment and from other animals.
■ Skin adaptations include the moist skin of amphibians, the scales of reptiles and fish, the shells of arthropods and mollusks, the feathers of birds, and the fur of mammals.

**Lesson Vocabulary**
animals    body parts    body coverings
**Note:** The activity on student page 25 may be used for guided discovery before you begin this lesson.

## FOCUS

...ose several students to act out a va-
...of animals. Have the class guess
...animals are being acted out. Talk
...how these animals move, what size
...e, and what body parts they have.

## Are Animals Different?

**Animals** are different.

Some are big.

Some are small.

How else are animals different?

1. body parts, body coverings, where t... live, what they eat... and so on

20

## TEACHER RESOURCE MASTERS

Math Connection    19

MATH CONNECTION    Ordering    Chapter 2

Name

**Which Is Bigger?**

Cut out the boxes below.
Paste the animals in order.
Start with the smallest.

| 1. insect | 2. spider | 3. bird | 4. cat |
|---|---|---|---|
| 1. | 2. | 3. | 4. |
| 5. dog | 6. goat | 7. bear | 8. elephant |
| 5. | 6. | 7. | 8. |

Each teaching cycle is a three-step lesson plan you can see at a glance. Just open your Teacher Edition to the first two pages of any lesson. Refer to the numbered teaching steps in the margins. Check out the other options, if you wish, on the pages that follow. Now you're ready to go!

The three teaching steps — Focus, Teach, and Apply — include strategies from a widely recognized teaching model.

**1** Focus: How do I start?

**2** Teach: How do I guide students to understanding?

**3** Apply: How do I close?

---

Animals have different **body parts**.

They use body parts to move.

1How do animals move?

2How can you move?

1. walk, run, crawl, swim, fly
2. walking, running, jumping, climbing, crawling, and so on

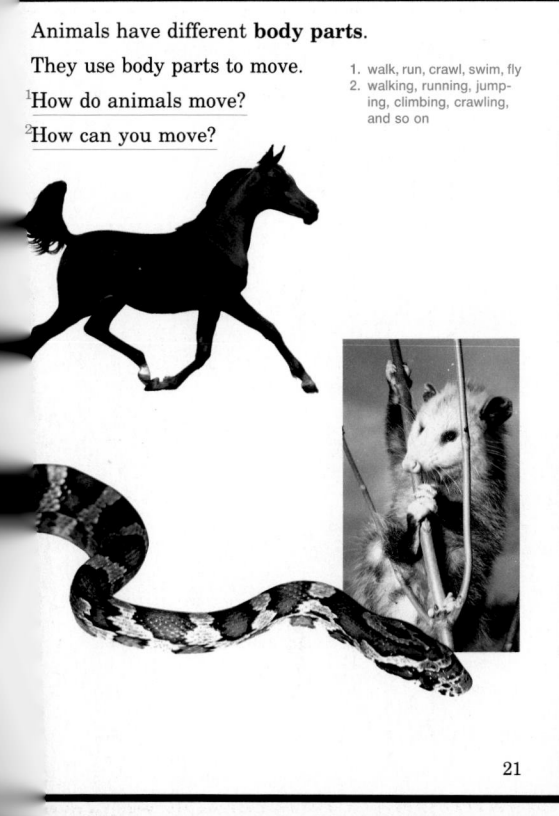

21

CHAPTER 2/LESSON 1
pages 20–25

## 2 TEACH

■ Discuss large and small animals. Have students name the largest and smallest animals they know.
■ Discuss how the body covering is related to an animal's life. One discussion might be how the animal's body covering affects where the animal lives. Ask: **How do body coverings help to keep animals safe?** *Shells, tough skin, and scales protect animals from predators. Hair and feathers protect an animal from the cold.*

### Guided Practice
■ Describe four different animals for students to draw without naming the animals. Check to see if students listened to your description of body parts or body coverings.
■ If necessary, use the **reteaching strategy** in OPTIONS.

### Independent Practice
■ Use the Teacher Resource Master **Independent Practice,** page 20.

## 3 APPLY

Have students **work cooperatively in groups** of four to make animal booklets. Each group should choose a body covering and include examples of animals with that body covering.

### Close
■ Show pictures of animals to the class. Have students identify the body parts and body coverings of each animal.

## OPTIONS

### Reteaching Strategy
Glue pictures of animals to 3 × 5 index cards. Label some blank cards with *swim, run, fly,* or *crawl.* Have students group the animals under the correct heading.

### Resource Options
■ Use Poster #2, "Did Someone Koala My Name?"

Chapter 2　**21**

---

## TEACHER RESOURCE MASTERS

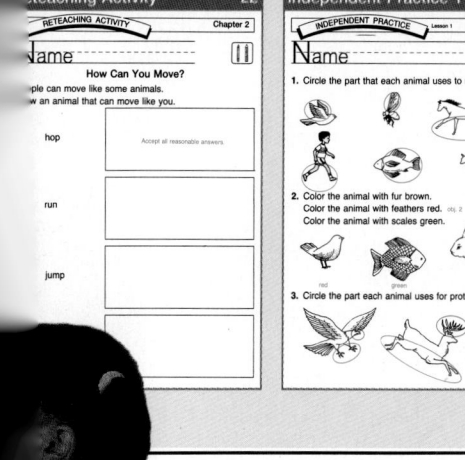

teaching Activity 22

RETEACHING ACTIVITY Chapter 2

Name

**How Can You Move?**
ple can move like some animals.
w an animal that can move like you.

Accept all reasonable answers

hop

run

jump

Independent Practice 1 20

INDEPENDENT PRACTICE Lesson 1 Chapter 2

Name

1. Circle the part that each animal uses to move.

2. Color the animal with fur brown.
Color the animal with feathers red.
Color the animal with scales green.

3. Circle the part each animal uses for protection.

**SCIENCE**
in Your World

Macmillan/McGraw-Hill

**SCIENCE**
in Your World

Macmillan/McGraw-

**SCIENCE**
in Your World

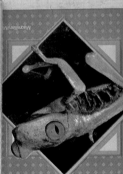

**SCIENCE**
in Your World

**SCIENCE**
in Your World

**SCIENCE**
in Your World

**SCIENCE**
in Your World

Science In Your World

# TEACHER REFERENCE GUIDE

FEATURING:
ABOUT THE
AUTHORS

SCOPE AND
SEQUENCE

PROGRAM
PHILOSOPHY
AND GOALS

THINKING
IN SCIENCE

TEACHING
STRATEGIES

READING
STRATEGIES

SCIENCE AT
HOME

SCIENCE FAIR

MATERIALS
LIST

RESOURCES

# ABOUT THE AUTHORS

## SENIOR AUTHORS

**Dr. Jay K. Hackett** is a professor of Earth Science Education at the University of Northern Colorado. He holds a B.S. in General Science, an M.N.S. in Physical Science, and an Ed.D. in Science Education with support in Earth Science. A resource teacher for elementary schools, he conducts numerous workshops and professional seminars. With over 30 years of teaching experience, he has taught and consulted on science programs across all levels and remains active in local, state, and national science professional organizations.

**Dr. Richard H. Moyer** is a professor of Science Education at the University of Michigan, Dearborn. He holds a B.S. in Chemistry and Physics Education, an M.S. in Curriculum and Instruction, and an Ed.D. in Science Education. With more than 20 years of teaching experience on all levels, he is currently involved in teacher training. He is the recipient of two Distinguished Faculty Awards. He conducts numerous workshops and in-service training programs for science teachers. Dr. Moyer is also the author of Merrill Publishing Company's *General Science* textbook.

## CONTRIBUTING AUTHORS

**Stephen C. Blume** serves as the Elementary Science Specialist for the St. Tammany Public School System in Slidell, LA. Mr. Blume holds a B.A. from St. Mary's University and an M.A. from Southeastern Louisiana University in elementary education. He is a member of the National Science Teachers Association, the Louisiana Science Teachers Association, and the Council for Elementary Science International. He is the author of several articles related to teaching science, as well as Macmillan/McGraw Hill's *Science Fair Handbook* and Merrill Publishing Company's *Science Connections*.

**Ralph M. Feather, Jr.,** is a teacher of geology, astronomy, and earth science and serves as Science Department Chair in the Derry Area School District in Derry, PA. He holds a B.S. in Geology and a M.Ed. in Geoscience from the Indiana University of Pennsylvania. He is a member of the Geological Society of America, the National Science Teachers Association, and the Association for Supervision and Curriculum Development, as well as many other professional organizations. Mr. Feather is co-author of Merrill Publishing Company's *Science Connections* and the Teacher Resource Package for *Focus on Earth Science*.

**Edward Paul Ortleb** is the Science Supervisor for the St. Louis Board of Education. He holds an A.B. in Education from Harris Teachers College and a M.A. in Education and an Advanced Graduate Certificate in Science Education from Washington University, St. Louis. Mr. Ortleb is a lifetime member of NSTA, having served as its president in 1978-79. He is a contributing author for the Teacher Resource Books for Merrill Publishing Company's *Accent on Science* and *General Science* and is co-author of Merrill Publishing Company's *Science Connections*.

**Dr. Barbara Swanson Thomson** is an associate professor in science education at The Ohio State University in Columbus, Ohio. Dr. Thomson received a B.S. from Michigan State University, an M.A. in reading and linguistics from The Ohio State University, and a Ph.D. in Science Education with a specialty in botany from The Ohio State University. She has held numerous national and local leadership positions in educational organizations. She conducts numerous workshops and inservice programs for teachers and has had teaching experience at all levels.

*Jay Hackett*

*Richard H. Moyer*

*Stephen C. Blume*

*Ralph M. Feather*

*Edward Ortleb*

*Barbara S. Thomson*

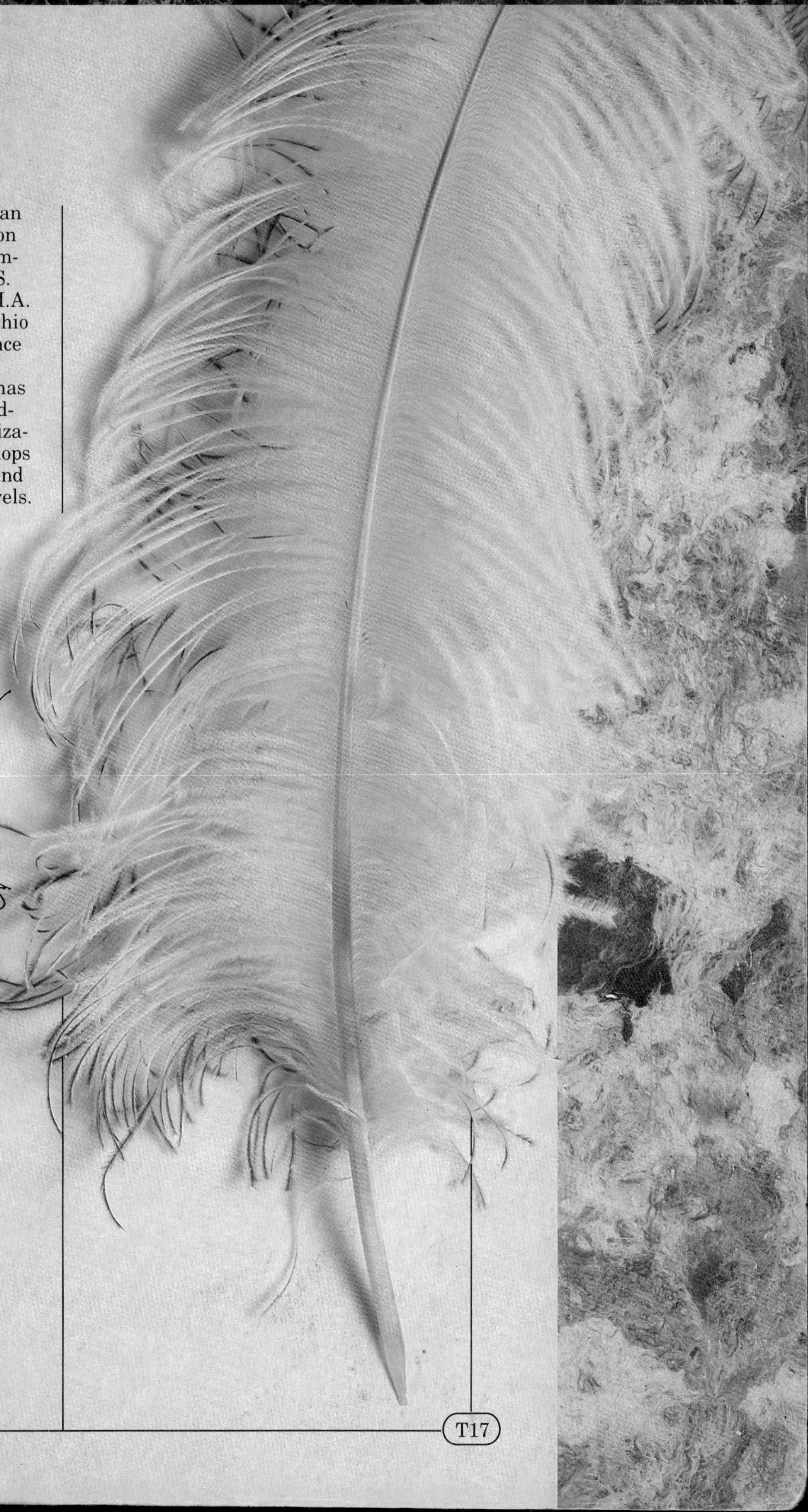

# SCOPE & SEQUENCE

# PROGRAM PHILOSOPHY AND GOALS

## PHILOSOPHY

*SCIENCE In Your World* is designed to offer a variety of meaningful experiences to develop children's natural curiosity about themselves and everything around them.

Appropriate learning experiences encourage children to explore and develop explanations for phenomena in the world. These experiences provide a framework that helps children make informed choices and decisions today and in the future.

Effective engagement in science enables children to understand and appreciate the impact of science and technology on society.

## GOALS

Active involvement in the *SCIENCE In Your World* philosophy, approach, and experiences will prepare children to do the following:

● Use critical-thinking process skills to solve problems and develop concepts.

● Integrate reading, writing, and mathematical thought processes to develop understandings in science.

● Recognize and explain cause-and-effect relationships in the world around them.

● Make informed choices and decisions that affect their environment and daily lives.

● Value the nature of science in its objectivity, limitations, and tentativeness.

● Understand and respect the impact of science on society and its use of technology.

# THINKING IN SCIENCE

**Cognitive Development**
Learning involves both awareness and judgement. *Cognitive development* is the process of development by which knowledge is acquired. Most of what science knows about cognitive development has come from observing children and finding similar patterns in the ways in which they think and acquire knowledge. Teachers and parents who know what to expect from children have a basis for developing appropriate and meaningful learning experiences.

At one time, scientists thought that children and adults learned in the same way. In this view, a child's mind was seen simply as an empty bucket into which a teacher could pour knowledge. A Swiss psychologist, Jean Piaget (1896-1980), is the person most responsible for advancements in researching cognitive development. We now know that cognitive development affects a child's learning to speak, read, and understand mathematical concepts and abstract ideas.

Piaget observed that people seem to go through four stages of cognitive development in the same order at approximately the same age ranges.

In 1972 Piaget said, "Children should be able to do their own experimenting and their own research. Teachers, of course, can guide them by providing appropriate materials, but the essential thing is that in order for a child to understand something, he must construct it himself, he must re-invent it."

*SCIENCE In Your World* applies our understanding of cognitive development in the following ways.

**1.** Experiences are designed to be appropriate to the general cognitive abilities of children at each age group.

**2.** Questions and experiences facilitate the development of certain operations at each grade level, including serial ordering, conservation, classification, and the formation of simple hypotheses.

**3.** Multiple exposure to certain types of thinking operations is provided throughout each grade level.

**4.** New concepts are introduced by providing familiar and concrete references.

**5.** Students learn and understand new concepts through motivating, hands-on activities.

By doing these things in education, we can appeal to children's strengths and stimulate the development of more advanced thinking patterns.

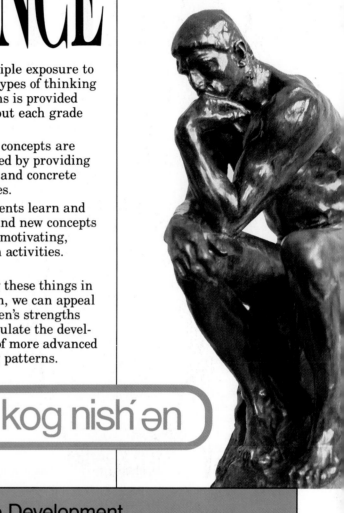

kog nish´ ən

## Four Stages of Cognitive Development

**Birth to two years**    **Sensory-Motor**      A child is self-centered and learns by senses.
Young children like to play peek-a-boo. They think that if you can't see them, they don't exist. A young child has to sense something by sight, sound, taste, smell, or touch to know it.

**Two to seven years**    **Preoperational**      Children tend to focus on only one aspect of an issue.
As a teacher, you may have met children who found it impossible to believe that you were also a parent. This is because a child in the preoperational stage focuses on only one aspect of an issue.

**Six to eleven years**    **Concrete-Operational**   Children can see two sides of an issue but have difficulty with abstract thought.
"That's not fair." "You cheated!" Rules, at this stage, become very important. Rules are concrete and should not change. Children are frustrated by exceptions in spelling or in games. To wonder about the appropriateness of a rule or a procedure is not part of the thinking process at this time.

**Eleven and older**    **Formal-Operational**      People have the ability to reason on an abstract level.

# THINKING IN SCIENCE

## CRITICAL THINKING

### Critical-Thinking Science Process Skills

What are *critical* thinking skills? The word *critical* can mean *evaluative,* and it can mean *crucial.* In education both definitions apply. Learning involves a crucial awareness and judgment. Our goal in education is to encourage the development of critical-thinking skills and to expand the potential for learning at each stage of cognitive development.

In 1956, Benjamin Bloom of the University of Chicago published a classification system for intellectual tasks that

specific listing of critical-thinking skills below.

Throughout the program, *SCIENCE In Your World* has conscientiously included experiences that help students develop, practice, and apply critical-thinking process skills. The process skills are carefully introduced and developed through the use of higher-level divergent questions, controlled experiments, and problem-solving and creative activities at each grade level. In addition, the *Application Activities,* all formal activities, and the *You Can…* activities

| | |
|---|---|
| **Observing** | Students use their sense of sight, sound, taste, smell, or touch to learn more about objects and events. |
| **Classifying** | Students sort or group objects or events based on common properties and/or categorize objects or events based on existing relationships among them. |
| **Inferring** | Students interpret, explain, and identify causes based on observed events and collected data. |
| **Communicating** | Students convey information in oral and written forms and visually through the use of graphs, charts, pictures, and diagrams. |
| **Recognizing and Using Spatial Relationships** | Students estimate the relative positions of both moving and nonmoving objects. |
| **Measuring** | Students identify and order length, area, volume, mass, and temperature to describe and quantify objects or events. |
| **Predicting** | Based on observations and inferences, students propose possible results or outcomes of future events. |
| **Using Numbers** | Students transfer or apply ordering, counting, adding, subtracting, multiplying, and dividing to quantify data where appropriate in investigations or experiments. |
| **Interpreting Data** | Students explain the meaning of information gathered in scientific situations. |
| **Forming Hypotheses** | Students first make an assumption and then draw out and test its logical consequences. |
| **Separating and Controlling Variables** | Students recognize the many factors that affect the outcomes of events. They understand the relationship of the factors to one another so that one factor (variable) can be manipulated while the others are controlled. |
| **Experimenting** | Students test hypotheses or predictions under conditions in which variables are both controlled and manipulated. |
| **Formulating Models** | Students construct mental, verbal, or physical representations of ideas, objects, or events. They then use the models to clarify explanations or to demonstrate relationships. |
| **Defining Operationally** | Students form a working definition that is based upon their actual experiences. |

has become known as Bloom's Taxonomy. The levels of thought he identified from simple to complex are **Knowledge, Comprehension, Application, Analysis, Synthesis,** and **Evaluation.** Bloom's Taxonomy forms the basis for the more

are specifically designed to practice critical-thinking process skills. This careful attention provides stimulation for your students to develop more advanced thinking patterns.

# THINKING IN SCIENCE

We know that competency in content is only one part of success in learning. When asked to *apply* a concept or to *interpret* an everyday situation in light of the concepts they have learned, many students become confused. Problem solving must be an integral part, as it is a natural part, of education.

A Problem-Solving Process or Model may be helpful to many students who do not know where to begin in solving a problem. Identifying the problem and then planning an effective strategy to solve it are the crucial steps in problem solving. You may want to suggest these nine steps as one way to attack a problem.

In 1949, Albert Einstein wrote, "There is not a single concept of which I am convinced that it will stand firm, and I feel uncertain whether I am in general on the right track." Solving difficult problems is one of the most complex things we do. Often we come to realize that the real problem is different from what we had originally thought. Or we discover that the solution we've derived does not really solve the problem. We do not always reach successful solutions on the first try. At any stage in the problem-solving process, we may need to go back to the beginning and start again.

*SCIENCE In Your World* offers students multiple opportunities to practice problem-solving skills as they read and actively participate in the activities in the student book. Activity suggestions in the teacher edition and the *Application Activities* in the back of each student edition are specifically designed as problems to solve.

As educators we can encourage students to try to solve problems. We can include problem solving in daily teaching, not only in science but in every area. If we focus on helping students use the process rather than merely get the right answer, we can help build the confidence needed to develop more advanced thinking skills.

## Problem Solving

**1** Verbalize the problem.
State the problem aloud and believe that you can solve it.

**2** Define the problem.
Analyze the information given and determine what you still need to know to solve the problem.

**3** Explore.
Brainstorm strategies for collecting and organizing information to solve the problem. Strategies for collecting data may be to observe, survey, or research known information. Strategies for organization might be to construct a table or graph, look for a pattern, talk to an expert, make a model, guess and check, work backwards, or use a process of elimination.

**4** Plan.
Decide on a strategy or group of strategies and list the steps needed to complete the plan.

**5** Collect information.
Using the plan, gather the data needed to solve the problem.

**6** Organize and analyze data.
According to your plan, complete the strategies needed to organize the information gathered into a usable form. Then analyze the data to find out what they tell you about the problem.

**7** Generate potential solutions.
Using the analysis of the data, brainstorm a list of possible solutions for the problem.

**8** Choose and explain the solution.
Review the procedures, data, and thought processes that led to your particular solution of the problem.

**9** Implement the solution.
Solve the problem.

# COOPERATIVE LEARNING

Research comparing competitive, individual, and cooperative learning indicates that cooperative learning results in the highest achievement, greatest motivation, and the most positive attitude, no matter what the student's age, the subject, or the learning activity may be.

## What Is Cooperative Learning?

Just putting students together to do something is *not* necessarily cooperative learning. Cooperative learning groups *learn* things together, not just do things together.

1. Cooperative learning requires more than individual accountability for mastering the assigned materials. Individuals are responsible for everyone else, as well.

2. Cooperative learning requires face-to-face interaction among group members.

3. Cooperative learning requires shared leadership responsibilities.

4. Cooperative learning requires students to use appropriate interpersonal and small-group skills that will be valuable in working in groups throughout their lives.

## The Teacher's Role in Cooperative Learning

1. Form the groups and assign a diverse group of students to each group.

2. Explain the roles of members in a group.

3. Explain the task and its goals.

4. Explain the criteria for success.

5. Monitor the cooperative behavior in the group and share your observations with the group.

6. Provide assistance with the task: give feedback, redirect questions, encourage thinking, manage conflict, and supply resources.

7. Provide closure for the lesson. Have students summarize what they've learned, and have them relate it to previous learning.

8. Evaluate the group process. Have groups rate themselves and write specific ways to improve.

9. Evaluate student learning. You might use individual or group tests and systems of extra points for groups achieving high marks overall.

## Student Roles in Cooperative Learning

In small groups, each group member may have more than one role. Among the tasks that need to be carried out are the following:

1. Facilitator—the person responsible for making sure the group stays on task and uses positive, cooperative learning strategies.

2. Recorder—the person who documents the group's observations, data, and answers to activity questions.

3. Gatherer of materials—the person responsible for getting the materials from the teacher.

4. Reader—the person responsible for reading the instructions to the group.

5. Performer—the person responsible for carrying out the activity procedures.

6. Interpreter/Observer—the person who explains what happens during the activity.

7. Custodian/Cleaner—the person responsible for returning all unused materials to the proper place and returning the group's working space to its original condition.

## Using Cooperative Strategies

To prepare students for cooperative learning, the following rules may be helpful.

1. Stay with your group. Moving around hinders progress.

2. To get ideas for procedures, use a brainstorming technique in which each person in the group takes turns coming up with an idea. During brainstorming no one can criticize another's idea.

3. Make group decisions by consensus.

4. Encourage each other to participate.

5. Use each other's names. Use eye contact.

TEACHING STRATEGIES

# INTEGRATING SCIENCE

**6.** Ask the teacher for help only after you have decided as a group that you need help.

**7.** Don't make negative personal remarks.

## How Is Cooperative Learning Used in *SCIENCE In Your World?*

Virtually all the activities in the student edition and the suggested activities in the teacher edition will work in a cooperative learning situation. Many of the activity pages make specific suggestions for working in a cooperative learning situation. In many cases, a cooperative learning group can be formed as students participate in the *Whole Class Projects* or *Science Fair Projects* that are listed on the teacher edition interleaf pages before each chapter.

You may also choose to form cooperative groups to read, study, or demonstrate knowledge of the concepts and methods explained in the text itself. ∎

## Integrating Science

We hear a lot about purposeful integration of the *language* arts: listening, speaking, reading, thinking, and writing. The language arts complement one another. When a student uses one, the others are reinforced. Language arts are the tools of thinking and learning across the curriculum. By the same token, no skill or subject can be taught in isolation. Subject areas interweave and overlap, and all learning involves an integration of the language arts. But what does integration mean specifically for science?

Science is truly integrated in the world. When children play in snow, when they help bake cookies, when they dig in sand, when they pick flowers, when they take care of their pets, they are engaged in scientific discovery, concepts, and methods.

Additionally, science naturally involves all of the language arts. Children practice reading, writing, listening, speaking, and critical thinking when they encounter scientific text, ideas, and activities. Science is a natural for developing interactive, cooperative group skills as students work in teams to complete activities. Science is particularly suited to the practice of critical-thinking skills as students encounter and solve problems.

Science is encountered constantly in social studies, math, and other curriculum areas. For example, scientific discoveries have changed the course of history. The study of geography goes hand in hand with the study of life, earth, and physical science. Science frequently relies on mathematic principles. And it is difficult to participate in physical education or learn about health without a scientific knowledge of the human body.

Literature, both fiction and nonfiction, complements your science curriculum, as well. Think of all you learned about spiders by reading *Charlotte's Web,* about deer from *The Yearling,* or about wild horses from *Misty of Chincoteague.*

*SCIENCE In Your World* is specifically designed to develop a student's understanding of science in human experience and the individual's role in the community and in society. The text involves real examples of the scientific phenomena that are explained. The activities and concepts are meant to be applied in real life.

In addition, throughout the teacher edition are specific ideas for math, language arts, social studies, art, physical education, home economics, and other curriculum integration in the *Connection* features. The student edition includes features such as *Science and… Math* that draw concrete analogies between science and other areas. The program also includes references in *Books to Read* at the end of each unit in the student and teacher editions and cross-disciplinary ideas in the Teacher Resource Books.

# TEACHING MODEL

**SCIENCE In Your World** makes it easy for you to develop your lesson plans for each part of your lesson cycle. Strategies for the achievement of each step in the cycle can be found in specific areas of the teacher edition. The Teaching Model below identifies these sections. It may be used in a variety of ways to meet the needs of different teaching situations and different lessons. The flexibility of **SCIENCE In Your World** allows for the use of this model in its entirety on a daily basis, allowing for all steps to be incorporated while you are involved in a single activity. It can also be adapted for a weekly structure or a structure determined by individual classroom needs.

| Step | Goal | *SCIENCE In Your World* |
|---|---|---|
| Focus | Focus students' attention. State goal or objective. | *Focus: Motivation strategies.* Student Edition: *Lesson Goals.* |
| Explanation | Input information. Teach to the objectives. | *Teach:* Teaching Tips. |
| Check Understanding | Make sure students understand the objective. | *Checking for Understanding; Reteaching Strategy.* |
| Guided Practice Check for Mastery | Guide students to make sure initial learning is successful. Observe and evaluate student performance. | Student in-text questions; Margin questions; Margin strategies; *Lesson Review* |
| Independent Practice Assess Mastery | Allow students to gain fluency through practice. Observe and evaluate student performance. | Use of *Independent Practice Masters* in the *Teacher Resource Book* for each lesson. |
| Closure | Make sure students understand and can apply what has been taught. | *Apply:* Application of lesson concepts. Summary statements to review concepts. |
| Extension | Build upon skills. | All Teacher Resource Book Activities; *Unit Review: Challenging Project, Books to Read; Lesson and Feature Options; Application Activities.* |

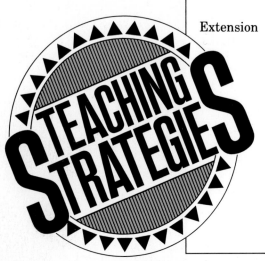

TEACHING STRATEGIES

# HINTS FOR CLASSROOM MANAGEMENT

### by Dr. Richard H. Moyer

There is no one right way to manage a science classroom just as there is no one right way to manage a classroom studying any subject. There are, of course, a few guidelines that are helpful to keep in mind regarding the smooth operation of an activity-oriented subject area like science.

## Preplan

Preplanning is probably the most important part of a successful lesson. Studying the Planning Guide at the beginning of each chapter in *SCIENCE In Your World* and skimming the student text and teacher margin material is essential for a smooth lesson that offers the teacher few "surprises."

Next, preview the activities you plan to have students do. It has been said often that science experiments always work—just not always the way you thought they would! Working through the activities and experiments ahead of time is the easiest way for teachers to be aware of how materials will work. In this way, you can also prepare your students for their subsequent experience.

## Organize Materials

Be sure you have adequate supplies of materials before you begin an activity. It is also valuable to think about how (and when) you will distribute materials to the class. You may wish to assign roles to group members in class. One role could be gatherer of materials: the person responsible for equipment and supplies.

It is also helpful to package small materials together to ease distribution. Plastic containers or food bags, shoe boxes, and egg cartons often work well for this purpose. Remember, it is also important to get materials back in an orderly manner. The use of containers and assigned students will be helpful for this task as well.

## Make Students Aware of Expectations

Be sure the students know what you expect of them. Discuss rules for appropriate behavior during science.

## Make Students Aware of Lesson Goals

A science activity will be more effective if students know why they are engaged in it. Before beginning an activity, review procedures with the class. Be sure students have well in mind *what it is they are trying to find out.*

## Make Effective Use of Human Resources

**Peer Tutoring** can enhance student understanding and retention. Peer tutoring is most effective when students of differing abilities are paired. Your role in peer tutoring is to train tutors to use positive reinforcement and good questioning strategies while maintaining their own language and learning styles as they teach each other.

**Reciprocal Teaching** is another method for making effective use of resources. Call on teachers, principals, parents, members of the community, and students who have specific expertise to help with particular lessons or activities. Make yourself available, as well, for lessons that require your expertise.

## Time on Science

Many teachers wonder about how much time they should spend on science every day. Each chapter introduction and formal activity in *SCIENCE In Your World* provides a Time Allotment for your planning purposes. Lessons were developed based on a daily 30-minute science period. However, depending on your state, district, or school guidelines or your personal preferences, the total amount of time you spend on science will vary. You may wish to extend some lessons and shorten others. You may wish to integrate some science chapters or activities with other curriculum areas. *SCIENCE In Your World* is designed to be adapted to your needs.

# TEACHING EXCEPTIONAL

The chart below provides you with general help in teaching exceptional students. In each chapter interleaf section in the teacher edition, *SCIENCE In Your World* also provides a *For Your Exceptional Students* feature that offers specific suggestions for help.

| | Description | Sources Of Help/Information |
|---|---|---|
| **Learning Disabled** | All learning disabled students have an academic problem in one or more areas, such as academic learning, language, perception, social-emotional adjustment, memory, or attention. | *Journal of Learning Disabilities* <br> *Learning Disability Quarterly* |
| **Behaviorally Disabled** | Children with behavior disorders deviate from standards for expectations of behavior and impair the functioning of others and themselves. These children may also be gifted or learning disabled. | *Exceptional Children* <br> *Journal of Special Education* |
| **Physically Disabled** | Children who are physically disabled fall into two categories –those with orthopedic impairments and those with other health impairments. Orthopedically impaired children have the use of one or more limbs severely restricted, so the use of wheelchairs, crutches, or braces may be necessary. Children with other health impairments may require the use of respirators or other medical equipment. | Batshaw, M.L., and M.Y. Perset. *Children with Handicaps: A Medical Primer*. Baltimore: Paul H. Brooks, 1981. <br> Hale, G. (Ed.). *The Source Book for the Disabled.* New York: Holt, Rinehart & Winston, 1982. <br> *Teaching Exceptional Children* |
| **Visually Disabled** | Children who are visually disabled have partial or total loss of sight. Individuals with visual impairments are not significantly different from their sighted peers in ability range or personality. However, blindness can affect cognitive, motor, and social development, especially if early intervention is lacking. | *Journal of Visual Impairment and Blindness* <br> *Education of Visually Handicapped* <br> American Foundation for the Blind |
| **Developmentally Handicapped** | A student with a developmental handicap experiences significant subaverage intellectual functions along with deficits in adaptive behavior. The deficits in both of these areas have significant impact on a student's developmental period of maturation. | Gearhart, B., Weishahn, M., and Gearhart, C. *The Exceptional Student in the Regular Classroom.* Columbus, Ohio: Merrill Publishing Company, 1988. |
| **Hearing Impaired** | Children who are hearing impaired have partial or total loss of hearing. Individuals with hearing impairments are not significantly different from their hearing peers in ability range or personality. However, deafness can affect cognitive, motor, and social development if early intervention is lacking. Speech development also is often affected. | *American Annals of the Deaf* <br> *Journal of Speech and Hearing Research* <br> *Sign Language Studies* |
| **Multicultural and/or Bilingual** | Multicultural and/or bilingual children often speak English as a second language or not at all. Customs and behaviors of people in the majority culture may be confusing for some of these students. Cultural values may inhibit some of these students from full participation. | *Teaching English as a Second Language Reporter* <br> R.L. Jones, ed., *Mainstreaming and the Minority Child.* Reston, VA: Council for Exceptional Children, 1976. |
| **Gifted** | Although no formal definition exists, these students can be described as having above average ability, task commitment, and creativity. Gifted students rank in the top 5% of their class. They usually finish work more quickly than other students, and are capable of divergent thinking. | *Journal for the Education of the Gifted* <br> *Gifted Child Quarterly* <br> *Gifted/Creative/Talented* |

# STUDENTS

In addition, many *Options* are labeled as basic, average, or advanced to guide you in your assignments.

## Tips For Instruction

1. Provide support and structure: clearly specify rules, assignments, and duties.
2. Establish situations that lead to success: use simple vocabulary.
3. Practice skills frequently–use games and drills to help maintain student interest.
4. Allow students to record answers on tape and allow extra time to complete tests and assignments.
5. Provide outlines or tape lecture material.
6. Pair students with peer helpers, and provide classtime for pair interaction.

1. Provide a carefully structured environment with regard to scheduling, rules, and room arrangement.
2. Clearly outline objectives and how you will help students obtain objectives. Seek input from them about their strengths, weaknesses, and goals.
3. Reinforce appropriate behavior and model it for students.
4. Do not expect immediate success. Instead, work for long-term improvement.
5. Balance individual needs with group requirements.

1. Assume that students understand more than they may be able to communicate.
2. Openly discuss with students any uncertainties you have about when to offer aid.
3. Ask parents or therapists what special devices or procedures are needed, and if any special safety precautions need be taken.
4. Allow physically disabled students to do everything their peers do, including participating in field trips, special events, and projects.
5. Help nondisabled students and adults understand the characteristics of physically disabled students.

1. Help the student become independent–make the student accountable for assignments.
2. Teach classmates how to serve as guides.
3. Eliminate unnecessary noise in the classroom.
4. Encourage students to use their sense of touch. Provide tactile models whenever possible.
5. Describe people and events as they occur in the classroom.
6. Provide taped lectures and reading assignments.
7. Team the student with a sighted peer for laboratory work.

1. Seat students away from distracting noises and outside activities.
2. Actively involve students with hands-on activities of short duration.
3. Sequence information from simple to complex.
4. Emphasize concrete, relevant experiences.
5. Provide immediate feedback.
6. Use frequent and continuing progress checks.
7. Use oral tests whenever possible.

1. Seat students where they can see your lip movements easily, and avoid visual distractions.
2. Avoid standing with your back to a window or light source.
3. Avoid moving around the room or writing on the board while speaking. Instead, use an overhead projector, which allows you maintain eye contact while writing.
4. Encourage students to face the speaker, even if students must move around during class discussions.
5. Write all assignments on the board, or provide written instructions.
6. If the student has a manual interpreter, allow both student and interpreter to select the most favorable seating arrangements.

1. Do not allow the language students bring to school to influence your expectations of their academic performances; however, beware of reverse discrimination.
2. Try to incorporate students' languages into your instruction. The help of a bilingual aide may be effective.
3. Include information on different cultures in the curriculum to aid students' self-image–avoid cultural stereotypes.
4. Encourage students to share their culture in the classroom.

1. Make arrangements for students to take selected subjects early.
2. Let students express themselves in art forms such as drawing, creative writing, or acting.
3. Make public services available through a catalog of resources, such as agencies providing free and inexpensive materials, community services and programs, and people in the community with specific expertise.
4. Ask "what if" questions to develop high-level thinking skills.
5. Emphasize concepts, theories, ideas, relationships, and generalizations.

TEACHING STRATEGIES

# EFFECTIVE USE OF ACTIVITIES

by Dr. Jay K. Hackett

## Guided Discovery

The heart of the elementary school science curriculum is involvement in meaningful guided discovery. This active participation in hands-on activities, guided by relevant thought-provoking questions, involves children in thought processes that help them develop problem-solving skills, reasoning, and understanding. Guided-discovery investigations emphasize science process skills such as observing, classifying, inferring, measuring, predicting, interpreting data, and drawing appropriate conclusions to develop higher-level thinking skills.

The effective use of guided-discovery investigations makes it possible for children to reconstruct previously developed explanations or concepts. Children develop explanations for common scientific phenomena observed in daily living experiences before they are exposed to formal science instruction in school. These explanations are often very different from what teachers expect. Surprisingly, these naive or mixed ideas often persist even after listening to more sophisticated explanations from the teacher and reading well-developed scientific explanations in textbooks. Many learning theorists and researchers believe these misconceptions can be restructured by involving children in new experiences that can't be explained using their previously developed ideas. Good guided-discovery activities can provide these experiences as well as the verbal interaction with peers and the teacher to help children recognize new relationships and construct more accurate generalizations.

## Guided-Discovery Activities in Science

Both the formal and supplemental activities in *SCIENCE In Your World* provide experiences through which students develop and reinforce or restructure concepts, as well as develop the ability to use process skills. The activity format, used consistently throughout the program, provides structure at the beginning of each investigation with some flexibility towards the close. This guided discovery focuses the attention of students on specific outcomes and at the same time stimulates intrinsic motivation so often provided by discovery.

## Pre- and Post-Lab Discussions

One of the genuine "secrets of success" employed by truly effective elementary school science teachers is the mastery of what some call pre-lab and post-lab discussion. In other words, both the proper introduction and the effective conclusion of the science activity are crucial to its success. A good pre-lab will accomplish the following:

● Stimulate interest or engage the student.

● Provide clues as to what is expected and set the purpose.

● Establish relevance to the learner.

T

In *SCIENCE In Your World* the problem statement that appears as the title of each activity in the student edition and the *Focus* section in the margin guide of the teacher edition provide suggestions for effective pre-lab discussion.

An effective post-lab discussion should accomplish these goals:

- Clearly identify a conclusion.
- Help students summarize or draw conclusions using their own words.
- Reveal how the conclusion applies to the everyday world of the child.

In *SCIENCE In Your World, What Did You Learn?* and *Using What You Learned* in the student edition and the *Apply/Close* section in the margin guide of the teacher edition provide ideas to accomplish the post-lab goals.

### Activities and Different Types of Students

Guided-discovery activities provide a variety of experiences to enhance learning through a variety of modes. Examples are summarized below.

**Visual Learners**  Students with a visual-learning preference are able to make first-hand observations, to compare and contrast, and to study charts, graphs, and pictorial representations.

**Auditory Learners**  Peer discussions in small groups coupled with post activity discussion to summarize findings and reach conclusions benefit students with an auditory preference for learning.

**Kinesthetic Learners**  Kinesthetic learners are aided by hands-on manipulation of equipment and materials during investigations.

Active involvement in hands-on activities also benefits students with certain learning disabilities. Many special students are quite capable of learning through participation in activities, but they can't read well or express their thoughts in writing. A number of research studies have shown that engagement in good activity-centered science programs has enhanced or even accelerated the language development of these students.

Activities often provide a vehicle to extend and enrich learning experiences for gifted and talented students. Participation in inquiry activities may bring out other questions and problems to pursue. These questions and problems are often excellent pursuits for gifted students. Extension of activities make excellent homework assignments to challenge gifted students.

Involvement in meaningful science investigations is participation in the nature of science itself. Experiences such as these help students appreciate the role of science and technology in our society and enhance the scientific literacy of our citizens.

# LEARNING CENTERS IN THE CLASSROOM

### by Dr. Jay K. Hackett

Many teachers who actively engage their students in guided discovery utilize learning centers as an integral part of their instruction. They have found that well-designed learning center activities provide motivation and help students become more self-directed and responsible. They also can provide for individual differences among students. Students may work at centers individually or in small, cooperative groups as a part of your regular ongoing science instruction. They may also use a learning center to pursue special interests and needs.

How can you set up a science learning center? One way is to set aside an area of your classroom to create a particularly rich learning environment. Use posters, pictures, collections, and other interesting materials to decorate this area. In this type of learning center, students can work on activities that you design to introduce or reinforce specific science concepts. Activities to develop process or problem-solving skills can also be effectively carried out. In addition, you can design science center activities for children to explore creative endeavors such as inventions, science poetry, and creative drama.

The teacher's role in the learning center is to organize the space, provide materials, and explain what students are to do and how to function in a learning center. To work independently, students need clear goals and directions for each activity. You may want to include a log at the learning center for students to record their progress. You may also want to confer with them to discuss their work at the learning center.

Many regular features found in the **SCIENCE In Your World** program lend themselves to science center activities. The *Application Activities* section at the back of every level of the student edition provides sixteen activities that could become part of the center. Suggestions provided in the *Unit Review* for projects and trade books suggested to enhance unit concepts also can become part of the center.

The *Planning Resources* page before each unit in the teacher edition of *SCIENCE In Your World* contains a *Science Center* feature. Each feature includes stated goals, a listing of necessary materials, and a well-developed procedure to assist you with implementation. Other features that make excellent science center activities include suggestions found in *Reinforcement, Enrichment,* and *Challenge.* All hands-on margin activities are preceded by a hands-on symbol that will alert you to their suitability for use in the science center.

Give science learning centers a try. You will find they broaden your instructional base and allow you to work more effectively with each of your students.

TEACHING STRATEGIES

# LIFE IN THE CLASSROOM

by Dr. Jay K. Hackett

Elementary students have a natural curiosity and interest in living organisms. For this reason, teaching science should include opportunities to develop a respect for life and all living things. Students need to understand the importance of providing humane care for pets, animals housed in the classroom, and animals used in science projects. In addition, teaching science provides an opportunity to demonstrate a noninvasive approach to the environment as students study plants and animals in their natural habitats.

You may be interested in setting up an aquarium or a terrarium for your class. In addition, students often wish to bring their own live plants and animals to share with the rest of the class. With plants and animals in the classroom, students can learn the importance and responsibilities of providing proper food, sufficient space, fresh water, and adequate light and ventilation for life to thrive. Additionally, observation of natural living patterns, such as growth rates or activity and rest patterns of plants, pets, fish, or domestic animals can be educational. Life in the classroom can be a valuable and stimulating educational experience for children providing certain conditions are met.

**1.** First, it is important to check school, local, and state guidelines regarding regulations on housing plants and animals in the classroom.

**2.** Secondly, in making assignments, such as leaf or bug collections, consider the impact that the assignment will have on the environment. Assignments can be adapted so that students will develop a conscientious attitude toward the environment.

**3.** All animal studies should be carefully supervised by the teacher. Experimental procedures must be ones that don't subject animals to pain or discomfort. Any behavioral studies or training should use only positive reinforcement.

**4.** Care of living things in the classroom must be directly supervised by a teacher experienced in proper care.

**5.** For animals in the classroom, animal quarters should be able to be cleaned easily. Proper temperature must also be maintained.

**6.** Weekends and vacation periods can create problems if there has been no formal planning for the care of animals in the class. Some type of schedule with school custodians or responsible students should be pre-arranged for those days when school is not in session. Some custodians may volunteer to care for animals during weekends or short vacation periods.

**7.** If it becomes necessary during long vacation periods, responsible students may be allowed to take the animals or plants home to care for them after parental permission has been obtained.

**8.** Copies of state and local regulations regarding animal care can be obtained from local veterinarians, the Humane Society, and the National Science Teachers Association, 1742 Connecticut Avenue N.W., Washington DC 20009.

Studying living organisms is not a small responsibility. However, with careful teacher planning, students can develop a respect for life as they learn the responsibility and cooperation required when caring for living things.

# SAFETY IN SCIENCE

Safety is of prime importance in every classroom, but science demands particular safety awareness. To aid in safety awareness, *SCIENCE In Your World* has carefully screened photographs to prevent showing potential safety hazards. References to specific safety practices appear in the written text and are often keyed to illustrations. Activities in which safety is a concern are identified by cautionary safety symbols. These symbols and an explanation for them appear on the following page. In addition, the material that accompanies each activity highlights teacher safety considerations and also includes tips on safety with plants, animals, fire, and other areas when appropriate.

The following safety guidelines are not inclusive but are meant to provide some general information for you in the science classroom.

## SAFETY RULES

**1.** Inspect materials and equipment for defects or potential hazards prior to the school year, and discard those that are unsafe.

**2.** Store all equipment and materials properly. Store potentially hazardous materials under lock and key.

**3.** Demonstrate the proper use of all materials used in the science classroom. Be familiar with any potential hazards. Use all appropriate safeguards.

**4.** Use the appropriate materials and equipment specified for each activity. Give clear, complete directions **BEFORE** students begin any activity.

**5.** Take appropriate precautions when using fire and/or heat sources. Be sure that you perform as a teacher demonstration all activity steps involving the use of a heat source.

**6.** Instruct students not to taste or touch substances or materials without your permission.

**7.** Stress the importance of not touching eyes, mouth, face, or other body parts while working with plants, animals, or chemicals. Instruct students to wash their hands thoroughly after each activity.

**8.** Stress the importance of appropriate behavior during all activities.

**9.** Provide supervision during each activity.

**10.** Familiarize students with first-aid, fire-drill, and other emergency procedures. Post instructions for these procedures in a prominent place.

# SAFETY SYMBOLS

Below are the safety symbols used throughout **SCIENCE In Your World** to alert you and your students to possible danger. Be sure that you review each symbol with the students and that they understand each symbol before beginning any activity. A blackline master with these symbols and their meanings also appears in the Appendix of the accompanying Teacher Resource Book.

**DISPOSAL ALERT**
This symbol appears when care must be taken to dispose of materials properly.

**BIOLOGICAL SAFETY**
This symbol appears when there is danger involving bacteria, fungi, and protists.

**OPEN FLAME ALERT**
This symbol appears when use of an open flame could cause a fire or an explosion.

**THERMAL SAFETY**
This symbol appears as a reminder to use caution when handling hot objects

**SHARP OBJECT SAFETY**
This symbol appears when a danger of cuts or puncture caused by the use of sharp objects exists.

**FUME SAFETY**
This symbol appears when chemicals or chemical reactions could cause dangerous fumes.

**ELECTRICAL SAFETY**
This symbol appears when care should be taken when using electrical equipment.

**PLANT SAFETY**
This symbol appears when poisonous plants or plants with thorns are handled.

**ANIMAL SAFETY**
This symbol appears whenever live animals are studied and the safety of the animals and the students must be ensured.

**RADIOACTIVE SAFETY**
This symbol appears when radioactive materials are used.

**CLOTHING PROTECTION SAFETY**
This symbol appears when substances used could stain or burn clothing.

**FIRE SAFETY**
This symbol appears when care should be taken around open flames.

**EXPLOSION SAFETY**
This symbol appears when the misuse of chemicals could cause an explosion.

**EYE SAFETY**
This symbol appears when a danger to the eyes exists. Safety goggles should be worn when this symbol appears.

**POISON SAFETY**
This symbol appears when poisonous substances are used.

**CHEMICAL SAFETY**
This symbol appears when chemicals used can cause burns or are poisonous if absorbed through the skin.

TEACHING STRATEGIES

# EVALUATION

Evaluation is a vital part of the teaching process, but it is often the most difficult thing to do. In many cases, teachers are insecure about assigning projects, activities, or writing because they are not sure of the best way to evaluate them. In science, as in other disciplines, there are a variety of evaluative strategies that a teacher can use. Different activities can be evaluated by different methods. The important thing is for you to decide which evaluative method you will use and to let the students know how their work will be evaluated when it is assigned.

**Summative Evaluation**
Usually when teachers first think of evaluation, they think about tests and grades. These tests are intended to sum up what the student knows about a subject. **Summative Evaluation** is normally conducted after formal study of a lesson, chapter, or unit. Summative Evaluation in *SCIENCE In Your World* includes the formal end-of-chapter tests provided in the student text. Here, test items are provided to help you ascertain student mastery of all objectives for each lesson. Activities in *SCIENCE In Your World* can also be summatively evaluated by assigning a grade to student activity worksheets from the *Teacher Resource Book*.

**Formative Evaluation**
Of course, evaluation involves much more than merely assigning grades. Evaluation is an ongoing process that can be used to guide student learning and diagnose difficulties students may be having. This type of evaluation is known as **Formative Evaluation.** Made *during* the course of study, it guides and promotes student learning.

Much of what teachers do informally in the classroom as they interact with their students is actually a type of formative evaluation. In the margin guide of *SCIENCE In Your World,* you will find many suggestions that will assist you in the formative evaluation of your students. These include suggested discussion questions as well as answers to student-text questions. Each lesson also includes a section entitled *Guided Practice.* This is designed to offer a mid-lesson check of student understanding of lesson concepts. If you determine the need, a *Reteaching Strategy* follows each of these checks.

Teachers may also wish to evaluate student performance on activities and process skills in science. As indicated above, the student activity worksheets can be used when completing the formal activities in the text. Formative evaluation of activities should also be accomplished through observation and discussion while students are

engaged in the activities. Ask students why they are doing certain steps of an activity while they are working. Be sure students are aware of what they are trying to find out. In other words, be sure students are aware of the goal of an activity before they begin and while they work through activities.

The evaluation component of the *Activity Book* can also be extremely helpful in evaluating process skill development. For each process skill, you will find a formal test (summative evaluation). Also included is an observational checklist for each process skill (formative evaluation). This checklist breaks down each process skill into component parts that are observable by the teacher.

In addition, it is also important for teachers to periodically assess students' attitudes toward science. Discuss with students what they like about science. In this way, you will gain insights into student interests.

# BY DR. RICHARD H. MOYER

## Holistic Evaluation

Holistic Evaluation is a method by which you can assess an activity or project as a whole. Holistic evaluation may be a general impression of the work and may require only a short observation. In some cases, you may wish to simply acknowledge completion of the assignment. In others, you may want to measure a student's work against certain general features, such as creativity, effort, or conformance to requirements. You need not individually analyze every bit of a student's work in order to evaluate it.

## Peer Evaluation/ Response Groups

Peer Evaluation can be of particular value especially if much of your classwork is done in cooperative groups. In many ways, peer evaluation goes on without any formal acknowledgement. For this reason, it is helpful to establish guidelines for peer evaluation even when cooperative groups are not used. These are some suggestions you may find helpful in explaining how to make a peer evaluation.

1. Listen carefully to the assignment explanation or description.

2. Comment on the best part of the work after the explanation is complete.

3. Ask questions about things you do not understand.

4. Give specific, constructive feedback.

In some cases, you may wish to form cooperative response groups for the purpose of sharing student work. As teacher, you should take an active role in setting up and monitoring these groups. They should consist of a mix of students who know and practice the guidelines above. The methods of sharing can vary. In some instances demonstrating or reading aloud may be appropriate. Circulating the assignment or making a copy and attaching an evaluation sheet for written comments may also be appropriate.

## Self-Evaluation

A major goal in education is to encourage children to become self-disciplined and eager to learn. We want students to internalize knowledge and skills. Having students make self-evaluations can demonstrate the responsibility each person has for his or her own work. It can develop greater self-reliance and independence. But self-evaluation is among the most difficult things people do because it requires critical-thinking skills and is so intertwined with self-concept and personality. There are, however, some guidelines that may help students organize their thoughts about themselves.

1. Develop a concrete checklist of items you want to evaluate before you begin an assignment. They may be based on the requirements for the assignment. Take the checklist out when the assignment is complete and evaluate each item.

2. Write a short paragraph before you turn in any assignment to evaluate how you think you did. Give yourself a grade if you want to.

3. Keep a record of your improvement on each assignment.

4. Establish your own goals for improvement for the next assignment.

5. Discuss your self-evaluation and goals for improvement with your teacher.

Whether you use summative, formative, holistic, peer, or self-evaluations, feedback is necessary for optimal student development.

*Excellent Report!*

# TEXT STRUCTURE

*SCIENCE In Your World* has been carefully designed and written to make it as easy as possible for your students to read.

## Logic
Each *SCIENCE In Your World* text is divided into four units: Life Science, Earth Science, Physical Science, and the Human Body. Each unit is subdivided into chapters, which are divided into lessons of study. The units, chapters, and lessons are of varying lengths, dependent on the information in them. Each lesson leads logically to the next, increasing a child's knowledge, interest, and confidence, and taking students to higher and higher levels of learning and understanding.

## Organization of Prose
A variety of expository text structures has been employed in *SCIENCE In Your World* depending on the subject matter in a particular lesson. For example, the lesson may be organized in time order if a historical context is called for. The text may also be organized in inductive order with the description of a cause and its effect, a problem and its solution, or a comparison and contrast.

Research has shown that reading comprehension improves when common text structures such as these are used.

## Readability
Several relevant factors concerning readability were considered in the writing of this program.

For one thing, careful attention was given to the concepts taught at each level. Our understanding of cognitive development served as the basis for selecting and planning experiences appropriate to the general cognitive abilities of each group at each grade level.

In addition, each lesson begins by relating the text to what the student already knows. This may mean using a poison ivy example to introduce a lesson on poisons or Magellan to introduce a chapter on oceans and seas. Throughout the text, real-life examples are used. For example, writing with a rock on the sidewalk is a streak test, and mushroom pizza describes a form of fungi. These features make the concepts interesting and easy for students to read, understand, and retain.

## Format
To facilitate reading, each page is attractively and simply laid out with clear titles and labels and bite-sized chunks of information.

To establish a purpose for reading, a list of goals that function as learning objectives begins each lesson in levels 3-6. After each lesson, summary statements are listed followed by review questions that zero in on the lesson goals.

The vocabulary chosen for each lesson complements the development of concepts. As each vocabulary word is introduced, it is boldfaced and, when appropriate, phonetically respelled.

Questions in the text have been directed to students to help them rethink the information they have read and to personalize the text material. In the margin of the intermediate texts, questions are included as guides for teachers and students to check reading comprehension and retention of information.

## Student Reference Material
*SCIENCE In Your World* provides students with a comprehensive Table of Contents, Index, Glossary, and Chapter and Unit Review to help them locate information in the text quickly.

## Photographs, Illustrations, Charts, and Graphs
Research has shown that visual representation of text material dramatically increases comprehension. For this reason, *SCIENCE In Your World* has been elaborately illustrated with attractive visual examples of science concepts and procedures. The pictures selected were also chosen with the student in mind. A variety of people are shown engaged in scientific discovery.

# PRIOR KNOWLEDGE AND EMERGENT LITERACY

## Prior Knowledge

People don't easily retain isolated bits of information. Piaget believed that people of all ages learn either by *assimilating* new information into a structure that we have already created or by changing our established structure to *accommodate* new information that doesn't fit. Either way, we activate prior knowledge when we learn something new.

An awareness of and an attempt to activate prior knowledge can help students make the connection between what is known and what is new. It reassures students that they already have a basic understanding of new concepts, and it gives them reference points for assimilating or accommodating new material.

Teachers can activate a student's prior knowledge simply by asking what he or she already knows about a topic. But *SCIENCE In Your World* has built-in features that allow students to do this independently. Each unit, chapter, and lesson begins by relating the upcoming text to what the student already knows. In addition, throughout the text, real-life examples are used. Furthermore, each lesson leads logically to the next, increasing a child's knowledge, interest, and confidence along the way.

By activating and developing their own knowledge on every page, *SCIENCE In Your World* enables students to comprehend science with ease, interest, and success.

## Emergent Literacy

Learning to read doesn't happen in one day. *Emergent literacy* is a term that is often used to describe the period of growth before children begin to read. It includes the language and print experiences children have before coming to school. It refers to the skills that mark the onset of reading: turning pages, moving eyes from left to right, developing awareness of the forms and functions of print, distinguishing between text and pictures, identifying logos and signs, scribbling, and playing with language rhymes and rhythms.

In *SCIENCE In Your World,* kindergartners and first graders are not expected to read everything in the text. But science provides an opportunity to develop this important skill while learning scientific content, concepts, and methods. *SCIENCE In Your World* encourages emergent literacy by activating students' prior knowledge, providing opportunities for whole-group reading with the *Big Books* for grades K-2, providing attractive, stimulating illustrations in the student texts, and offering writing and hands-on activities that make young students *want* to read more.

## READING STRATEGIES

# WRITING FOR SCIENCE

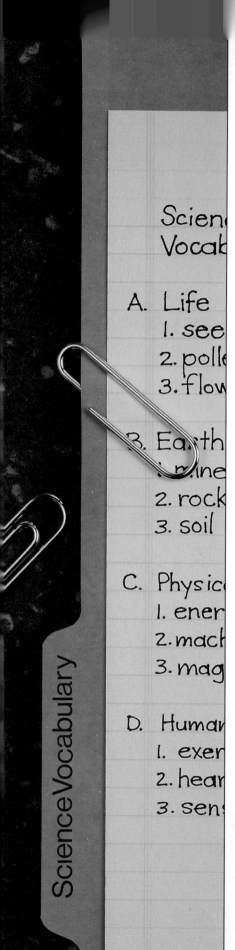

Writing, a reading strategy? Yes! Research shows that the process of writing is really a process of thinking. Writing helps activate prior knowledge, generate new ideas, organize thoughts, synthesize ideas, summarize learning, and apply language conventions. Writing promotes student thinking and improves reading comprehension. It enhances learning in every discipline, including science.

## Writing for Comprehension
Writing something down can aid comprehension immediately. The following ideas show how writing can help some specific problems.

When students cannot understand a verbal description of a process, have them
- draw a picture or series of pictures and label the parts of the process.
- write down each stage of the process, and number the consecutive stages.

When students have trouble remembering vocabulary words, have them
- draw a semantic map of the word. Write the word in the center of a paper. In bubbles or with lines around the word, write examples or synonyms of the word.
- find a sentence that contains the word. Rewrite the sentence in their own words. Ask a question about the sentence. Then read the sentence to someone else to see if the meaning of the word is clear.
- make a direct comparison chart listing the confusing word and words like it down the side. Across the top, list characteristics or meanings of each of the words. Then mark the characteristics or meanings that apply to each word.

## Types of Writing for Science
When people think of scientific writing, they generally think of written lab reports that state the following:

Description of Problem
Hypothesis
Background Information
Methods Used
Analysis of Results
Discussion
Summary
Conclusions

But this is not the only form of writing scientists do. All types of writing can help develop scientific literacy. Below are examples of the scientific application of each form of writing.

**Expressive Writing**  A daily or weekly personal journal can record a student's thoughts, ideas, and observations.

**Descriptive Writing**  Description is the stuff scientific investigation is made of. Descriptive writing is in all other forms of writing.

**Expository Writing**  Expository writing is transfer of information. Reports, summaries, and instructions enable students to communicate what they have learned.

**Persuasive Writing**  As in lab reports, persuasive writing enables students to present their knowledge in a factual, logical, and persuasive manner.

**Narrative Writing**  Narrative writing can be a biography of a famous scientist or can tell the story of how a student arrived at a particular conclusion.

**Poetry**  Especially in the early grades, poetry can be used to sum up or describe an experience.

## Teaching Writing for Science
Writing for science is no different from any other type of writing instruction. The writing process provides the best method for planning, executing, and evaluating writing for the greatest number of students.

**Prepare**  Identify the purpose and audience for your writing. Do any necessary research and make an outline or plan for writing.

**Write**  Follow your plan to write. Don't worry about making mistakes. Just get your thoughts down on paper.

**Revise**  Read your writing. Check for logic, clarity of ideas, missing or unnecessary information, rhythm, and flow.

**Edit**  Proofread your writing for errors in spelling, punctuation, grammar, and vocabulary.

**Share**  Share your work with other people: your teacher, a response group, your friends, or family. Ask for feedback.

# DISCUSSION

Scientists are well aware of the importance of discussion when they write reports of their experiments. Discussion involves consideration of a problem or question. Factors that affect the data one way or another can be brought out and considered.

In the classroom, discussion can be one of the most valuable tools a teacher can use to help students learn. A good discussion offers students opportunities to verbalize what they know and find out what others discovered. It is a vehicle for bringing up questions and problems and getting help to solve them. Discussion also provides the teacher with a good way to evaluate student progress and understanding.

A discussion can also be a horrible experience for students who are not prepared, for students who don't trust their classmates or teacher, or in classrooms in which a particular student or the teacher dominates every discussion.

Good discussions occur when everyone speaks, normally quiet people are fluent, people listen to each other and are flexible, original ideas are generated, problems are solved, and the group doesn't want the discussion to end.

There are certain rules that can be applied to encourage good discussions.

1. Discussion should be limited to groups of students who are prepared to discuss a particular topic.

2. The agenda for the discussion should be specific and understood by all participants.

3. A time limit should be set for the discussion.

4. A facilitator, the teacher or a student, should be assigned to keep the group on the topic, discourage negative comments, and make sure everyone gets an adequate chance to speak.

5. At the end of the discussion, the group should come to a consensus about what was accomplished.

Throughout *SCIENCE In Your World* there are multiple opportunities for discussion groups. On pages T30 and T31 are suggestions for pre- and post-lab discussions. But the completion of any activity, chapter review, or even a failed experiment can provide fodder for a good discussion.

# READING STRATEGIES

agenda

# THE ART OF QUESTIONING IN SCIENCE

by Dr. Richard H. Moyer

It has been said that the greatest potential for learning comes when a teacher asks the right question. Asking good questions is indeed an art. Good questioning strategies can lead to much more effective lessons and a higher-level understanding of science concepts.

Educators classify classroom questions in many ways. On these pages we will look at three·common ways to classify classroom questions. We find these are helpful for teachers interested in fostering higher-level and critical-thinking skills among their students.

**Divergent and Convergent Questions**
One of the simplest ways to classify questions is by whether they are open-ended or closed. Open-ended questions are usually referred to as **divergent** and closed-ended questions as **convergent**. Divergent questions have many possible answers, while convergent questions have few (or only one) possible correct response. "How could you group these objects?" is an example of a divergent question. There are, of course, multiple possible appropriate responses. The value of such a question is that it stimulates classroom discussion and involvement of students.

On the other hand, "Is this a correct grouping of the objects?" is an example of a convergent question. There is only one possible correct response: yes or no. Since it requires only that the student be able to recognize whether the grouping is correct or not, it requires lower-level thought on the student's part.

Neither type of question is necessarily "better" than the other. However, you should strive for a mix of the two. Unfortunately, convergent questions most often dominate classroom discussions. This generally results in lower-level discussions and the active involvement of few students.

Divergent questions should be used to stimulate higher-level thinking as well as inquiry and creative thinking in the classroom. Convergent questions, on the other hand, are helpful to focus on a single answer or to direct students' attention to certain events or ideas.

**Literal, Interpretive, Critical, and Creative Questions**
Another way to classify questions is to think of them as requiring a literal, interpretive, critical, or creative response. Below is a description of each type of question.

**Literal**   Requires simple regurgitation of information. Literal questions, like convergent questions, have right or wrong answers. They can be used to ascertain if a student is aware of some information. "What color was the litmus paper?" is an example of a literal question.

**Interpretive**   Requires some analysis on the part of the student, who must show that information has been comprehended. Students may have to put pieces of information together or interpret data to answer the question. "How might salt affect perspiration?" is an example of an interpretive question.

**Critical**   Requires students to evaluate information or procedures. They must rely on their own knowledge and judgment to answer this type of question. "What is wrong with this procedure?" is an example of a critical question.

**Creative**   Requires students to use their imaginations to create a solution to a problem. They must use their knowledge and critical judgment to develop an adequate solution. "How can we make this procedure work?" is an example of a creative question.

READING S·T·R·A·T·E·G·I·E·S

Again, the important thing to do when asking questions is to mix them up. Science does not have only right and wrong answers to phenomena, but it does have some. So a variety of types of science questions is not only good for students, but also is highly appropriate.

**Levels of Critical-Thinking Questions**
It is also helpful to think about classifying classroom questions in terms of Bloom's Taxonomy of Educational Objectives. The levels of thought Bloom identified from simple to complex are summarized below.[1]

It is important to consider the *level* of the questions we ask in the classroom. Again, a mix of levels is in order. Lower-level questions are useful to focus attention on specific details or events, but are not appropriate to develop critical-thinking or inquiry skills. To that end, you should try to ask questions that reflect the higher levels from Bloom's Taxonomy. Keep in mind that lower-level questions are not bad or undesirable. What is undesirable is to only ask lower-level questions.

More specifically, asking questions that require students to perform the Critical-Thinking Science Process Skills described on page T22 would also engage them in a variety of levels of thinking. Are you asking questions related to the science processes that students use to analyze the results of activities or draw inferences from their observations? Such questions are important to help students gain the experiences necessary to develop inquiry and critical-thinking skills.

Developing better classroom questioning skills requires much practice. It is easier to think about than to actually do. However, the positive results of carefully thinking about and analyzing our questioning techniques pays off in countless ways.

Throughout the program, *SCIENCE In Your World* has provided all types of questions for students and teachers. From the *Lesson Review, Chapter Review,* and margin questions in the student text to the numerous questions in the teacher edition, *SCIENCE In Your World* provides a unique blend of thoughtful questions to develop advanced thinking skills in science.

## Bloom's Taxonomy Of Educational Objectives

| | |
|---|---|
| **Knowledge** | Recalling facts or memorizing. |
| **Comprehension** | Describing in your own words, interpreting, translating from one medium to another. |
| **Application** | Problem solving, applying information to produce a result. |
| **Analysis** | Finding underlying structure, breaking down a process, identifying motives. |
| **Synthesis** | Creating unique and original products. |
| **Evaluation** | Resolving differences of opinion or controversies; making value decisions about issues. |

[1]Carin and Sund. 1989. *Teaching Science Through Discovery,* 6th ed., p.159. Columbus, OH: Merrill Publishing Company.

# SCIENCE AT HOME

**by Dr. Jay K. Hackett**

Teachers have long been aware of the positive relationship between student success in school and the interest and involvement of parents in support of the education of their children. This interest and support are carried out in a variety of ways.

There are many excellent opportunities for home-school collaboration and cooperation in using *SCIENCE In Your World.* Each of these has much potential for improving the performance of students as well as increasing the scientific literacy of both students and parents. In addition, cooperative efforts such as these can establish strong positive reinforcement and support among teachers, students, and parents.

Let's look at several suggested home-school activities and how they might be conducted.

1.   Inform parents that you will be asking their child to take home the activity worksheets completed in daily science activities. Ask them to find a convenient time for their child to tell another family member what was done and what was learned.

2.   Establish a regular practice of sending home the *Family Science* activity found in your *Teacher Resource Book.* Encourage both students and family members to do the hands-on activities at home and discuss the results. Send a letter home encouraging parents to take part in these home activities.

3.   Solicit help from parents when needed. For example, send a science materials scavenger hunt list to help build your inventory of common equipment, materials, and supplies such as candles, paper cups, flashlight batteries, liquid soap, baby food jars, waxed paper, and so on.

4.   Ask for volunteer family aids to help you with a science materials inventory, investigations, and other tasks.

5.   Ask parents to encourage their child to bring home science trade books from the school resource center or public library. Encourage them to read with their child or have the child share what was read with other family members.

6.   Hold a special after-school, hands-on science workshop for family members and their children. Conduct several interesting hands-on activities with the student and a family member participating as a team. Use activities that utilize common household materials and supplies. Workshops such as these could be particularly helpful for parents hesitant to do the *Family Science* activity with their child.

7.   Send a letter home asking parents to encourage their child to watch science-related television programs such as *Mr. Wizard, 3-2-1 Contact, National Geographic Specials, Nova,* and others. Suggest that they provide a short period of time at dinner or before bedtime to have the child tell what was learned from the program.

8.   Encourage parents during school visitations or by letter to make family visits to local museums, the zoo, a botanical garden, or planetarium.

Cooperative activities between school and home such as these will require initial planning and follow through on your part. But the potential rewards for all involved will be worth it. Activities such as these offer special encouragement and benefits for females and minority students and family members. Give some of these suggestions, or others you create, a try. Share the positive results with your colleagues and encourage them to try similar activities, too.

# SCIENCE FAIR

**by Dr. Jay K. Hackett**

Every year science fairs are held at class, school, district, state, and national levels. If you are not aware of your school's science fair schedule, ask your principal about it because participation in science fair projects is one of the most motivating and meaningful learning experiences your students can have. When involved in science fair projects, students actively experience the nature of science itself. Students get first-hand experience in designing and using an organized procedure for solving a problem. They use scientific methods and develop critical-thinking process skills as they add to their knowledge about the world in which they live.

Many students are frightened by the idea of entering a science fair. But all science fair projects simply begin with questions. Why do some balls bounce higher than others? Why are plants green? What do ants eat? What would happen if…? When students become accustomed to asking questions and seeking answers, they are ready to identify problems and set up procedures for seeking solutions.

To help students develop questioning minds, you can encourage them to ask questions about their observations. You can set up interesting classroom displays, collections, pictures, and bulletin boards. You can even set up a questions corner where students can write down questions about the displays, and, of course, you could contribute your own questions to the list. Talk about all of your questions in class, and have students help you decide which ones need further investigation.

To get students used to the idea of a science fair, particularly in primary grades, it is helpful to conduct a class science project. Help students pose several interesting questions. Decide on one interesting question and the resultant problem. Ask students, "What do you want to know? How can you find out?" Using the problem-solving process, help them design a logical procedure for conducting the experiment. Allow small groups of students to assume responsibility for different parts of the investigation. Interpret the results and cooperatively arrive at a conclusion. Now each student has participated in a model science project and has become more confident in his or her own ability to identify and successfully complete an individual science fair project.

*SCIENCE In Your World* provides a variety of features to assist you in using science projects as a regular part of your science instruction. Each unit review provides a selected list of science fair project ideas. Chapter interleaf pages provide suggestions for whole-class science projects as well as additional science fair project ideas. In addition, the program provides you with a *Science Fair Handbook.* This handbook provides guidelines and ideas for developing science fair projects along with helpful tips for organizing and conducting a science fair in your school. Blackline masters of entry forms, judging criteria, and award certificates are also provided. *SCIENCE In Your World* makes it easy for your students to think of themselves as scientists as they develop successful science fair projects.

# MATERIALS LIST

## LEVEL ONE

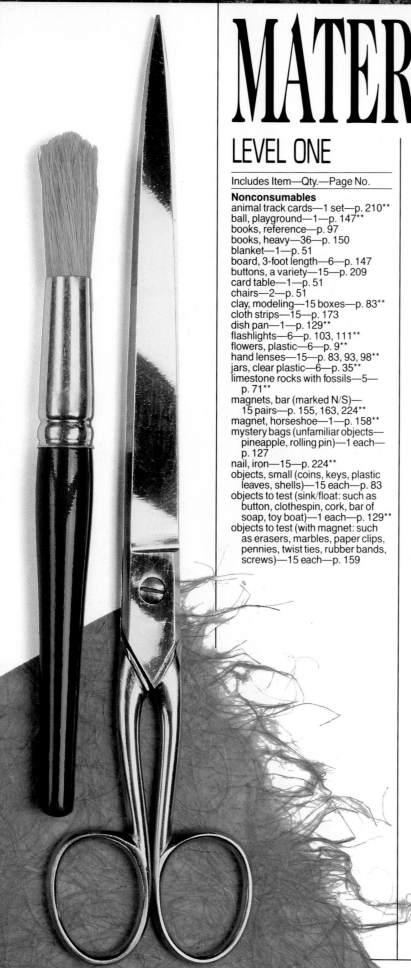

Includes Item—Qty.—Page No.

**Nonconsumables**
animal track cards—1 set—p. 210**
ball, playground—1—p. 147**
books, reference—p. 97
books, heavy—36—p. 150
blanket—1—p. 51
board, 3-foot length—6—p. 147
buttons, a variety—15—p. 209
card table—1—p. 51
chairs—2—p. 51
clay, modeling—15 boxes—p. 83**
cloth strips—15—p. 173
dish pan—1—p. 129**
flashlights—6—p. 103, 111**
flowers, plastic—6—p. 9**
hand lenses—15—p. 83, 93, 98**
jars, clear plastic—6—p. 35**
limestone rocks with fossils—5—
   p. 71**
magnets, bar (marked N/S)—
   15 pairs—p. 155, 163, 224**
magnet, horseshoe—1—p. 158**
mystery bags (unfamiliar objects—
   pineapple, rolling pin)—1 each—
   p. 127
nail, iron—15—p. 224**
objects, small (coins, keys, plastic
   leaves, shells)—15 each—p. 83
objects to test (sink/float: such as
   button, clothespin, cork, bar of
   soap, toy boat)—1 each—p. 129**
objects to test (with magnet: such
   as erasers, marbles, paper clips,
   pennies, twist ties, rubber bands,
   screws)—15 each—p. 159

overlays, transparent—30—p. 79**
paper clips—1 box—p. 134, 158,
   224**
pet—classroom—p. 30
people to interview—p. 46
postcards, beach-scene—6—p. 216
rocks, assorted (suggested: granite,
   limestone, marble, obsidian,
   pumice, shale)—1 each—p. 93**
rope—6 pieces—p. 177**
ruler, centimeter—30—p. 213**
scissors—30—p. 14, 19, 25, 134,
   184, 193, 196
shells—assorted small—15—
   p. 83**
toothbrush—individual—p. 183

**Consumables**
bag, paper—60—p. 62, 184, 222**
bag, plastic—30—p. 71
bird food—1 bag—p. 217**
cardboard tubes (paper towel
   or toilet paper)—60—p. 44
chalk, assorted colors—30—p. 87**
chalk, white—15 pieces—p. 107**
cloth strips—15—p. 173
crackers, saltine—1 box—p. 123*
crayons—30 boxes—p. 11, 19, 22,
   25, 59, 62, 76, 97, 143, 155, 183,
   189, 196, 198, 208, 209, 212, 218,
   219, 222
cups, clear plastic—61—p. 9, 14, 41,
   158, 223**
cups, 3-oz. paper—30—p. 123**
dehydrated or instant foods,
   variety—1 bag each—p. 114
dried fruits, variety—1 bag—p. 114
egg cartons—30—p. 19
daisies, fresh with long stems—
   150—p. 5*
glue—30 bottles—p. 14, 19, 25, 155,
   184, 193, 196
grapefruit rinds, halves—15—
   p. 217*
ice cubes—15—p. 223
juice, apple—half gallon—p. 223*
magazines, old—60—p. 25, 184
markers, felt-tip—30—p. 79, 196**
matte spray—1 can—p. 87
milk—half gallon—p. 123*

newspapers—tall stack—p. 184,
   220
paper, assorted construction—
   2 packages—p. 14, 19, 134,
   196, 222
paper, drawing—8 packages—p. 11,
   22, 76, 87, 97, 183, 196, 212, 223
paper, large drawing—2 packages—
   p. 25, 59, 143, 189, 198, 208, 218,
   219
paper, brown kraft—1 roll—p. 193
paper, graph—30 sheets—p. 143
paper, lined tablet—5 tablets—p. 11,
   44, 46, 97, 212, 221
paper, newsprint—1 package—
   p. 93, 98
pattern, air spinner—15—p. 134
pattern, magnet maze—30—p. 155
plates, paper—1 large package—
   p. 155, 184**
posterboard—2 large sheets—
   p. 111
seeds, lima beans—150—p. 9, 14,
   41**
soils (clayrich, humus, sandy)—
   4 cups each—p. 98**
soil, potting—1 40-lb bag—p. 9, 14,
   41**
string—1 ball—p. 107**
sweet potatoes—6—p. 35*
tape, masking—1 roll—p. 44
tape, wide transparent—1 roll—p. 41
thread, heavy—1 spool—p. 5**
toothpaste—as needed—p. 183
toothpicks, round—1 box—p. 5, 35**
water, tap (warm and cold)—as
   needed—p. 30, 35, 41, 114, 129,
   158
yarn, heavy jute—2 skeins—p. 139**
yarn, 4-ply knitting—2 skeins—p. 51,
   217, 222**

*perishable
**included in Materials Kit

# RESOURCES

## Film/Filmstrip Suppliers

**Academy Films**
Box 1023
Venice, CA 90291

**Agency for Instructional Technology (AIT)**
Box A
Bloomington, IN 47401

**AIMS Media**
6901 Woodley Avenue
Van Nuys, CA 91406

**American Forest Institute**
1250 Connecticut Avenue, NW
Suite 320
Washington, DC 20036

**Barr Films**
P.O. Box 5667
3490 East Foothill Boulevard
Pasadena, CA 91107

**Beacon Films**
1250 Washington Street
Box 575
Norwood, MA 02062

**Benchmark Films, Inc.**
145 Scarborough Road
Briarcliff Manor, NY 10510

**Bullfrog Films, Inc.**
Oley, PA 19547

**Carolina Biological Supply Co.**
2700 York Road
Burlington, NC 27215

**Centre Productions, Inc.**
1800 30 Street, Suite 307
Boulder, CO 80301

**Centron Educational Films**
Div. of Simon & Schuster
108 Wilmot Road
Deerfield, IL 60015

**Clearvue, Inc.**
5711 N. Milwaukee
Chicago, Il 60646

**Coronet/MTI Film & Video**
Distributors of LCA
108 Wilmot Road
Deerfield, IL 60015

**Counselor Films**
1728 Cherry Street
Philadelphia, PA 19103

**CRM/McGraw-Hill**
P.O. Box 641
Del Mar, CA 92014

**Davidson Films, Inc.**
231 "E" Street
Davis, CA 95616

**Educational Media International**
Box 1288
175 Margaret Place
Elmhurst, IL 60126

**Encyclopaedia Britannica Educational Corporation**
425 N. Michigan Avenue
Chicago, IL 06011

**Filmakers Library, Inc.**
133 E. 58th Street, 703A
New York, NY 10022

**Films for the Humanities, Inc.**
Box 2053
Princeton, NJ 08540

**Films, Inc.**
1213 Wilmette Avenue
Wilmette, IL 60091

**Gateway** (now Coronet)

**Handel Film Corporation**
8730 Sunset Boulevard
West Hollywood, CA 90069

**Hawaii State Dept. of Education**
1390 Miller Street
Honolulu, HA 96813

**Indiana University Audiovisual Center**
Bloomington, IN 47405-5901

**International Film Bureau, Inc.**
332 S. Michigan Avenue
Chicago, IL 60604

**Journal Films, Inc.**
930 Pitner Avenue
Evanston, IL 60202

**Knowledge Unlimited**
Box 52
Madison, WI 53701

**Learning Corp. of America**
(now Coronet)

**Library Filmstrip Center**
205 E. Locust Street
Bloomington, IL 61701

**Mar/Chuk Film Industries, Inc.**
P.O. Box 61
Mount Prospect, IL 60056

**Macmillan Video**
Macmillan Publishing Co.
866 Third Avenue
New York, NY 10022

**MTI Teleprograms** (now Coronet)

**National Audiovisual Center**
8700 Edgeworth Drive
Capitol Heights, MD 20743

**National Film Board of Canada**
1251 Avenue of the Americas
New York, NY 10020

**National Geographic Society Educational Services**
17th and "M" Streets, NW
Washington, DC 20036

**New World Video**
1888 Century Park E
Los Angeles, CA 90067

**Paramount** (now AIMS Media)

**Phoenix/BFA Educational Media**
Division of Phoenix Films
468 Park Avenue S
New York, NY 10016

**Professional Research, Inc.**
930 Pitner Avenue
Evanston, IL 60202

**PBS Video**
475 L'Enfant Plaza, SW
Washington, DC 20024

**Pyramid Film & Video**
Box 1048
Santa Monica, CA 90406

**Society for Visual Education, Inc.**
1345 Diversey Parkway
Chicago, IL 60614

**Stanton Films**
2417 Artesia Boulevard
Redondo Beach, CA 90278

**Sterling Education Films, Inc.**
241 E. 34th Street
New York, NY 10016

**Walt Disney Educational Media Co.**
500 S. Buena Vista Street
Burbank, CA 91521

**Weston Woods Studios, Inc.**
389 Newtown Turnpike
Weston, CT 06883

**Wombat Productions, Inc.**
250 W 57 St., Suite 916
New York, NY 10019

film film film

# RESOURCES

## VIDEOTAPE

### Videotape Suppliers

**Agency for Instructional Technology (AIT)**
Box A
Bloomington, IN 47401

**AIMS Media**
6901 Woodley Avenue
Van Nuys, CA 91406

**Barr Films**
P.O. Box 5667
3490 East Foothill Boulevard
Pasadena, CA 91107

**Beacon Films**
1250 Washington Street
Box 575
Norwood, MA 02062

**Bullfrog Films**
Oley, PA 19547

**Carolina Biological Supply Co.**
2700 York Road
Burlington, NC 27215

**Centre Productions, Inc.**
1800 30th Street, Suite 207
Boulder, CO 80301

**Centron Educational Films**
Division of Simon & Schuster
108 Wilmot Road
Deerfield, IL 60015

**Coronet/MTI Film & Video**
Distributors of LCA
108 Wilmot Road
Deerfield, IL 60015

**Educational Media International**
Box 1288
175 Margaret Place
Elmhurst, IL 60126

**Encyclopaedia Britannica Educational Corporation (EBEC)**
425 N. Michigan Avenue
Chicago, IL 60611

**Filmakers Library, Inc.**
133 E. 58th St., 703A
New York, NY 10022

**Films for the Humanities, Inc.**
Box 2053
Princeton, NJ 08540

**Films, Inc.**
733 Green Bay Road
Wilmette, IL 60091

**Handel Film Corp.**
8730 Sunset Boulevard
Los Angeles, CA 90069

**Hawkhill Associates, Inc.**
125 E. Gilman Street
Madison, WI 53703

**International Film Bureau, Inc.**
332 S. Michigan Avenue
Chicago, IL 60604

**Learning Corp. of America**
(now Coronet)

**Macmillan Video**
866 Third Avenue
New York, NY 10022

**Media Projects, Inc.**
P.O. Box 2008
Portland, OR 97208

**National Audiovisual Center**
8700 Edgeworth Drive
Capitol Heights, MD 20743

**National Film Board of Canada**
1251 Avenue of the Americas
New York, NY 10020

**National Geographic Society Educational Services**
17th and M Street, NW
Washington, DC 20036

**New World Video**
1888 Century Park, East
Los Angeles, CA 90067

**Perennial Education, Inc.**
930 Pitner Avenue
Evanston, IL 60202

**Phoenix/BFA Educational Media**
Division of Phoenix Films
468 Park Avenue S
New York, NY 10016

**Professional Research Inc.**
930 Pitner Avenue
Evanston, IL 60202

**Pyramid Film & Video**
Box 1048
Santa Monica, CA 90406

**Society for Visual Education**
1345 W. Diversey Parkway
Chicago, IL 60614

**Time-Life Video**
Time-Life Building
1271 Avenue of the Americas
New York, NY 10020

**University of California Extension Media Center**
2223 Fulton Street
Berkeley, CA 94720

**University of Texas**
Audiovisual Unit
7703 Floyd Curl Drive
San Antonio, TX 78274

**University of Utah Instructional Media Services**
207 Milton Bennion Hall
Salt Lake City, UT 84112

**University of Wisconsin Bureau of Audio Visual Instruction**
1327 University Avenue
P.O. Box 2093
Madison, WI 53701

**Walt Disney Educational Media Co.**
500 S. Buena Vista Street
Burbank, CA 91521

**Wombat Productions, Inc.**
250 W. 57 Street, Suite 916
New York, NY 10019

# RESOURCES

## TV Programs

### Public Broadcasting Service

**"All About You"**
30—15 minute lessons
Primary—Health
Teacher Guide

**"Community of Living Things"**
15—15 minute lessons
Intermediate—Science
Teacher Guide

**"Discovering"**
20—15 minute lessons
Intermediate—Science
Teacher Guide

**"Dragons, Wagons & Wax"**
30—15 minute lessons
Primary—Science
Teacher Guide

**"Human Community"**
15—15 minute lessons
Intermediate—Life,
Environmental
Teacher Guide

**"The Inside Story with Slim Goodbody"**
8-15 minute lessons
Primary—Health
Teacher Guide

**"L-4"** (Man's relationship
with environment—Earth
and Space)
16—15 minute lessons
Intermediate—Science
Teacher Guide

**"Owl TV"**
30 minutes
Primary/Intermediate

**"Search for Science"**
30—15 minute lessons
Intermediate—Science
Teacher Guide

**"3-2-1 Contact"**
30 minutes
Intermediate/Jr. High—
Science
Write: Children's TV
Workshop for teacher guides.

**"Up Close & Natural"**
15—15 minute lessons
Primary—Science
Teacher Guide

**"Zoo Zoo Zoo"**
16—15 minute lessons
Primary—Natural Science
Teacher Guide

### Nickelodeon

**"Mr. Wizard's World"**
30 minutes
Intermediate/Jr. High

# RESOURCES

## Software Suppliers

**Activision, Inc.**
2350 Bayshore Parkway
Mountain View, CA 94043

**AIMS Media**
6901 Woodley Avenue
Van Nuys, CA 91406

**Bantam Books**
666 Fifth Avenue
New York, NY 10103

**BrainBank, Inc.**
220 Fifth Avenue
New York, NY 10001

**Collamore Educational
Publishing**
125 Spring Street
Lexington, MA 02173

**Diversified Educational
Enterprises**
725 Main Street
Lafayette, IN 47901

**Educational Activities, Inc.**
1937 Grand Avenue
Baldwin, NY 11510

**Educational Materials &
Equipment Co.**
P.O. Box 17
Pelham, NY 10803

**Educational Technology**
6150 N. 16th Street
Phoenix, AZ 85016

**Focus Media, Inc.**
839 Stewart Avenue
Garden City, NY 11530

**Grolier Electronic
Publishing, Inc.**
95 Madison Avenue
New York, NY 10016

**Intellectual Software**
562 Boston Avenue
Bridgeport, CT 06610

**January Productions**
249 Goffle Road
P.O. Box 66
Hawthorne, NJ 07507

**K–12 MicroMedia**
6 Arrow Rd.
Ramsey, NJ 07446

**Learning Well**
200 South Service Road
Roselyn Heights, NY 11577

**Marshfilm/Marshware, Inc.**
P.O. Box 8082
Shawnee Mission, KS 66208

**MECC**
3490 Lexington Avenue,
North
St. Paul, MN 55126

**Micro Power & Light Co.**
12810 Hillcrest Rd., Suite 120
Dallas, TX 75230

**Mindscape**
3444 Dundee Road
Northbrook, IL 60062

**Orange Cherry Software**
P.O. Box 427
Bedford Hills, NY 10507

**Right On Programs**
1737 Veterans Highway
Central Islip, NY 11722

**Simon & Schuster**
P.O. Box 2987
New York, NY 10185

**Spectrum Software**
75 Todd Pond Road
Lincoln, MA 01773

**Teach Yourself by
Computer Software, Inc.**
2128 West Jefferson Road
Pittsford, NY 14534

**T.H.E.S.I.S.**
P.O. Box 147
Garden City, MI 48135

**Unicorn Software**
2950 East Flamingo Road,
#B
Las Vegas, NV 89121

**World Book Discovery, Inc.**
510 Merchandise Mart Plaza
Chicago, IL 60654

# software

# RESOURCES

## Scientific Equipment Suppliers

**Aquarium and Science Supply Co.**
1610 North Kings Highway
Cherry Hill, NJ 08034
(609) 795-5302/5303

**Carolina Biological Supply Co.**
2700 York Road
Burlington, NC 27215
(919) 584-0381

**Central Scientific Co.**
(CENCO)
11222 Melrose Avenue
Franklin Park, IL 60131
(312) 451-0150

**Connecticut Valley Biological Supply Co., Inc.**
82 Valley Road
P.O. Box 326
Southampton, MA 01073
(800) 628-7748

**Delta Education, Inc.**
P.O. Box M
Nashua, NH 03061-6012
(800) 258-1302

**Edmund Scientific Co.**
101 E. Gloucester Pike
Barrington, NJ 08007
(609) 547-3488

**Fisher Scientific Co.**
Educational Materials Div.
4901 W. LeMoyne St.
Chicago, IL 60651
(800) 621-4769

**Frey Scientific Co.**
905 Hickory Lane
Mansfield, OH 44905
(419) 589-9905

**Grau-Hall Scientific Corp.**
6501 Elvas Avenue
Sacramento, CA 95819
(916) 455-5258

**Kons Scientific Co., Inc.**
P.O. Box 3
Germantown, WI 53022-0003
(800) 242-5667

**Learning Things, Inc.**
68A Broadway
P.O. Box 436
Arlington, MA 02174
(617) 646-0093

**McKilligan Supply Corp.**
435 Main Street
Johnson City, NY 13790
(607) 729-6511

**Nasco**
901 Janesville Avenue
Fort Atkinson, WI 53538
(414) 563-2446

**Sargent-Welch Scientific Co.**
7300 N. Linder Avenue
Skokie, IL 60077
(312) 677-0600

**Schoolmasters Science**
745 State Circle
P.O. Box 1941
Ann Arbor, MI 48106
(313) 761-5072

**Science Kit and Boreal Laboratories**
777 East Park Drive
Tonawanda, NY 14150
(800) 828-7777

**Ward's Natural Science Establishment, Inc.**
5100 W. Henrietta Road
P.O. Box 92912
Rochester, NY 14692-9012
(800) 962-2660

# RESOURCES

INSTRUCTIONAL AIDS · PERIODICALS

## Instructional Aids

**American Geophysical Union**
2000 Florida Avenue, NW
Washington, D.C. 20009
(202) 462-6903

**American Nuclear Society**
555 N. Kensington Avenue
LaGrange Park, IL 60525
(312) 352-6611

**Astro Media**
Div. of Kalmbach Pub. Co.
1027 N. Seventh Street
Milwaukee, WI 53233
(414) 272-2060

**Astronomical Society of the Pacific**
1290 24th Avenue
San Francisco, CA 94122
(415) 661-8660

**Cambridge Development Lab**
1696 Massachusetts Avenue
Cambridge, MA 02138
(800) 637-0047

**Creative Dimensions**
P.O. Box 1393
Bellingham, WA 98227
(206) 733-5024

**Hansen Publications**
1098 South 200 West
Salt Lake City, UT 84101
(800) 321-2369

**H. S. Center for Educational Resources**
T-281 HSB SB-56
University of Washington
Seattle, WA 98195
(206) 545-1186

**Hubbard Scientific Company**
P.O. Box 104
1946 Raymond Drive
Northbrook, IL 60062
(800) 323-8368

**Ideal School Supply Company**
11000 S. Lavergne Avenue
Oak Lawn, IL 60453
(312) 425-0800

**Lawrence Hall of Science**
Discovery Corner
University of California
Berkeley, CA 94720
(415) 642-1016

**MMI Corp.**
2950 Wyman Parkway
P.O. Box 19907
Baltimore, MD 21211
(301) 366-1222

**NASA**
National Aeronautics & Space Administration
Washington, DC 20546

**National Dairy Council**
6300 North River Road
Rosemont, IL 60018-4233
(312) 696-1020

**National Geographic Educational Services**
Dept. 76, P.O. Box 1640
Washington, DC 20013

**Nystrom**
3333 Elston Avenue
Chicago, IL 60618
(800) 621-8086

**Scavenger Scientific Supply Company**
P.O. Box 211328
Auke Bay, AK 99821

**The Science Man Co.**
A Div. of TSM Marketing, Inc.
4738 N. Harlem Avenue
Harwood Heights, IL 60656
(312) 867-4441

**Scott Resources/ESNR Division**
P.O. Box 2121
401 Hickory Street
Fort Collins, CO 80522
(303) 484-7445

**Society for Nutrition Education**
2140 Shattuck Ave., Suite 1110
Berkeley, CA 94704

**Society for Visual Education, Inc.**
1345 Diversey Parkway
Chicago, IL 60614
(312) 525-1500

## Science Periodicals for Students

### Primary
*Animal Kingdom*
New York Zoological Society
Bronx, NY 10460

*Chickadee*
Young Naturalist Foundation
59 Front Street
Toronto, Ontario M5E 1B3,
Canada

*Scienceland*
Scienceland, Inc.
501 Fifth Avenue
New York, NY 10017

*Your Big Backyard*
National Wildlife Federation
8925 Leesburg Pike
Vienna, VA 22184-0001

### Elementary
*Animals*
Massachusetts Society for the Prevention of Cruelty to Animals
350 S. Huntington Avenue
Boston, MA 02130

*Current Science*
Xerox Education Publications
1250 Fairwood Avenue
Columbus, OH 43216

*Dolphin Log*
Cousteau Society
Membership Center
930 West 21st Street
Norfolk, VA 23517

*Kind*
The Humane Society of the U.S.
Youth Membership Division
2100 L Street, NW
Washington, DC 20037

*National Geographic World*
National Geographic Society
17th and M Street, NW
Washington, DC 20036

*Odyssey*
1027 N. 7th Street
Milwaukee, WI 53233

*Owl*
P.O. Box 2878
Des Moines, IA 50320

*Ranger Rick*
National Wildlife Federation
8925 Leesburg Pike
Vienna, VA 22184-0001

*Science World*
Scholastic, Inc.
P.O. Box 644
Lyndhurst, NJ 07071

*3-2-1 Contact*
Box 53051
Boulder, CO 80322-2933

*Zoo Books*
Wildlife Education, Inc.
P.O. Box 85271
San Diego, CA 92138

*Zoonooz*
Zoological Society of San Diego, Inc.
Box 551
San Diego, CA 92112

# RESOURCES

BOOKS

## Elementary Science Methods Books

Abruscato, Joseph. *Teaching Children Science.* Englewood Cliffs, NJ: Prentice-Hall, 1982.

*Building Basic Skills in Science.* Chicago, IL: Contemporary Books, Inc., 1982.

Carin, Arthur and Robert Sund. *Teaching Science Through Discovery.* Columbus, OH: Merrill Publishing Co., 1985.

Friedl, Arthur. *Teaching Science to Children: An Integrated Approach.* Westminster, MD: Random House, 1986.

Gega, Peter C. *Science in Elementary Education.* New York: John Wiley & Sons, 1986.

Harlan, Jean. *Science Experiences for the Early Childhood Years.* Columbus, OH: Merrill Publishing Co., 1984.

Iatridis, Mary D. *Teaching Science to Young Children: A Resource Book.* New York: Garland Publishing, 1986.

Kintsch, W. *Methods & Tactics in Cognitive Science.* Hillsdale, NJ: Erlbaum, Assoc., 1984.

McGill, Ormond. *Science Magic: One Hundred One Experiments You Can Do.* New York: Arco Publishing, Inc., 1984.

Stull, Elizabeth C. and Carol L. Price. *Science and Math Enrichment Activities for the Primary Grades.* West Nyack, NY: The Center for Applied Research in Education, Inc., 1987.

## Earth Science Resource Books

Bakker, Robert T. *The Dinosaur Heresies.* New York: William Morrow & Co., 1986.

Ballard, Robert D. *Exploring Our Living Planet.* Washington, DC: National Geographic Society, 1983.

Cattermole, Peter and Patrick Moore. *The Story of the Earth.* New York: Cambridge University Press, 1985.

Cooke, Donald A. *The Life and Death of Stars.* New York: Crown Pubs., Inc., 1985.

Darling, David J. *Discovering Our Universe.* Minneapolis: Dillon Press, Inc., 1985.

Dietrich, R.V. and Reed Wicander. *Minerals, Rocks and Fossils.* New York: John Wiley and Sons, 1983.

Forrester, Frank. *1001 Questions Answered About the Weather.* New York: Dover Publications, 1981.

Giovanelli, Ronald G. *Secrets of the Sun.* New York: Cambridge University Press, 1984.

Preiss, Bryon, Editor. *The Planets.* New York: Bantam Books Inc., 1985.

Redfern, Ron. *The Making of a Continent.* New York: Times Books, 1983.

Turk, Jonathan. *Introduction to Environmental Studies,* 2nd Edition. New York: Saunders College Publishing, 1985.

## Life Science Resource Books

Beller, Joel. *Experimenting with Plants.* Simon & Schuster, 1985.

Bodanis, David. *The Body Book: A Fantastic Voyage to the World Within.* Boston: Little, Brown & Co., 1984.

Department of the Interior, United States Fish and Wildlife Service. *Endangered and Threatened Wildlife and Plants.* Washington, DC: United States Government Printing Office, 1986.

Dowden, Anne. *From Flowers to Fruit.* New York: Crowell Junior Books, 1984.

Ferry, Georgina, Editor. *The Understanding of Animals.* New York: Basil Blackwell, 1984.

Gardner, Eldon J. *Human Heredity.* New York: John Wiley & Sons, 1983.

Gibbons, Bob. *How Flowers Work: A Guide to Plant Biology.* New York: Sterling Publishing Co., 1984.

Hoage, R.J., Editor. *Animal Extinction: What Everyone Should Know.* Washington, DC: Smithsonian, 1985.

Scheeler, Phillip and Donald E. Bianchi. *Cell Biology: Structure, Biochemistry, and Function.* New York: John Wiley & Sons, 1983.

Tributsch, Helmut, translated by Miriam Varon. *How Life Learned to Live: Adaptation in Nature.* Cambridge, MA: MIT Press, 1985.

Waldrop, Victor, Editor. *Incredible Animals A to Z.* Vienna, VA: National Wildlife Federation, 1985.

## Physical Science Resource Books

Dobbs, Roland. *Electricity and Magnetism.* Boston: Routledge and K. Paul, 1984.

Feynman, Richard P. *QED: The Strange Theory of Light and Matter.* Princeton, NJ: Princeton University Press, 1985.

Hess, Fred C. *Chemistry Made Simple.* New York: Doubleday and Co., 1984.

Holden, Alan and Phyllis Morrison. *Crystals and Crystal Growing.* Cambridge, MA: MIT Press, 1982.

Levine, Ira N. *Physical Chemistry.* New York: McGraw-Hill, 1983.

Milne, Lorus J. and Margery Milne. *Nature's Great Carbon Cycle.* New York: Atheneum Publishers, 1983.

Pierce, John R. *The Science of Musical Sound.* New York: W.H. Freeman, 1983.

Ramage, Janet. *Energy: A Guidebook.* New York: Oxford University Press, 1983.

Segre, Emile. *From Falling Bodies to Radio Waves.* New York: W.H. Freeman, 1984.

Walton, Alan J. *Three Phases of Matter,* 2nd Edition. New York: Clarendon Press, 1983.

# SCIENCE
## In Your World

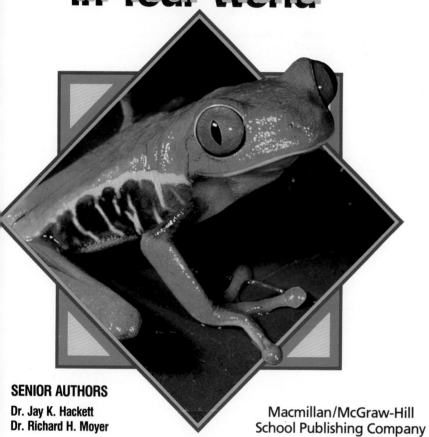

**SENIOR AUTHORS**
Dr. Jay K. Hackett
Dr. Richard H. Moyer

Macmillan/McGraw-Hill
School Publishing Company

## ACKNOWLEDGMENTS

For permission to reprint copyrighted material, grateful acknowledgment is made to the following authors, publishers, and agents. All possible care has been taken to trace the ownership of every selection included and to make full acknowledgment of its use. If any errors have inadvertently occurred, they will be corrected in subsequent editions, provided notification is sent to the publisher.

*Harper & Row, Publishers, Inc.:* Text from "Look" from *All That Sunlight* by Charlotte Zolotow, illustrated by Walter Stein. Text copyright © 1967 by Charlotte Zolotow.

*Florence Parry Heide:* "Rocks" by Florence Parry Heide, reprinted with permission of the author, Florence Parry Heide.

*Macmillan:* "The Little Turtle" reprinted/translated with permission of Macmillan Publishing Company from *Collected Poems* by Vachel Lindsay. Copyright © 1920 by Macmillan Publishing Company; renewed 1948 by Elizabeth C. Lindsay.

## CREDITS

**Series Editor:** Jane Parker
**Design Coordinator:** Kip Frankenberry
**Series Production Editor:** Helen Mischka
**Level Editor:** Linda A. Montgomery
**Contributing Editors:** Mary Duncan Garza, Lisa K. Higgins
**Production Editor:** Janet B. Arledge
**Designer:** Jeff Kobelt
**Artist:** Richard Metzger
**Photo Editor:** Mark Burnett

Macmillan/McGraw-Hill School Division
866 Third Avenue
New York, New York 10022

Printed in the United States of America

ISBN 0-675-16225-4                    9 8 7 6 5 4 3 2

# SENIOR AUTHORS

**Dr. Jay K. Hackett**
University of Northern Colorado

**Dr. Richard H. Moyer**
University of Michigan-Dearborn

# CONTRIBUTING AUTHORS

**Stephen C. Blume**
Elementary Science Curriculum Specialist
St. Tammany Public School System
Slidell, Louisiana

**Ralph M. Feather, Jr.**
Teacher of Geology, Astronomy, and Earth Science
Derry Area School District
Derry, Pennsylvania

**Edward Paul Ortleb**
Science Supervisor
St. Louis Board of Education
St. Louis, Missouri

**Dr. Barbara Swanson Thomson**
Associate Professor in Science Education
The Ohio State University
Columbus, Ohio

### CONTRIBUTING WRITER

**Ann H. Sankey**
Science Specialist
Educational Service District 121
Seattle, Washington

### READING CONSULTANT

**Barbara S. Pettegrew, Ph.D.**
Director of the Reading/Study Center
Assistant Professor of Education
Otterbein College, Westerville, Ohio

### SAFETY CONSULTANT

**Gary E. Downs, Ed.D.**
Professor
Iowa State University
Ames, Iowa

## GIFTED AND MAINSTREAMED CONSULTANTS

**George Fichter**
Educational Consultant
Programs for Gifted
Ohio Department of Education
Worthington, Ohio

**Timothy E. Heron, Ph.D.**
Professor
Department of Human Services, Education
The Ohio State University
Columbus, Ohio

## CONTENT CONSULTANTS

**Robert T. Brown, M.D.**
Associate Professor of Clinical
Pediatrics Dir., Section for
Adolescent Health The Ohio State Univ.
Children's Hosp. Columbus, Ohio

**Henry D. Drew, Ph.D.**
Chemist, U.S. FDA
Div. of Drug Analysis
St. Louis, Missouri

**Judith L. Doyle, Ph.D.**
Physics Teacher
Newark High School
Newark, Ohio

**Todd F. Holzman, M.D.**
Child Psychiatrist
Harvard Com. Health Plan
Wellesley, Massachusetts

**Knut J. Norstog, Ph.D.**
Research Associate
Fairchild Tropical Garden
Miami, Florida

**James B. Phipps, Ph.D.**
Prof., Geol./Oceanography
Grays Harbor College
Aberdeen, Washington

**R. Robert Robbins, Ph.D.**
Assoc. Professor
Astronomy Department
University of Texas
Austin, Texas

**Sidney E. White, Ph.D.**
Professor
Department of Geology/Mineralogy
The Ohio State Univ.
Columbus, Ohio

## REVIEWERS: Teachers and Administrators

**Virginia Ceruti,** Cleveland Elementary School, Norwood, MA; **Sister Teresa Fitzgerald,** CSJ, Office of Catholic Education, Brooklyn, NY; **Carmen G. Guerra,** Felipe R. Perez Elementary, Brownsville, TX; **JoAnn Hamm,** Danville Board of Education, Danville, KY; **Donna Jackson,** Hazel Avenue Elementary School, West Orange, NJ; **Norma Jones,** Austin Tracy School, Lucas, KY; **Barbara Kmetz,** Trumbull High School, Trumbull, CT; **Carol D. Massey,** John Glenn Elementary, San Antonio, TX; **Lee Dell McCarty,** United Methodist Publishing House, Nashville, TN; **Corinne Measelle,** Palm Beach County School Board, West Palm Beach, FL; **Waltina Mr'oczek,** Beachwood Elementary School, Beachwood, OH; **Deanna Owen,** Travis Magnet Elementary, Odessa, TX; **Linda Payne,** Whitesville Elementary School, Whitesville, KY; **Patrice Burns Reitblatt,** Westwood Terrace Elementary, San Antonio, TX; **Rosemary Schmitz,** Galm Elementary, San Antonio, TX; **Peggy Smith,** Special Education Resource Teacher, Fort Worth, TX; **Frank Stone,** Floranada Elementary School, Fort Lauderdale, FL; **Lana Tarlton,** Cook Elementary School, Austin TX; **Diane Thomas,** Northwest Crossing Elementary, San Antonio, TX; **Vivian Torres,** Leon Valley Elementary, San Antonio, TX; **Dr. Rosa White,** Cutler Ridge Elementary School, Miami, FL

# Table of Contents

## Unit 1 — Life Science 2

iv  denotes ACTIVITY.
See page x for ACTIVITIES TABLE OF CONTENTS.

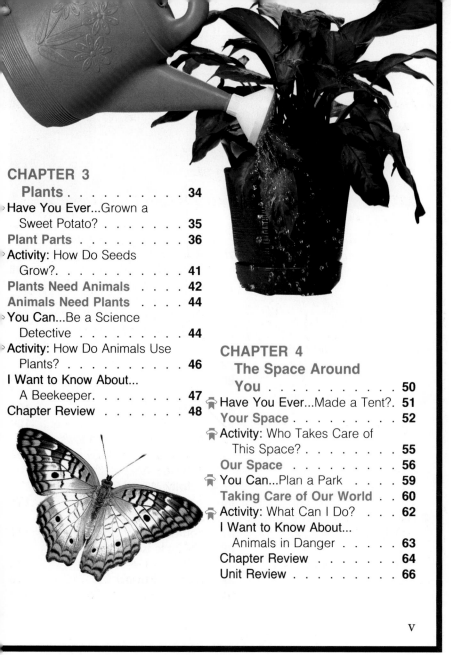

v

denotes ACTIVITY.
See page x for ACTIVITIES TABLE OF CONTENTS.

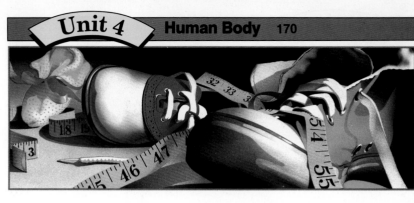

## Unit 4  Human Body  170

🔊 denotes ACTIVITY.
See page x for ACTIVITIES TABLE OF CONTENTS.

### You Can...

### Activities

## Process Skill Models

## Problem Solving Activities

## SCIENCE IS . . . UNDERSTANDING

Students need to be scientifically literate to be prepared to contribute to the world of today and tomorrow. **SCIENCE In Your World** introduces students to famous scientists and accepted scientific facts, concepts, theories, and laws.

Edward O. Wilson is a professor of entomology (a branch of zoology that deals with insects) at Harvard University. This quote is taken from an article in *Time* on October 13, 1986.

You may wish to discuss with students what this quote means. They may or may not know the cliché, "When you have seen one, you've seen them all." But they should quickly recognize that all things are not alike. Every thing on Earth is unique, even the students in the class.

Further, you may wish to take two objects (two leaves, for example) and have the class compare and contrast them. In addition, students could describe how this year will be different from last year.

# Science is…
# Understanding

"When you have seen one ant, one bird, one tree, you have not seen them all."
Edward O. Wilson   American scientist (1986)

How do living things grow?
What do animals need to live?
How do we use plants?
**Science has some answers for you.**

xii

# Science is...
# Discovering

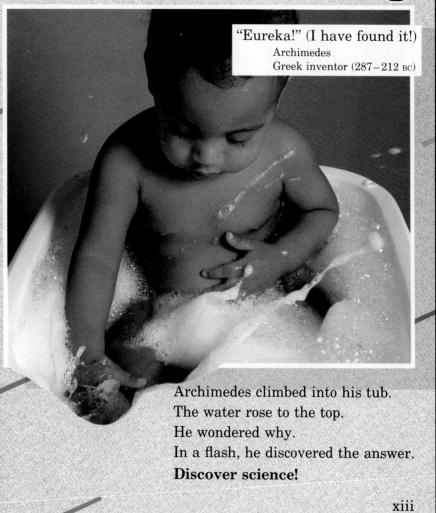

"Eureka!" (I have found it!)
Archimedes
Greek inventor (287–212 BC)

Archimedes climbed into his tub.
The water rose to the top.
He wondered why.
In a flash, he discovered the answer.
**Discover science!**

xiii

## SCIENCE IS . . . DISCOVERING

**SCIENCE In Your World** puts students in the role of scientists as they understand and use scientific methods to question, observe, describe, classify, measure, predict, hypothesize, and draw conclusions to solve problems in their world. Students will engage in literal, interpretive, critical, and creative thinking skills as they rediscover their world through scientific eyes.

Archimedes was an ancient Greek physicist and inventor. He was also the most celebrated mathematician of ancient times. "Eureka" is a famous quote, which many students may have heard from watching a television program called *Eureka's Castle*. It is shouted when a person makes a sudden discovery. It is also California's state motto.

The story behind the quote is that Archimedes was given the task of determining the purity of gold in a crown. Archimedes realized, as he stepped into his bath, that when a solid body is immersed in a liquid, it apparently loses weight, and this apparent loss of weight equals the weight of the liquid it displaces. A given weight of gold would displace less water than an equal weight of silver (which is less dense than gold). In his excitement at his discovery, Archimedes ran home naked, shouting, "Eureka!"

Although your students may not understand the principle of water displacement, they may remember the idea of shouting "Eureka!" when they make a discovery.

You may wish to lead a discussion about discoveries they have made. They may have realized how fast a car with closed windows heats up on a hot day. They may have dug into sand at a beach and found water. They may have a pet that has had babies. All of these are incidents at which these young scientists may shout, "Eureka!"

## SCIENCE IS . . . DECIDING

Science is more than concepts and discovery. **SCIENCE In Your World** recognizes that science involves important decision-making skills as well. Students can work to solve today's and tomorrow's problems by learning how to make responsible decisions. The scientific decisions made in the realms of life, earth, and physical science affect our lives today and the lives of many future generations.

This proverb is often attributed to Ben Franklin's *Poor Richard's Almanac* (1733) along with "Early to bed and early to rise, makes a man healthy, wealthy, and wise." But it is really an anonymous saying that has been current since the nineteenth century.

You may wish to take this opportunity to talk with your class about foods that are good for them and decisions they make about what to eat every day. Ask them what they do to stay healthy. Do they eat an apple a day?

Science is...

# Deciding

"An apple a day keeps the doctor away."

Anonymous Old Saying

How can you stay healthy?
What choices can you make?
**Science can help you decide.**

xiv

# Science is...

# Applying

Applying

"...cience is experiment;
...ience is trying things."
Jacob Bronowski
English scientist (1908–1974)

Scientific inventions can help you.
The elevator helps people every day.
Have you used it?

## SCIENCE IS . . . APPLYING

Scientific knowledge can affect all aspects of students' lives at home, in school, in the community, in the world, and in the universe. Applying the scientific principles they learn in **SCIENCE In Your World** today, students can better understand and make decisions about the world around them.

Jacob Bronowski was born in Poland and educated at Cambridge University in England. He was trained as a mathematician, but after studying the effects of atomic bombing, he began to study the future direction of science. He has written several books, including *Science and Human Values* (1956) and *The Ascent of Man* (1973). This quote is from his book *A Sense of the Future*, published in 1977.

You may wish to ask students what they think an experiment is. They may have tried an experiment to see how their parents would behave if they acted a certain way. They may have tried different ways to train a pet or different uses for a common object. You might convey the idea that, in a way, all experiments involve science because they involve a scientific method. Most inventions have involved experiments and trying things. Experimenting leads to useful knowledge.

For the elevator example, you may wish to ask students if they have ever ridden on an elevator and explain how it is different from an escalator. In 1861, the American inventor Elisha G. Otis patented a steam-powered elevator. Later, steam power was replaced by hydraulic power and then by electricity. Over the years, more safety devices and automatic controls have been introduced.

## SCIENCE IS . . . THINKING SCIENTIFICALLY

This year in **SCIENCE In Your World,** students will go far beyond learning facts and understanding established scientific methods. Like scientists, they will use their minds to think about their world in new ways, solve problems, and develop ideas.

To help them think scientifically, the six critical thinking process skills listed here on the student pages are taught in **Process Skill Models** on sudent pages 208-214. These models introduce students to process skills that are appropriate to their developmental cognitive stage and are practiced over and over in the formal activities. In each model, a process skill is explained, described in a sample, and practiced in specific activities.

These models immediately precede the Problem Solving Activities that are cor-related with individual lessons. To aid your students in thinking like scientists from the beginning of the school year, you may wish to assign all of the models during the first several days of science class.

The Process Skill Models also appear in the *Activity Book,* pages 1-12.

Science is...

Classifying

Inferring

Observing

xvi

Using Numbers

Communicating

Measuring

Find out all about these process skills on pages 208-214 of this science book.

in your world...

1

# SCIENCE IS . . . IN YOUR WORLD

Science is everywhere! What makes a plant grow? How high is the sky? Why is it blue? How do fish breathe? How do animals communicate? How does a TV set work? How deep is the sea? How does bread rise? How do babies learn to talk? All the questions that people wonder about the world involve science. Using the scientific knowledge we have today and the scientific methods we can learn in **SCIENCE In Your World,** we can seek the answers to the wonders of the world.

You may wish to make a list of questions children have about the world and show how their questions involve science. Many of their questions may have complex answers that scientists have not yet been able to discover. Have students think of themselves as the scientists of the future who will be able to understand more than ever before.

# Life Science

## Classroom Centers

*I have no time to plan! Where can I find ideas for bulletin boards, audio visuals, and so on? Look no further!*

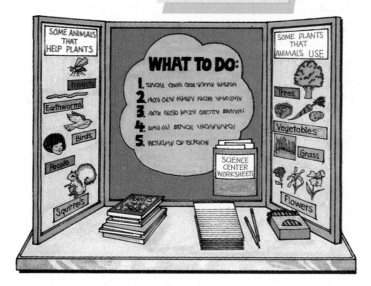

## Bulletin Board

**Goals:** The purpose of this bulletin board is to show that animals are living things and require food, water, and air to breathe. Choose a habitat and illustrate its components so students can see how life's needs are met in that habitat.

**Materials:** habitat background mural
construction-paper animals and plants

**Procedure:** This bulletin board can be constructed as a class project. Paint a background mural of a habitat. The habitat could be a desert, ocean, forest, or grassland. Include physical features appropriate to the habitat. Make construction-paper animals and plants representative of living things that exist in that habitat. Glue these to the background mural. Be sure that food and water sources are shown. Label the bulletin board as suggested in the illustration.

## ⬚ Science Center

**Goals:** Students will examine an assortment of pictures of plants and animals and explain how they are important to one another. You may find other suggestions in the margin material suitable for additional science center activities.

**Materials:** pictures of a variety of animals and plants
construction paper     crayons
markers     pencils
reference books     ruled paper

**Procedure:** Cut out an assortment of pictures of animals that help plants and display these on one side of a backboard as shown. On the other side of the board, display a variety of pictures of plants that are used by animals. In the center, direct the students to look at the pictures and (1) select an animal and tell how the animal helps a plant; or (2) select a plant and tell how the plant is used by animals. Have students write stories based on their choices and illustrate their work. Have students complete a science center worksheet found on page 205 in the Teacher Resource Package.

## Places to Go, People to See

### Field Trip Ideas

Arrange to visit a zoo and hear a presentation given by a zoo staff member. Many zoos allow children to have direct (supervised) contact with some of the zoo animals.

Arrange for a guided walk through a city or state park.

### Speakers and Visitors

Invite a volunteer or worker from a local humane society, zoo, or pet shop to talk to students about caring for living things.

Contact your local zoo and arrange to have a wild animal "visitor." Some zoos transport small, safe animals to schools for educational purposes.

## Audiovisuals for the Students

 ### Film and Filmstrips

*Animal Babies,* 16 mm, 10 min., color, Encyclopaedia Britannica Educational Corp.

*Animals Move in Many Ways,* 16 mm, 10 min., color, Phoenix BFA Educational Media.

*Learning About Flowers and Their Seeds,* 16 mm, 14 min., color, Encyclopaedia Britannica Educational Corp.

*Seeds and How They Travel,* 1 filmstrip, 1 cassette, 14 min., National Geographic Society.

 ### Videotapes

*All About Animals: Insects,* 12 min., color, AIMS Media.

*A Grain of Wheat,* 8 min., color, Phoenix Films and Video.

 ### Computer Software

*Animal Kingdom*   Teaches about different classes of animals from prehistoric animals to amphibians, reptiles, insects, and mammals. Sound effects and color graphics.
Type: Tutorial
Hardware: Apple II+, IIe, Commodore 64
Supplier: Unicorn Software

*Fantastic Animals*   Includes three activities: Mixed Up Animals; Animal Arcade; and Take the Animals Home. Students learn body parts and appropriate environments.
Type: Games
Hardware: Apple II+, IIe, IIc, Commodore 64, IBM PC, PCjr
Supplier: Bantam Books

## Resources for the Teacher

 ### Materials at Little/No Cost

Stokes Seeds          W. Atlee Burpee Co.
Box 548               300 Park Avenue
Buffalo, NY 14240     Warminster, PA 18974
Seed catalogs are free from many seed companies.
A wide variety of free leaflets and reports on animals can be obtained by writing for a list of publications from your state's Department of Natural Resources, Division of Wildlife.

 ### Resource Books

Beller, Joel. *Experimenting With Plants.* New York: Simon & Schuster, 1985.

Embrey, Joan and Ed Lucaire. *Joan Embrey's Collection of Amazing Animal Facts.* New York: Dell Publishing Co., 1984.

Palmer, E. Lawrence and Seymour Fowler. *Fieldbook of Natural History,* 2nd Edition. New York: McGraw-Hill, 1975.

# UNIT 1

## Life Science

### UNIT CONCEPTS

**Chapter 1**
- The world is made up of living and nonliving things.
- Plants and animals, including people, are living things.

**Chapter 2**
- Animals are different in their sizes, body parts, and body coverings.
- Animals live in different habitats.

**Chapter 3**
- All plants have certain plant parts.
- Plants need animals to perform certain functions.
- Animals use plants in a variety of ways.

**Chapter 4**
- Each individual has personal space in the environment.
- People share their space with other living things.
- Each person is responsible for personal and shared space in the environment.

*Be prepared! Chapter concepts appear in one neat package right here.*

*Life Science*

2

*Literature in a science book? You bet! Relate science to what students are reading.*

T here was a little turtle.

He lived in a box.

He swam in a puddle.

He climbed on the rocks.

from "The Little Turtle"
Vachel Lindsay

3

# ACTIVITY CENTER

For fun, hands-on, independent activities that integrate reading, writing, math, and technology with the chapters in this unit, have students complete some or all of the Activity Center Activities below. Look for specific chapter references in the Lesson Planning Guides.

**Reading:** 1 Is It Living? 2 Name That Story, 3 Plant a Garden, 4 Your Space
**Writing:** 1 Is It Alive? 2 If I Could Be... 3 Pleasing Plants, 4 My Space
**Math:** 1 Animal Maker, 2 Seed Sort, 3 Nuts About Patterns, 4 Flower Power
**Technology:** 1 Using Wood, 2 My Favorite Food, 3 We Wear Plants, 4 Too Much Trash

## CONNECTING LITERATURE TO SCIENCE

### Understanding the Selection
■ Call attention to the turtle in the illustration and encourage students to tell what they know about turtles.
■ Read the poem aloud. Then have students read the poem aloud with you.
■ Ask: **Where does the poet say the turtle lived?** *in a box* **Why do you think the turtle lived in a box?** *It was a pet.*
■ Ask students to name and discuss some other animals that make good pets. Record the responses in a cluster diagram. See the example below.

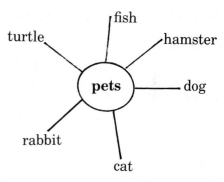

### Relating the Selection to Unit Concepts
■ Ask students where turtles usually live. Possible answers: *rivers, ponds, lakes.*
■ Discuss how animals in the wild care for themselves and how people care for some animals. Ask: **What are some ways in which animals in the wild take care of themselves?** Possible answers: *They find food; they find homes; they protect themselves.*
■ Ask: **How do people take care of animals?** Possible answers: *feed them; take them outside; play with them.*

### Relating the Selection to the Student's World
■ Have students identify the small photograph and tell where a lion cub might live. Possible answers: *in a den, in the zoo, in the wild*
■ Ask: **If this lion lived in the wild, how would it take care of itself?** Possible answer: *hunt for food and shelter.*
■ Ask: **If this lion lived in the zoo, how would it be taken care of?** Possible answers: *It would be fed; it would get help if it were sick.*

# What Is a Living Thing?

*Plan ahead—*
*See each lesson*
*in the chapter*
*at a glance:*
*objectives, vocabulary,*
*materials, and all*
*program supplement*

## Planning Guide

| Lessons | Objectives | Vocabulary |
|---|---|---|
| **Chapter Introduction** pp. 4, 5 | | |
| **Lesson 1 Living and Nonliving Things** pp. 6–9 | 1. **Identify** the differences between living and nonliving things. <br> 2. **Recognize** some common characteristics of living things. | nonliving things <br> living things |
| **Lesson 2 Many Living Things** pp. 10–15 | 3. **Determine** that a wide variety of plants and animals are living things. <br> 4. **Identify** people as living things. <br> 5. **Describe** growth as a characteristic of living things. | |
| **Chapter Review** pp. 16, 17 | | |

# Planning Guide

| Text Activities | | Teacher Resource Masters | Other Components |
|---|---|---|---|
| **Title/Skill** | **Materials per Group** | | |
| **Have You Ever . . . Made a Crown?** p. 5<br>Observing<br>Time Allotment: 30 minutes | daisies<br>heavy thread<br>toothpick | | **Activity Center:** "Is It Living"; "Is It Alive"; "Using Wood" |
| **Is It Living or Nonliving?** p. 9<br>Observing<br>Time Allotment: 20 minutes<br><br>**Do You Have a Clue?** p. 216<br>Observing/inferring<br>Time Allotment: 20 minutes | 2 lima bean seeds<br>2 cups of soil<br>a plastic flower<br>pencil and paper<br><br>paper<br>pencil<br>crayons | Transparency Master, p. 1<br>♦ Family Science, p. 2<br>Activity Worksheet, p. 3<br>Independent Practice, p. 8<br>Language Arts Connection, p. 159 | Poster #1<br>Big Book, p. 1<br>Activity Book, p. 34 |
| **You Can . . . Think Smart,** p. 11<br>Observing/Communicating<br>Time Allotment: 15 minutes | pencil and paper<br>crayons | Activity Worksheet, p. 4<br>Critical Thinking, p. 5<br>▲ Critical Thinking, p. 6<br>Math Connection, p. 7<br>Independent Practice, p. 9<br>♦ Reteaching Activity, p. 10<br>Language Arts Connection, p. 160 | Big Book, p. 2<br>Activity Book, pp. 13, 14 |
| **Do Living Things Grow?** p. 14<br>Observing/Measuring<br>Time Allotment: 20 minutes | a lima bean seed<br>3 paper strips<br>a cup of soil<br>glue<br>scissors<br>pencil and paper | | |
| | | Test A, p. 11<br>Test B, p. 12 | Color Transparencies #1a and #1b |

♦ Basic / ▲ Advanced / All other masters are for use by all students.

# What Is a Living Thing?

*Need ideas for exceptional students or extra science projects? No problem! Here they are!*

## For Exceptional Students

### ESL/LEP

**Chapter 1/Lesson 2, Page 12**
Help students learn about growth and change by asking each child to keep a monthly growth chart throughout the year. Make a class graph each month and discuss the changes. Ask students to share other ways they might change during the year.

Your class may want to select a nearby tree to adopt for the year. Take a class picture beside the tree each month. Display the pictures in order. Each month discuss the change in the tree, students, weather, and clothing.

**Chapter 1/Lesson 1, Page 8**
Make and label sets of cards to play the game Concentration. Sets could include matching baby animals and adult animals or living and nonliving things. Magazines or old science books are good sources for pictures.

### Gifted

**Chapter 1/Lesson 2, Page 12**
To emphasize the diversity of life for your able and talented students, have them choose one group of like animals or plants, such as monkeys or conifers. Gather books or pictures and ask students to choose four different examples of life in one group and list how each is different from another.

### Mainstreamed

**Chapter 1/Lesson 1, Page 8**
**Learning Disabled:** Cut out magazine pictures. Show a picture to the students. Have students identify the living and nonliving items in the picture. Ask students to respond orally or in writing. Encourage students to find as many items as possible in the picture. Repeat the activity with other pictures.

## Projects to Do

### Whole Class Science Project

Choose a class pet to raise for the year. If one needs to be purchased, discuss how the money will be obtained. Emphasize the needs of the animal before the purchase. Make a list of all the items that will be needed to care for the pet. Set up a schedule for the care and maintenance of the pet. Keep a growth chart for the pet.

### Science Fair Projects

Individual students could do one of the following projects:

1. Plant some flower seeds in each of two cups. Care for one cup of seeds regularly with water and light. Put the other cup in a dark area. Water regularly. Make a chart to record what you do and what happens.
2. Study the life cycle of a tadpole or a caterpillar. Display artwork or pictures that show the various stages. Write about each stage of development.

Language Arts Connection 159

LANGUAGE ARTS CONNECTION · Language Study Skills Noting Details · Big Book 1

Name · Use with Chapter 1, Lesson 1.

**How Are Living Things Alike?**

Circle the things that are the same in each picture.

Answers will vary.

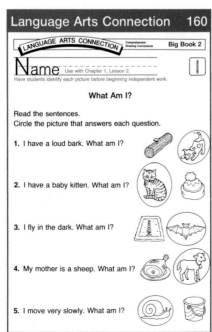

Language Arts Connection 160

LANGUAGE ARTS CONNECTION · Comprehension Drawing Conclusions · Big Book 2

Name · Use with Chapter 1, Lesson 2.

Have students identify each picture before beginning independent work.

**What Am I?**

Read the sentences.
Circle the picture that answers each question.

1. I have a loud bark. What am I?
2. I have a baby kitten. What am I?
3. I fly in the dark. What am I?
4. My mother is a sheep. What am I?
5. I move very slowly. What am I?

# CHAPTER 1

pages 4–17

## Chapter Concepts
■ The world is made of living and nonliving things.
■ Plants and animals, including people, are living things.

## Chapter Background
■ Energy is needed for life activities to continue. Animals consume food, while plants manufacture their own. Plants produce their own energy using water, air, light, and nutrients in the soil. Animals must ingest food to obtain energy.

## Looking Ahead
■ Invite a volunteer or worker from a local humane society, zoo, or pet shop to talk to students about caring for living things to **Close** Lesson 2.

## Look for These Symbols

    —Hands-on activity
    —Cooperative learning
    —Overhead transparency
◆  —Basic/Reinforcement
●  —Average/Enrichment
▲  —Advanced/Challenge
    —Science Center
    —Calculator Practice

*Watch for these easily recognizable symbols that tell you at a glance what type of learning experience is described.*

# SCIENCE
In Your World

4

# CHAPTER 1

# *What Is a Living Thing?*

Have you ever chased a butterfly?

Do you like the smell of flowers?

Our world is full of living things.

## ACTIVITY

### Have You Ever...

## Made a Crown?

1. Use a toothpick.

2. Make a hole in a flower stem.

3. Put another stem through the hole.

4. Repeat several times.

5. Tie the ends together.

What else can you make with flowers?

*Use this short, quick, fun activity to spark student interest and tap prior knowledge.*

*What are the four parts of every effective lesson? PREPLAN, FOCUS, TEACH, APPLY*

## PREPLAN

**Time Allotment:** 30 minutes

**Objectives**
1. **Recognize** that the world is full of living things.
2. **Observe** and make a crown of flowers.

**Setup**
To conduct the activity, collect the following materials for each student or **cooperative learning group.**

daisies          heavy thread          toothpick

## 1   FOCUS

■ Discuss the pictures on pages 4 and 5.

## 2   TEACH

■ Read the chapter title and introductory paragraph.
■ Ask: **Is a baby chick a living thing? Where does a baby chick come from?** *Yes. It hatches from an egg that a hen has laid.*

### Have You Ever . . .
■ If daisies aren't available, dandelions or other long-stemmed, nonpoisonous wildflowers may be used.
■ Display a crown made from flowers.

**Student Responses**
Answers may include a necklace or a bracelet.

## 3   APPLY

SC Choose another project for students to make something from natural things. Pine cones, sweet gum balls, shells or milkweed pods can be used.

**Close**
■ Point out that the world is made up of living and nonliving things. Tell students they will learn more about living things as they read Chapter 1.

# PREPLAN

## Lesson Objectives
1. **Identify** the differences between living and nonliving things.
2. **Recognize** some common characteristics of living things.

## Science Background
■ Cells of living things require air and water in order for processes to be conducted in the cells.
■ Oxygen is a critical gas needed for many different processes. Oxygen is required for respiration which releases energy from food.

## Lesson Vocabulary
nonliving things        living things

**Note:** The activity on student page 9 may be used for guided discovery before you begin this lesson.

# 1   FOCUS

■ Have a collection of living and nonliving things to show students. Ask them to determine which are living and which are nonliving. Ask them to explain why they put each item into a certain category. Make a class list of some similarities and some differences.

*1. Focus— Engage your students and prepare them for what's to come!*

# Living or Nonliving?

Some things are living.

Some things are not.

[1]How can you tell?

1. Most living things move on their own, grow, breathe, and so on.

*PREPLAN— What do you need? Lesson objectives and science background, of course.*

6

# TEACHER RESOURCE MASTERS

**Nonliving things** are not alive.

They do not need food.

They do not need water.

They do not need air.

*2. TEACH —*
*Use one or more of*
*these stimulating*
*teaching suggestions.*
*Guided and independent*
*practice make checking*
*for understanding*
*a snap.*

*3 APPLY*
*No lesson is*
*complete without*
*applying what*
*has been learned.*
*Lesson closure ties*
*up any loose ends*

7

## TEACHER RESOURCE MASTERS

*Students*
*having trouble?*
*Reteaching*
*Suggestions give*
*them another*
*chance.*

Independent Practice 1    8

INDEPENDENT PRACTICE   Lesson 1    Chapter 1

**N**ame

1. Circle the living things.   obj. 1

2. Circle what all living things need.   obj. 2

## 2   TEACH

Distribute some rocks, some cookies, two potted plants, and a teddy bear. Ask the students to decide what is living and what is nonliving. Ask: **Was anything made from something living?** *Cookies are made from plant materials that were once living.*

### Guided Practice

Divide students into **cooperative groups** of two. Give each pair a picture of a nonliving or a living thing. Ask each pair to tell the class something about its picture. Have the class classify all the pictures as living or nonliving.
■ If necessary, use the **reteaching strategy** in OPTIONS.

### Independent Practice

■ Use the Teacher Resource Master **Independent Practice,** page 8.

## 3   APPLY

■ Use Application Activity, "Do You Have a Clue?," on student page 216.
SC Have the class make a class collage or class list of living and nonliving things.

### Close

■ Use the pictures from Guided Practice and have students write a story about a living or nonliving thing. Encourage students to use inventive spelling.

## OPTIONS

### Reteaching Strategy

Give each student a small bean or coleus plant. Charge the students with keeping their plants alive. What do living things need? How can we provide these needs? A possible living animal that could be used by each learner is a mealworm.

### Resource Options

■ Use Poster #1, "A Tide Pool."

# OPTIONS

### LANGUAGE CONNECTION

**Writing:** Make a class list of things that are nonliving. Have students choose one item from the list. Students can write a story to explain how they know the item is nonliving.

### 🖩 MATH CONNECTION

Pose the following problem to your students. Have them complete the number sentence to solve it.

Toby made a list of living and nonliving things. He had 4 living things on his list. Toby had 9 things on his list in all. How many nonliving things were on Toby's list? (5)

**Science and Technology:** Use "I WANT TO KNOW ABOUT . . . Saving Squirrels," student page 15, with this lesson.

◆ **Reinforcement:** Ask a parent to lend the class a pet for a day. Have students plan for the needs of the pet.

● **Enrichment:** Have some of the students expand their plant activities by using plant food. Have them compare the plants that have been given plant food with those that have not.

▲ **Challenge:** Have interested students ask friends, neighbors, or family about caring for living things. Have them find out how people keep their plants healthy.

### Resource Options

■ Use Big Book, page 1, "Different People," and Teacher Resource Master **Language Arts Connection,** page 159.
■ Use Activity Book, page 34, "Do You Have a Clue?"

**Living things** need food.

They need water and air.

They need food, water, and air to stay alive.

[1]Are you a living thing?

1. Since we need food, water, and air, we are living things.

Use Application Activity on page 216.

8

# TEACHER RESOURCE MASTERS

**Transparency Master** 1

TRANSPARENCY MASTER    Chapter 1

**What Do Living Things Need?**

Discuss with students how food, water, and air are only objects depicted that are absolutely necessary for all living things.

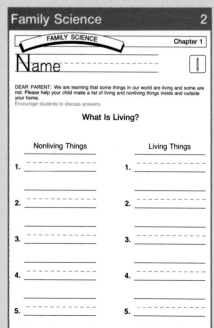

**Family Science** 2

FAMILY SCIENCE    Chapter 1

Name

DEAR PARENT: We are learning that some things in our world are living and some are not. Please help your child make a list of living and nonliving things inside and outside your home.
Encourage students to discuss answers.

**What Is Living?**

| Nonliving Things | Living Things |
|---|---|
| 1. _____ | 1. _____ |
| 2. _____ | 2. _____ |
| 3. _____ | 3. _____ |
| 4. _____ | 4. _____ |
| 5. _____ | 5. _____ |

# Is it living or nonliving?

## What you need

2 lima beans          plastic flower

2 cups of soil        pencil and paper

## What to do

1. Fill two cups with soil.

2. Plant a plastic flower in one cup.

3. Push two seeds into the other cup.

4. Add a little water to each cup every day.

5. Draw pictures to tell about the changes.

*Where? When? Scientific discoveries begin with questions. Use the informal activities to foster inquiry and advanced thinking skills.*

9

## ACTIVITY RESPONSES

Accept all reasonable student responses to questions during any activity discussion.

*Employ the tried and true lesson approach of PREPLAN, FOCUS, TEACH, and APPLY.*

*Don't forget to use the Activity Worksheet in the Teacher Resource Book and watch out for those safety symbols.*

## PREPLAN

**Time Allotment:** 20 minutes

**Process Skill:** Observing

### Objectives

1. **Observe** differences between living and nonliving plants.

2. **Identify** some needs of living plants.

### Setup

Have all equipment ready and label each pot with the letter A or B. Each child or **cooperative learning group** should have one A pot and one B pot.

**Cooperative Grouping:** fives—Assign roles as explained on T24.

## 1 | FOCUS

■ Ask students if they can name some living and nonliving things. Have students suggest ways to determine the differences between living and nonliving things.

## 2 | TEACH

■ Have students put the plastic flower in cup A and the seeds in cup B.

■ After the activity is completed on day one, ask students to predict what will happen by day three, five, and so on.

■ Use Teacher Resource Master **Activity Worksheet,** page 3, with this activity.

## 3 | APPLY

■ Write a group story using a nonliving object and pretend it will come to life. What does it look like? Can it talk? Does it crawl, slither, walk, or run? Let students illustrate this new "living" critter.

### Close

■ Discuss living and nonliving things. Ask: **When a nonliving thing is made to look like a living thing, how can we tell if it is alive?** *It does not move, grow, need water, and so on.*

## PREPLAN

*Friendly narrative style brings students into the world of science by activating prior knowledge and experience.*

### Lesson Objectives

**3. Determine** that a wide variety of plants and animals are living things.

**4. Identify** people as living things.

**5. Describe** growth as a characteristic of living things.

### Science Background

■ Life is indicated by six main features. All organisms have these characteristics. All organisms are made of cells that grow, develop, reproduce, use energy, and need food. All cells have structures that allow the organism to carry out its life processes. The nucleus is the control center of the cell.

■ Scientists classify organisms into five main kingdoms to identify, compare, and discuss the variety of living things. The kingdoms are Monera, Protist, Fungi, Plant, and Animal. Viruses are not classified as organisms because they do not have all the features of living things.

**Note:** The activity on student page 14 may be used for guided discovery before you begin this lesson.

## 1  FOCUS

■ Mount several pictures of animals and plants on cardboard. Have students take turns pretending they are an animal or plant. Interview each student. Ask them about where they live, what they eat, and so on.

■ Start an experience chart for the class. List all the animals students have seen. Add to the list as they remember additional ones. You could also start a plant list.

# Many Living Things

Living things are all around us.

Animals are living things.

Plants are living things.

How many living things can you name?

1. Encourage students to name a variety of plants and animals.

10

## TEACHER RESOURCE MASTERS

 ACTIVITY

# You Can...

## Think Smart

Draw a picture of yourself.
Are you like other living things?
Make a list to tell how.

*Easy-to-do, fun handson activities help students reinforce important science concepts.*

11

## TEACHER RESOURCE MASTERS

*And what's more, find reduced Teacher Resource Master pages right when you want them.*

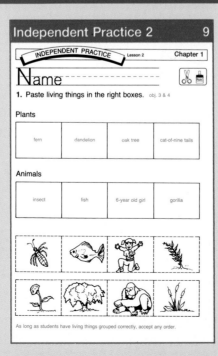

Independent Practice 2          9

INDEPENDENT PRACTICE   Lesson 2   Chapter 1

Name

**1.** Paste living things in the right boxes.  obj. 3 & 4

Plants

| fern | dandelion | oak tree | cat-of-nine tails |
|------|-----------|----------|-------------------|

Animals

| insect | fish | 6-year old girl | gorilla |
|--------|------|-----------------|---------|

As long as students have living things grouped correctly, accept any order.

## 2 TEACH

■ Review with students the reasons that people are living things.
■ Have the class line up according to height. Discuss growth as a characteristic of living things.

### Guided Practice

■ Give each student a sheet of newsprint. Show them how to fold the paper into three equal parts. Ask students to draw three stages of growth for an animal or a plant.
■ If necessary, use the **reteaching strategy** in OPTIONS.

### Independent Practice

■ Use the Teacher Resource Master **Independent Practice,** page 9.

## 3 APPLY

Have students work in **cooperative groups** to make an alphabetical living things booklet.

### Close

■ Invite a volunteer or worker from a local humane society, zoo, or pet shop to talk to students about caring for living things.

## OPTIONS

### Reteaching Strategy

Read *Wild Animals and Their Babies* by Jan Pfloog to the class.

### Resource Options

■ Use Big Book, page 2, "Ligers and Tigons," and Teacher Resource Master **Language Connection,** page 160.
■ Refer to page 13 for teaching strategies for **You Can . . . Think Smart.**

# OPTIONS

### LANGUAGE CONNECTION

**Writing:** Read *The Caterpillar and the Polliwog* by Jack Kent. Talk about why the tadpole doesn't notice itself changing. Ask students how *they* change. Have students write their own story or poem about how they have changed since they were babies. Or students may want to pick an age and write about how they will change from their present age to the new age.

### MATH CONNECTION

Make a class graph showing the number of living animals and the number of living plants in the classroom. When the graph is complete, have students add the two numbers to find the total number of living things in the room.

♦ **Reinforcement:** Show the students pictures of animals and plants. Discuss their different sizes. Discuss growth of baby animals. Ask students if they have ever seen puppies or kittens growing and changing. Ask them to tell how the animals changed.

### Resource Options
■ Use Activity Book, pages 13 and 14, "Classifying."

*There's still more. Resource Options show you where to find all the supplemental materials you'll need to teach the lesson.*

Most living things grow.
They change as they grow.
You are a living thing.
You change as you grow, too.

*Use the Reading, Writing, and Math Connections to travel across the curriculum.*

12

# TEACHER RESOURCE MASTERS

Critical Thinking     5

CRITICAL THINKING/PROBLEM SOLVING   Classifying/Sequencing   Chapter 1

Name

**How Have You Changed?**
Look at each picture.
Draw how you have changed.

Drawings will vary.
Accept all reasonable answers.

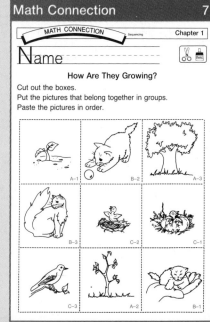

Math Connection     7

MATH CONNECTION   Sequencing   Chapter 1

Name

**How Are They Growing?**
Cut out the boxes.
Put the pictures that belong together in groups.
Paste the pictures in order.

1. food, water, and air    2. They will grow to look like their parents.

[1]What do living things need to grow?

[2]How will these baby animals change?

13

# OPTIONS

## YOU CAN . . . THINK SMART

**Process Skills:** Observing/Communicating

**Objective: Recognize** the characteristics that make people living things.

### Setup/Teach

■ Provide time for students to share their lists with the class. You might also add to their lists.

### Student Responses

Answers will vary but might include moving, eating, playing, being afraid. Other responses are also possible.

🖐 SC ● **Enrichment:** Have students collect pictures of animals to illustrate *big* and *small*. Have them put big animals in one group and small animals in another group. Label the animals with their names. Display the groups of pictures.

🖐 ▲ **Challenge:** Have interested students **work cooperatively** to create a play about an animal. The play might begin with the animal as a baby and show how it grows and changes. Students might perform the play for the rest of the class.

*Students aren't all alike. That's why you need specific reinforcement, enrichment, and challenge ideas.*

*Don't recognize these symbols? Remember that the key appears on the first page of the chapter.*

# TEACHER RESOURCE MASTERS

**Critical Thinking** 6

CRITICAL THINKING/PROBLEM SOLVING  Challenge        Chapter 1

## Name

### Living Things Change And Grow
Show how living things change and grow.
Draw pictures to show what happens.
Be sure students have indicated growth in their drawings.

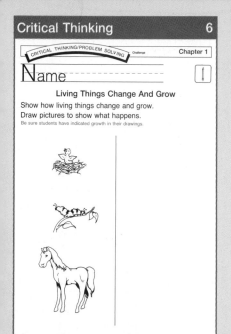

**Reteaching Activity** 10

RETEACHING ACTIVITY        Chapter 1

## Name

### Animals Grow
All animals grow.
Find how the animals grow.
Draw lines.

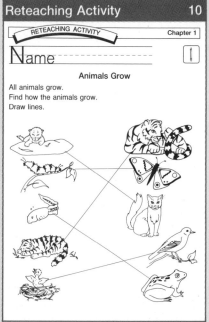

# PREPLAN

**Time Allotment:** 20 minutes

**Process Skills:** Observing/Measuring

## Objectives

1. **Measure** the growth of plants.
2. **Infer** that seeds are living.
3. **Identify** growth with living things.

## Setup

Write each student's name on a cup using a waterproof marker.

**Cooperative Grouping:** twos—Assign roles as explained on page T24.

## 1 FOCUS

■ Have students hold the seeds in their hands. Ask if the seeds are living. Have students suggest ways they can find out. Summarize the discussion on an experience chart.

## 2 TEACH

■ Demonstrate a strip-measuring technique to students. Have them record the growth of their plants.
■ Monitor the care given each plant to assure a successful activity.
■ Use the Teacher Resource Master **Activity Worksheet,** page 4.

## 3 APPLY

■ Have students tell about other ways to measure the growth of living things.

## Close

■ Compare the students' measurements. Ask: **Did all the seeds grow at the same rate?** Discuss with students how they know that their seeds are alive.

## Do living things grow?

## What you need

| | |
|---|---|
| a lima bean | a cup of soil |
| 3 paper strips | scissors |
| glue | pencil and paper |

## What to do

1. Plant the seed in a cup of soil.
2. Put the cup in a sunny place.
3. Add water to the soil.
4. How tall is your plant growing?
5. Use paper strips to measure.

14

## ACTIVITY RESPONSES

Accept all reasonable student responses to questions during any activity discussion.

# I WANT TO KNOW ABOUT...

## Saving Squirrels

*Introduce students to careers and technology with I Want to Know About...*

Some squirrels put nuts on electric poles.

This can hurt the squirrels.

And it can make our lights go out.

We can put plastic owls on the poles.

Squirrels are afraid of owls.

The squirrels will put the nuts somewhere else.

### Science and Technology

15

## TEACHER RESOURCE MASTERS

## Feature Background

■ The three main groups of squirrels in the United States are fox or gray squirrels; red squirrels; and flying squirrels. In all, there are more than 300 kinds of squirrels.

■ Squirrels eat nuts, seeds, corn, berries, fruit, and mushrooms. They gather food for winter and store it in the ground, in trees, or in their dens.

■ Squirrels live in hollow tree trunks or nests.

■ Squirrels are born in litters that range in size from two to six. The baby squirrels' eyes are closed, and they have no fur.

## Feature Vocabulary

squirrels
electric
plastic

## Teaching Suggestions

■ Discuss with students why squirrels store food for winter. Make a class list of other animals that gather food for winter.

■ Discuss with students that the plastic owls scare the squirrels, because owls prey upon the squirrels' young. Tell students that scarecrows are used in the same way to scare birds away from crops.

■ Explain to students how and why the electric company found a solution to its problem that protects the squirrels.

pages 16, 17

**Chapter Closure:** Use these pages to re-view and reinforce chapter concepts.

### What I Learned

Have students read the rebus summary statements aloud to be sure they inter-pret the pictures correctly. After each sentence, discuss other possible words that would also make the sentence true.

### Words I Know

Use any or all of the following sugges-tions to reinforce the chapter vocabulary. Write each science word or word group on the chalkboard. Ask students to read them. Add the words to the class science list or have students write the words in their individual science word books. Ask students to tell about these words to help you evaluate their comprehension. Have students use each science word or word group in a sentence.

*Evaluation doesn't have to be hard on you or your students. With two types of tests and the easy-to-use blackline masters, you can be sure understanding is there.*

*Recap chapter highlights with these summary statements and literal and critical thinking questions.*

## CHAPTER REVIEW 1

### What I Learned

• Some things are living, and some are not.

Living things need  ,  , and air.

food          water

 and  are living things.

Plants          animals

 and  grow and change.

Plants          animals

So do you!

### Words I Know
nonliving things          living things

16

## TEACHER RESOURCE MASTERS

Test A                    11

TEST A          Recalling Facts          Chapter 1

Name Each question is worth 25 points.

Color only the nonliving things. obj. 1 & 4
Students should color all items circled.

pages 16, 17

## What I Know

*Use the picture to answer the questions.*

1. What are some nonliving things?

2. What do living things need to grow?

3. What are some living things?

4. How do living things change?

17

## What I Know

Have students refer to the pictures to answer the questions and extend concepts.
**1.** Answers may include books, toys, bed, baseball equipment, and so on.
**2.** Living things need food, water, and air.
**3.** Living things in the picture include fish, bird, and kitten. The presence of people is inferred.
**4.** Living things grow bigger or heavier; they may change the kinds of activities they like to do as they grow older.

# OPTIONS

### Resource Options
Use Color Transparencies #1a and #1b.

# TEACHER RESOURCE MASTERS

Test B          12

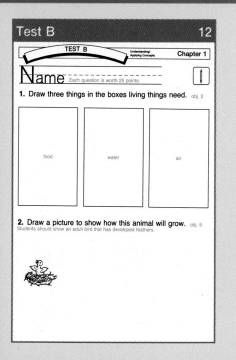

TEST B    Understanding/Applying Concepts    Chapter 1

Name Each question is worth 25 points.

**1.** Draw three things in the boxes living things need. obj. 2

| food | water | air |

**2.** Draw a picture to show how this animal will grow. obj. 5
Students should show an adult bird that has developed feathers.

**CHAPTER**
**2**

# Animals

## Planning Guide

| Lessons | Objectives | Vocabulary |
|---|---|---|
| **Chapter Introduction** pp. 18, 19 | | |
| **Lesson 1 Are Animals Different?** pp. 20–25 | 1. **Describe** how animals use body parts to move. <br> 2. **Identify** different body coverings of animals. <br> 3. **Infer** how some animals protect themselves. | animals <br> body parts <br> body coverings |
| **Lesson 2 Where Animals Live** pp. 26–31 | 4. **Name** some animal habitats. <br> 5. **Recognize** that animals in the wild care for themselves. <br> 6. **Explain** how people care for some animals. | habitat |
| **Chapter Review** pp. 32, 33 | | |

# Planning Guide

| Text Activities | | Teacher Resource Masters | Other Components |
|---|---|---|---|
| **Title/Skill** | **Materials per Group** | | |
| **Have You Ever . . . Made a Turtle?** p. 19 Inferring/Observing Time Allotment: 30 minutes | egg cartons scissors glue colored markers or crayons construction paper | | Activity Center: "Name That Story"; "If I Could Be"; "Animal Maker"; "My Favorite Food" |
| **You Can . . . Make a Chart,** p. 22 Communicating Time Allotment: 30 minutes | drawing paper crayons | Activity Worksheet, p. 15 Critical Thinking, p. 17 ▲ Critical Thinking, p. 18 Math Connection, p. 19 Independent Practice, p. 20 ◆ Reteaching Activity, p. 22 Language Arts Connection, pp. 161, 162, 163 | Poster #2 Big Book, p. 3 Big Book, p. 4 Big Book, p. 5 Activity Book, p. 15 |
| **How Can You Group Animals?** p. 25 Classifying Time Allotment: 30 minutes | animals pictures scissors crayons a large sheet of paper glue | | |
| **How Do We Care for Pets?** p. 30 Communicating/Inferring Time Allotment: 15 minutes to set up and a few minutes each day per group per week | a pet pet food water a log pencil | Transparency Master, p. 13 ◆ Family Science, p. 14 Activity Worksheet, p. 16 Independent Practice, p. 21 Language Arts Connection, p. 164 | Poster #1 Big Book, p. 6 Activity Book, p. 17 |
| | | Test A, p. 23 Test B, p. 24 | Color Transparencies #2a and #2b Software: "Hunting With A Camera" |

◆ **Basic** / ▲ **Advanced** / All other masters are for use by all students.

# CHAPTER 2

# *Animals*

## ESL/LEP

**Chapter 2/Lesson 1, Page 24**
Play the game 'I Have-Who Has'. Begin by placing the names of many different kinds of animals in a paper bag. Students reach in and select an animal name. Have students draw a picture of their animal. Hold up a word card with words such as claws, teeth, fur, or scales on it. Students whose animals have that characteristic stand up and show their picture. You may want to vary the game by changing the directions. Instead of standing ask students to touch their toes five times or stand up and turn around.

**Chapter 2/Lesson 2, Page 29**
Write the word *habitat* on the chalkboard. Pronounce the word together and discuss its meaning. To help students gain a better understanding of the word, make habitat dioramas using shoe boxes. They can make scenes depicting the jungle, zoo, farm, or woods. Discuss the similarities and differences in each habitat. Ask students to make a list of the animals that might live in each.

## Gifted

**Chapter 2/Lesson 2, Page 29**
Help students discover ways to identify groups of animals such as mammals, reptiles or birds, and draw examples of each group.

## Mainstreamed

**Chapter 2/Lesson 1, Page 24**
**Visually Impaired:** Gather a variety of animal coverings. As the students touch these coverings, have them name animals with similar coverings. Play a game where each student feels a covering and then names an animal with a covering like it.

**Chapter 2/Lesson 2, Page 29**
**Developmentally Handicapped:** In one column, paste pictures of different animals (examples: polar bear, bird, cow). In a second column, paste pictures of habitats (examples: Arctic region, meadow, farmland). Have students match animals with habitats and predict what might happen if an animal's habitat changed too quickly.

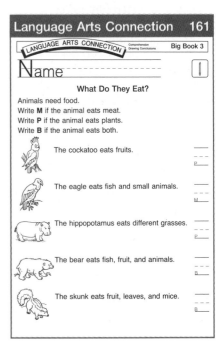

# Projects to Do

## Whole Class Science Project

Give students directions for making animal cubes. Have students complete the squares with the following information.

Square 1: name of the animal

Square 2: a colorful picture of the animal

Square 3: where the animal lives

Square 4: how the animal moves

Square 5: how the animal protects itself

Square 6: what its body covering is

After all six squares are completed, students should cut around the cube's outline and fold it into shape. Use glue or tape to hold the cubes together.

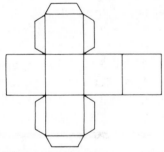

## Science Fair Projects

Individual students could do one of the following projects:

1. Using wild bird seeds that have been colored with red, blue, green, and yellow food coloring, find out if seed color is an important factor in food gathering for wild birds.

2. Using various types of seeds at a bird feeder, find out if certain wild birds prefer certain kinds of seed.

3. Using plaster of paris casts of animal tracks, find out what wild animals live near your home.

4. Using amphibian eggs that have been gathered from a local pond in the spring, find out if variations in pond water temperature affect the development of the eggs.

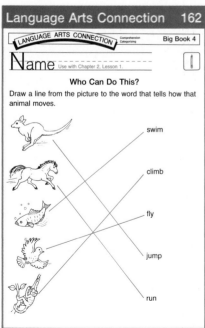

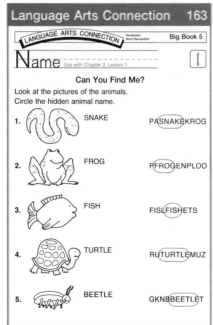

**Language Arts Connection 162**

LANGUAGE ARTS CONNECTION — Comprehension Categorizing — Big Book 4

Name — Use with Chapter 2, Lesson 1.

### Who Can Do This?

Draw a line from the picture to the word that tells how that animal moves.

swim
climb
fly
jump
run

**Language Arts Connection 163**

LANGUAGE ARTS CONNECTION — Vocabulary Word Recognition — Big Book 5

Name — Use with Chapter 2, Lesson 1.

### Can You Find Me?

Look at the pictures of the animals. Circle the hidden animal name.

1. SNAKE — PASNAKEKROG
2. FROG — PFROGENPLOO
3. FISH — FISLFISHETS
4. TURTLE — RUTURTLEMUZ
5. BEETLE — GKNBBEETLET

**Language Arts Connection 164**

LANGUAGE ARTS CONNECTION — Vocabulary Compound Words — Big Book 6

Name — Use with Chapter 2, Lesson 2.

### Putting Words Together

Put two words together to make a new word.
Write the new word on the line.
Draw a picture to show what the new word names.
Draw where it lives.

butter ___butterfly___ fly
*Animal habitats will vary, but may include flowers.*

grass ___grasshopper___ hopper
*Animal habitats will vary, but may include a grassy area.*

bull ___bullfrog___ frog
*Animal habitats will vary, but may include a lily pad.*

rattle ___rattlesnake___ snake
*Animal habitats will vary, but may include a rocky area.*

# CHAPTER 2

pages 18–33

## Chapter Concepts
- Animals are different in their sizes, body parts, and body coverings.
- Animals live in different habitats.

## Chapter Background
- Animals are classified mainly on the basis of body structure. These structural similarities or differences may be internal, external, or developmental.
- Scientists have classified animals into two major groups: invertebrates and vertebrates. Invertebrates are animals without backbones. Vertebrates are animals with backbones and internal skeletons.
- Organisms and the environment in which they live make up large habitats known as ecosystems.
- Examples of ecosystems include the polar regions, tundra, taiga, temperate forest, grassland, desert, rain forest, fresh water, and ocean.

## Looking Ahead
- Selection a filmstrip or video on animals living in a particular habitat to **Close** Lesson 2.

## Look for These Symbols
- —Hands-on activity
- —Cooperative learning
- —Overhead transparency
- ◆ —Basic/Reinforcement
- ● —Average/Enrichment
- ▲ —Advanced/Challenge
- SC —Science Center
- —Calculator Practice

SCIENCE
In Your World

18

# CHAPTER 2

# Animals

Have you ever seen a squirrel climb a tree?

Do you have a dog or a cat?

What animals live in your neighborhood?

## Have You Ever...

## Made a Turtle ?

1. Cut out part of an egg carton.
2. Use it to make a shell.
3. Make a circle for the head.
4. Make four circles for the feet.
5. Glue the body parts in place.
6. Color your turtle with markers.

How does a turtle move?

19

---

## PREPLAN

**Time Allotment:** 30 minutes

### Objectives
1. **Infer** that animals are different.
2. **Observe** and make a craft turtle.

### Setup
To conduct the activity, collect the following materials for each student or **cooperative learning group:**

| | |
|---|---|
| egg cartons | scissors |
| glue | colored markers |
| construction paper | or crayons |

## 1   FOCUS

■ Ask students to describe the picture on page 18. Ask students to relate any experience they may have had visiting farm animals.

## 2   TEACH

■ Read the chapter title and introductory paragraph. Discuss animals found on farms, in the neighborhood, at the zoo, and so on.

### Have You Ever . . .
■ Display photographs of actual turtles as well as a model craft turtle for student observation and discussion.

### Student Responses
Possible answers include: *a turtle crawls on four legs, it pulls its legs and head inside its shell.*

## 3   APPLY

Have students describe the body parts and body coverings of turtles. Ask students to work in **cooperative groups** and create another kind of animal.

### Close
■ Tell the students that they will learn more about different animals and where they live in Chapter 2.

# PREPLAN

## Lesson Objectives

1. **Describe** how animals use body parts to move.
2. **Identify** different body coverings of animals.
3. **Infer** how some animals protect themselves.

## Science Background

- The largest animal is the blue whale, which can grow to more than 30 meters long.
- The smallest insect is the fairyfly, which is only about 0.2 millimeters long.
- Animals have different body parts that enable them to move in different ways. Wings enable some animals to fly. Long legs make fast runners.
- Animals have body coverings that allow them to adapt to various environments. The body covering provides protection from the environment and from other animals.
- Skin adaptations include the moist skin of amphibians, the scales of reptiles and fish, the shells of arthropods and mollusks, the feathers of birds, and the fur of mammals.

## Lesson Vocabulary

animals    body parts    body coverings

**Note:** The activity on student page 25 may be used for guided discovery before you begin this lesson.

# 1  FOCUS

- Choose several students to act out a variety of animals. Have the class guess which animals are being acted out. Talk about how these animals move, what size they are, and what body parts they have.

# Are Animals Different?

**Animals** are different.

Some are big.

Some are small.

[1]How else are animals different?

1. body parts, body coverings, where they live, what they eat, and so on

20

# TEACHER RESOURCE MASTERS

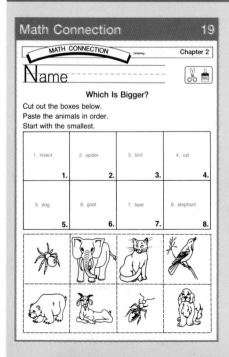

Math Connection                    19

MATH CONNECTION · Ordering · Chapter 2

**N**ame

**Which Is Bigger?**

Cut out the boxes below.
Paste the animals in order.
Start with the smallest.

| 1. insect | 2. spider | 3. bird | 4. cat |
|---|---|---|---|
| 1. | 2. | 3. | 4. |
| 5. dog | 6. goat | 7. bear | 8. elephant |
| 5. | 6. | 7. | 8. |

Animals have different **body parts**.

They use body parts to move.

How do animals move?

How can you move?

1. walk, run, crawl, swim, fly
2. walking, running, jumping, climbing, crawling, and so on

21

## TEACHER RESOURCE MASTERS

| Reteaching Activity | 22 |
| --- | --- |

RETEACHING ACTIVITY — Chapter 2

**Name**

**How Can You Move?**

People can move like some animals.
Draw an animal that can move like you.

hop — Accept all reasonable answers.

run

jump

climb

| Independent Practice 1 | 20 |
| --- | --- |

INDEPENDENT PRACTICE — Lesson 1 — Chapter 2

**Name**

1. Circle the part that each animal uses to move. obj. 1

2. Color the animal with fur brown.
Color the animal with feathers red. obj. 2
Color the animal with scales green.

red   green   brown

3. Circle the part each animal uses for protection. obj. 3

## 2  TEACH

■ Discuss large and small animals. Have students name the largest and smallest animals they know.

■ Discuss how the body covering is related to an animal's life. One discussion might be how the animal's body covering affects where the animal lives. Ask: **How do body coverings help to keep animals safe?** *Shells, tough skin, and scales protect animals from predators. Hair and feathers protect an animal from the cold.*

### Guided Practice

■ Describe four different animals for students to draw without naming the animals. Check to see if students listened to your description of body parts or body coverings.

■ If necessary, use the **reteaching strategy** in OPTIONS.

### Independent Practice

■ Use the Teacher Resource Master **Independent Practice,** page 20.

## 3  APPLY

Have students **work cooperatively in groups** of four to make animal booklets. Each group should choose a body covering and include examples of animals with that body covering.

### Close

■ Show pictures of animals to the class. Have students identify the body parts and body coverings of each animal.

## OPTIONS

### Reteaching Strategy

Glue pictures of animals to $3 \times 5$ index cards. Label some blank cards with *swim, run, fly,* or *crawl.* Have students group the animals under the correct heading.

### Resource Options

■ Use Poster #2, "Did Someone Koala My Name?"

## OPTIONS

### YOU CAN . . . . MAKE A CHART
**Process Skill:** Communicating

**Objective: Construct** a chart to record observed data.

**Setup/Teach:**
■ Provide students with paper to complete the chart. Instruct them as to how to set up the chart and record data.

Ask students to work in pairs and describe their chart to their partner.

### LANGUAGE CONNECTION
**Writing:** Write the following sentences on the chalkboard: My favorite animal is the _____. Its body is covered with _____. Put the following list on the board from which the students can choose an answer to this second sentence: fur, scales, shells, hair, skin, feathers. Ask students to write sentences about the animal's body parts, movement, and protection. Compile a list of the words they may need to use.

### Resource Options
■ Use Big Book, page 3, "Tooth Troubles," and Teacher Resource Master **Language Connection** page 161.
■ Use Big Book, page 4, "Wishy Washy," and Teacher Resource Master **Language Connection** page 162.
■ Use Big Book, page 5, "Animals on the Move," and Teacher Resource Master **Language Connection** page 163.
■ Use Activity Book, pages 15 and 16, "Measuring."

Animals use body parts to stay safe.
Some animals use sharp teeth to bite.
Some use claws to protect themselves.

**ACTIVITY**
## You Can...
### Make a Chart
Can body parts keep you safe?
Make a chart.
Tell how you stay safe each day.

How I stay safe

22

## TEACHER RESOURCE MASTERS

Animals have different **body coverings**.

¹What body coverings do you see?

²What body coverings do you have?

1. hair, shells, scales, feathers, and skin    2. hair and skin

23

## TEACHER RESOURCE MASTERS

### Critical Thinking                                    17

CRITICAL THINKING/PROBLEM SOLVING Classifying/Graphing    Chapter 2

Name

#### Animal Coverings

Count the animals with each kind of body covering.
Color that many boxes in the chart.
Tell about your chart.

| Animal Coverings Chart | | | | | |
|---|---|---|---|---|---|
| skin | | | | | |
| fur | | | | | |
| feathers | | | | | |
| shell | | | | | |
| scales | | | | | |

CHAPTER 2/LESSON 1

pages 20–25

## OPTIONS

◆**Reinforcement:** Have students collect pictures of animals to illustrate the concepts *big* and *small*. Have them put big animals in one group and small animals in another. Have them write the name of the animal below its picture. Display the groups of pictures.

●**Enrichment:** You may wish to extend student knowledge and experience of animals by implementing an "Animal of the Day" exhibit. Each day, display a picture of an unfamiliar animal in its natural habitat. Encourage students to find the name of the animal. Place books near the exhibit for students to seek information. You may want to award a "Zoologist of the Day" certificate to the first student who is successful in finding the animal. Share information about the animal with students.

SC ▲**Challenge:** Direct students to make an alphabetical list of animals, a–ant, b–butterfly, c–cougar, and so on. Have students make an "animal pictionary" using their lists. They could draw or cut out animal pictures. The extent of this project will depend on the ability of the students.

### MATH CONNECTION

Have students collect ten pictures of animals from old magazines. Have them make a pictograph showing the ways animals move by pasting the pictures in the appropriate columns.

#### Animals Move in Many Ways

| | |
|---|---|
| Walk | |
| Fly | |
| Swim | |
| Crawl | |
| Hop | |

## OPTIONS

### LANGUAGE CONNECTION

**Writing:** Have students choose two animals they find interesting and combine them to make one animal. Combine name parts of the animal too. Direct students to write a poem and create an animal. You may want students to use paints or mold their animals out of clay. A sample is given below.

#### The Allibee

The allibee is a silly thing.
It bites the flowers and doesn't sting.

▲**Challenge:** Have students choose an animal and write a factual story about it. Have them include information about what the animal eats, where it lives, and so on.

### HEALTH CONNECTION

Invite someone from your local humane society or a veterinarian to speak to the students about how they help injured or sick animals. Ask them to talk about new medical procedures to treat animals.

---

## Some body coverings keep animals safe.

[1]Can you guess how?

1. camouflage in surroundings as protection from predators

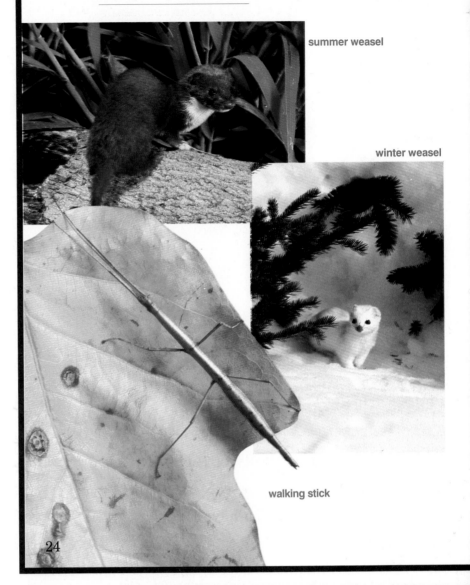

summer weasel

winter weasel

walking stick

24

---

## TEACHER RESOURCE MASTERS

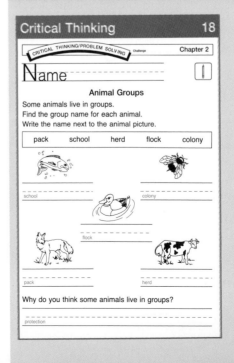

Critical Thinking                    18

CRITICAL THINKING/PROBLEM SOLVING  Challenge        Chapter 2

Name

#### Animal Groups

Some animals live in groups.
Find the group name for each animal.
Write the name next to the animal picture.

| pack | school | herd | flock | colony |

school

colony

flock

pack

herd

Why do you think some animals live in groups?

protection

## How can you group animals?

### What you need

animal pictures     large sheet of paper

scissors     glue

crayons     pencil and paper

### What to do

1. Find pictures of different animals.

2. How are your animals alike?

3. How are your animals different?

4. Group your animals.

## ACTIVITY RESPONSES

Accept all reasonable student responses to questions during any activity discussion.

## PREPLAN

**Time Allotment:** 30 minutes

**Process Skill:** Classifying

### Objectives

1. **Classify** animals by recognizing similarities.

2. **Infer** that animals could be grouped in a variety of ways.

### Setup

Have pictures of animals available or magazines with animal pictures for students to cut out.

**Cooperative Grouping:** twos—Assign roles as explained on T24.

## 1   FOCUS

■ Have students suggest ways that animals that are alike can be grouped, such as movement, body parts, body coverings, and size.

## 2   TEACH

■ Have each pair of students classify the animals in one specific way. Each pair may make a poster of their classification system and share it with the class.

■ Use Teacher Resource Master **Activity Worksheet,** page 15, for this activity.

## 3   APPLY

■ Discuss with students what they think is the best way to group animals. Explain that because there are so many kinds of animals, scientists group those that are most alike.

### Close

■ Ask students what they learned about their animal groups. Here are some possible observations.

1. Animals might have the same body covering but be in different groups.

2. Grouping animals differently may move some animals into different groups.

## PREPLAN

### Lesson Objectives

**4. Name** some animal habitats.

**5. Recognize** that animals in the wild care for themselves.

**6. Explain** how people care for some animals.

### Science Background

■ Organisms adapt to a specific environment.

■ A habitat contains the life needs of the organism such as proper food, water, air, light, temperature, pressure, space, soil, and shelter.

■ Zoos keep endangered species from becoming extinct by operating breeding programs. Modern zoos try to simulate the natural environment of the animals. Zoos provide opportunities for scientists to study animals under controlled conditions.

### Lesson Vocabulary

habitat

**Note:** The activity on student page 30 may be used for guided discovery before you begin this lesson.

## 1   FOCUS

■ Make up some pictures of animals in out-of-place habitats such as a rabbit in an undersea setting, a bear on a city street, or a fish in the forest. Show these pictures to students. Ask them what is wrong with the picture. Use the discussion to establish that habitats help animals meet certain needs.

# Where Animals Live

Animals live in different places.

The place an animal lives is its **habitat.**

26

## TEACHER RESOURCE MASTERS

Many animals live in the wild.

Wild animals have different habitats.

[1]Where do these animals live?

1. habitats include a forest, desert, and an ocean

## 2 TEACH

- Ask students to brainstorm a list of foods that wild animals might eat and how they might find that food. Suggest birds as the first group of animals students should think about.
- Ask students to name some ways we take care of pets.

On the chalkboard or overhead projector, write the names of the habitats shown here. Encourage students to name some animals that can be found in each habitat. List the animals that they name under the correct habitat.

### Guided Practice

Have groups of students **work cooperatively** to use tempera paint or colored chalk to make a habitat.

- If necessary, use the **reteaching strategy** in OPTIONS.

### Independent Practice

- Use the Teacher Resource Master **Independent Practice,** page 21.

## 3 APPLY

Give each student an animal word or picture card. Have students look or read one another's card. Decide as a class how everyone could be grouped. Suggestions might include wild animals, pets, farm or zoo animals.

### Close

- Use a film or video to show students animals living in a particular habitat.

## TEACHER RESOURCE MASTERS

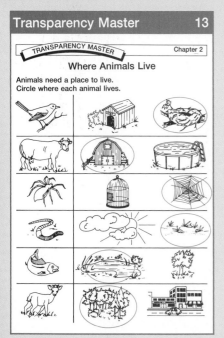

Transparency Master 13

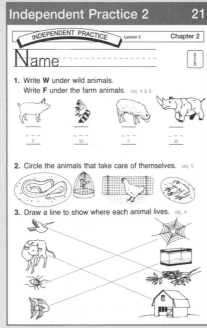

Independent Practice 2 21

## OPTIONS

### Reteaching Strategy

Direct students to consider their own habitat. Discuss how food, water, and air needs are met. Have students draw their habitat.

### Resource Options

- Use Poster #1, "A Tide Pool."

# OPTIONS

### LANGUAGE CONNECTION

**Reading:** Read the story *Raccoon Baby* by Berniece Freschet to your students. Have students tell you what happened in the story. Record the responses on the chalkboard. Place the story events in the proper sequence by numbering them. You may want students to copy the responses in the correct sequence on a piece of paper.

### LANGUAGE CONNECTION

**Reading:** Read *Is Anyone Home?* by Ron Maris to your students. Ask students to tell you where the story takes place. Make a class list of all of the descriptions of the setting.

SC ◆ **Reinforcement:** Write these sentences on the board leaving blanks where indicated.

1. _____, _____, and _____ live in the forest.
2. _____, _____, and _____ live in zoos.
3. _____, _____, and _____ live on farms.

Have students make rebus statements by copying the sentences and filling in the blanks with pictures. They can use cutout pictures or draw them.

### Resource Options

■ Use Big Book, page 6, "But As for Me," and Teacher Resource Master **Language Connection** page 164.
■ Use Activity Book, pages 17 and 18, "Inferring."

Wild animals take care of themselves.
They find their own food.
They find their own homes.

28

# TEACHER RESOURCE MASTERS

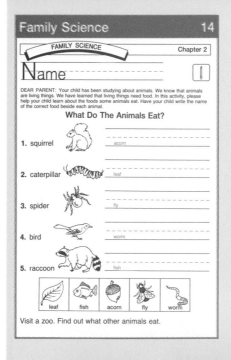

Family Science                                              14

FAMILY SCIENCE                        Chapter 2

Name                                              |

DEAR PARENT: Your child has been studying about animals. We know that animals are living things. We have learned that living things need food. In this activity, please help your child learn about the foods some animals eat. Have your child write the name of the correct food beside each animal.

**What Do The Animals Eat?**

1. squirrel — acorn

2. caterpillar — leaf

3. spider — fly

4. bird — worm

5. raccoon — fish

leaf   fish   acorn   fly   worm

Visit a zoo. Find out what other animals eat.

Some wild animals live in a zoo.

We care for these animals.                    1. pets and farm animals

[1]What other kinds of animals need care?

29

TEACHER RESOURCE MASTERS

## OPTIONS

● **Enrichment:** Have students find pictures of animals in their habitats. Have them tell the name of the animal, the kind of habitat, and some of the ways the animal gets the things it needs from the habitat.

▲ **Challenge:** Ask students to bring in empty aluminum food trays. Provide each student with gravel, clay, soil, and a variety of plants, such as mosses or twigs. Have students design habitats and make models of various animals to put in them. The shiny base of the tray may be left exposed to simulate water in a pond or stream.

### ART CONNECTION

Give students a sheet of white construction paper. Fold the paper lengthwise so that one-third of it is separated from the rest. This third will be flat and represent the foreground in the picture. Have students draw and color a habitat on the large section of the paper. Have students draw pictures of animals or cut them out of magazines. Put paper tabs on the animal pictures and glue them onto the foreground. Have students write a sentence or a story about their habitat pictures.

**Career:** Use "I WANT TO KNOW ABOUT . . . A Zoo Dentist," student page 31, with this lesson.

## PREPLAN

**Time allotment:** Allow 15 minutes to set up this activity and a few minutes every day for a week.

**Process Skills:** Communicating/Inferring

### Objectives

1. **Infer** that pets have needs that must be met by people.
2. **List** ways people meet pet needs.

### Setup

Obtain a small pet for student groups to take care of for a month. Have the necessary equipment and supplies ready.

■ Provide each student group with **Activity Worksheet** 16 to use as a log.

**Cooperative Grouping:** fours—Assign roles as explained on page T24.

## 1 FOCUS

■ Display pictures of people feeding, watering, brushing, and exercising their pets. Ask students to discuss ways the owners are giving their pets what they need.

## 2 TEACH

■ **Safety Considerations:** Make sure students know the proper way of handling and feeding the animal.

■ Use Teacher Resource Master **Activity Worksheet,** page 16 for this activity.

## 3 APPLY

■ Compile a list of things that all pet owners should do to properly care for their pets.

### Close

■ Discuss with students the importance of pet care.

---

## ACTIVITY

## How do we care for pets?

### What you need

| a pet | pet food | water |
| pencil | log | |

### What to do

1. Take care of a pet for a week.
2. Make a log to tell what you do.
3. What did your pet eat?
4. Did you give your pet water?
5. What else did your pet need?

30

## ACTIVITY RESPONSES

Accept all reasonable student responses to questions during any activity discussion.

# I WANT TO KNOW ABOUT...

## A Zoo Dentist

Dr. John Barr cares for zoo animals.

He is a zoo dentist.

Sometimes animals have sore teeth.

Dr. Barr has special tools in many sizes.

He helps animals feel better.

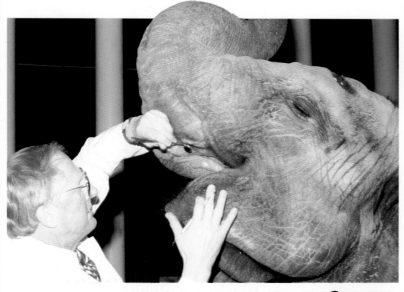

*Career*

31

**TEACHER RESOURCE MASTERS**

### Feature Background

■ A zoo dentist has a degree in dentistry. Some have additional training in veterinary medicine.

■ Zoo dentists work on many types of animals. A snake may need to have a fang cleaned or removed. Larger mammals may have teeth filled, pulled, polished, aligned, or sealed (occlusal sealant), have gum surgery, or have plaque removed.

■ Zookeepers give animals the kinds of food that they would eat in the wild. For example, carnivores need to eat fleshy meat to keep their teeth, gums, and face and neck muscles strong and healthy.

■ A zoo dentist may need to anesthetize an animal to work on it. The zoo dentist must be protected from the animal, and the animal must be protected from any unnecessary pain or discomfort.

### Feature Vocabulary

dentist

teeth

### Teaching Suggestions

■ Discuss with students the importance of good dental care. Ask students why they think animals might need a dentist. Emphasize the importance of a good diet for pets. Remind students not to give junk food to animals, because animals cannot brush their teeth.

■ Tell students that different animals have different types of teeth. Zoo dentists must figure out how to treat each type of animal. Usually the zoo dentist must make an immediate diagnosis, decide on the course of treatment, and perform any necessary treatment in one short session.

■ Tell students that the elephant in this photograph is named Bud. He lives at the Columbus Zoo, in Columbus, Ohio. Bud is the only male African forest elephant in the United States, and is one of only two in the Western Hemisphere. He is 15 years old. Most African forest elephants live to be 60-65 years old.

pages 32, 33

**Chapter Closure:** Use these pages to review and reinforce chapter concepts.

## What I Learned

Have students read the rebus summary statements aloud to be sure that students interpret the pictures correctly. After each sentence is read, discuss other words that might make the sentence true.

## Words I Know

Use any or all of the following suggestions to reinforce the chapter vocabulary. Write each science word or word group on the chalkboard. Ask students to read them. Add the words to the class science list or have students write the words in their individual science word books. Ask students to tell about these words to help you evaluate their comprehension. Have students use each science word or word group in a sentence.

**CHAPTER REVIEW**

**2**

### What I Learned

- Some animals use , , or  to move.

  wings    fins    legs

- Some animals have body coverings of ,

  fur

  , or  .

  feathers    scales

- Some animals live in a , an , or a  .

  desert    ocean

  forest

### Words I Know

**body parts**    **body coverings**    **habitat**

32

## TEACHER RESOURCE MASTERS

Test A    23

TEST A    Recalling Facts    Chapter 2

Name _____ 

Each question is worth 12 points.

**1.** Draw lines from the animals to their habitat. obj. 4

**2.** Put an **X** on the wild animals. obj. 5

## What I Know

*Use the picture to answer the questions.*

1. How do some animals protect themselves?

2. What are some body coverings?

3. What is a habitat?

4. How do wild animals care for themselves?

5. How do people care for animals?

## What I Know

Have students refer to the picture to answer the questions and extend concepts.

1. Body coverings, camouflage in a habitat, or body parts protect animals.

2. Body coverings include shells, scales, feathers, skin, fur or hair.

3. A habitat is the place an animal lives where all its needs are met.

4. Wild animals find their own food, water, and shelter.

5. People provide food, water, and shelter for pets and zoo and farm animals.

## OPTIONS

### Resource Options
Use Color Transparencies #2a and #2b.

## TEACHER RESOURCE MASTERS

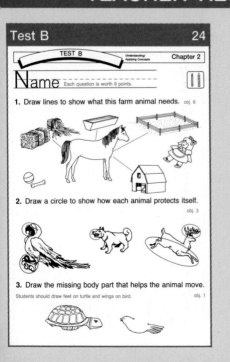

# Plants

## Planning Guide

| Lessons | Objectives | Vocabulary |
|---|---|---|
| Chapter Introduction pp. 34, 35 | | |
| Lesson 1 Plant Parts pp. 36–41 | 1. **Recognize** roots, stems, leaves, and flowers as parts of plants.<br>2. **Tell** how plants use plant parts. | plants<br>leaves<br>stems<br>roots<br>flowers |
| Lesson 2 Plants Need Animals pp. 42, 43 | 3. **Identify** ways in which plants need animals.<br>4. **Recognize** animals that aid plants. | pollen |
| Lesson 3 Animals Need Plants pp. 44–47 | 5. **Give examples** of plants that we use for food.<br>6. **Communicate** how animals need plants.<br>7. **Describe** ways that people use plants. | |
| Chapter Review pp. 48, 49 | | |

# Planning Guide

| Text Activities | | Teacher Resource Masters | Other Components |
|---|---|---|---|
| **Title/Skill** | **Materials per Group** | | |
| **Have You Ever . . . Grown a Sweet Potato?** p. 35<br>Observing<br>Time Allotment: 30 minutes | clear plastic jar<br>sweet potato<br>toothpicks<br>water | | **Activity Center:** "Plant a Garden"; "Pleasing Plants"; "Seed Sort"; "We Wear Plants"; "Flower Power" |
| **How Do Seeds Grow?** p. 41<br>Observing/Communicating<br>Time Allotment: 20 minutes | 2 lima bean seeds<br>a clear plastic cup<br>water<br>tape<br>soil<br>pencil and paper | Transparency Master, p. 25<br>◆ Family Science, p. 26<br>Activity Worksheet, p. 27<br>Critical Thinking, p. 29<br>▲ Critical Thinking, p. 30<br>Math Connection, p. 31<br>Independent Practice, p. 32<br>Language Arts Connection, pp. 165, 166 | Big Book, p. 7<br>Big Book, p. 8 |
| | | ◆ Reteaching Activity, p. 35<br>Independent Practice, p. 33<br>Language Arts Connection, p. 167 | Big Book, p. 9 |
| **You Can . . . Be a Science Detective,** p. 44<br>Observing<br>Time Allotment: a few minutes each day | empty paper rolls<br>yarn<br>masking tape<br>construction paper | Activity Worksheet, p. 28<br>Independent Practice, p. 34<br>Language Arts Connection, pp. 168, 169 | Big Book, p. 10<br>Big Book, p. 11<br>Activity Book, pp. 35, 36 |
| **How Do Animals Use Plants?** p. 46<br>Communicating<br>Time Allotment: 30 minutes<br><br>**Feed the Birds,** p. 217<br>Observing/Inferring<br>Time Allotment: 30 minutes | people to interview<br>pencil<br>logs<br><br>empty grapefruit half<br>yarn or string      pencil<br>bird food | | |
| | | Test A, p. 36<br>Test B, p. 37 | Color Transparencies #3a and #3b |

◆ Basic  /  ▲ Advanced  /  All other masters are for use by all students.

# Plants

## For Exceptional Students

## ESL/LEP

### Chapter 3/Lesson 1, Page 45

To help students learn about plants, have students make a poster showing how we use plants. Have students fold a large piece of paper in half. Label one side of the paper with the word *Plants*. Have students draw pictures of plants on this half. Label the other half with the words *Uses of Plants*. Students need to cut out and glue pictures from old magazines to show how these plants are used.

### Chapter 3/Lesson 1, Page 40

Write the words *flowers, roots, stems,* and *leaves* on the chalkboard. Review the pronunciation of these words. Give each student a piece of string or yarn (for roots), green construction paper shapes (for leaves and stems), and colored tissue paper shapes (for flowers). Once students have learned to recognize the word with the plant part, have students try the following activity. Ask students to work with a partner and sit back-to-back. Students take turns placing the stem, leaves, and flowers on a piece of paper, describing the position. The partner places the parts in the described locations. Compare the two pictures.

## Gifted

### Chapter 3/Lesson 1, Page 40

Have students gather and discuss the characteristics and classification of five plants from their yard or neighborhood. They should attach each plant to a sheet of plain white paper and label the roots, stems, leaves, and flowers where appropriate. Have students answer questions like these: How are the plants alike? How are they different? How can people find out what kind of plants they are? The students should look up the plants in reference books and label them with the correct common name.

## Mainstreamed

### Chapter 3/Lesson 1, Page 40

**Mild Behavior Disorders:** Direct students to remove several leaves with their stem from a mature coleus plant and place the leaves upright in water. Have students record how many days pass before they observe root development. Have them count the number of roots after five days and ten days. Plant the rooted cuttings in soil and water them as necessary. Have students name and label their plant.

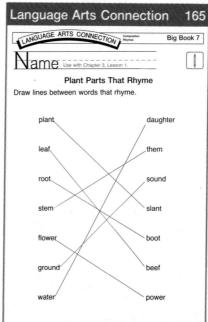

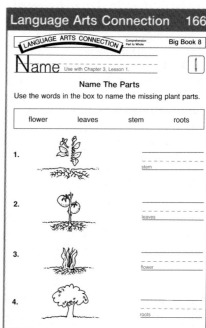

# Projects to Do

## Whole Class Science Projects

Have students make a dry potpourri. Contact a local florist and ask if he or she would supply you with discarded roses. Obtain seeds of caraway, coriander, anise, and cloves, spruce or pine leaves, and orange or lemon rind. Spread out the petals, leaves, and rind on a sheet of newspaper to air-dry for a few days. Provide each student with a square of muslin and a piece of colored yarn. Students should place their aromatic plant fragments within the muslin square. They can draw up the four corners and close it with a rubber band and then cover this with the yarn. Some students may need help in tying a bow.

## Science Fair Projects

Individual students could do one of the following projects:

1. Find out if temperature affects the germination of radish seeds. Sprout seeds in separate plastic cups that are provided with different temperatures.
2. Make a miniature garden with mosses, herbs, and other small plants or with cacti. Provide all the necessary conditions for healthy plant growth.
3. Choose three or four different kinds of seeds. Sprout them in separate plastic cups with a damp sponge and compare the growths of the roots. How are roots of different plants the same? How are they different?

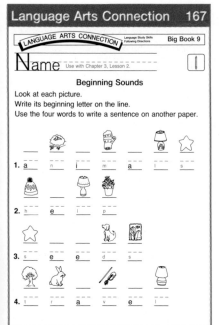

**Language Arts Connection  167**

LANGUAGE ARTS CONNECTION  Language Study Skills  Following Directions  Big Book 9

Name  Use with Chapter 3, Lesson 2.

**Beginning Sounds**

Look at each picture.
Write its beginning letter on the line.
Use the four words to write a sentence on another paper.

1. a _ n _ i _ m _ a _ l _ s
2. h _ e _ l _ p
3. s _ e _ e _ d _ s
4. t _ r _ a _ v _ e _ l

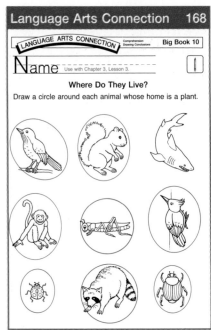

**Language Arts Connection  168**

LANGUAGE ARTS CONNECTION  Comprehension  Drawing Conclusions  Big Book 10

Name  Use with Chapter 3, Lesson 3.

**Where Do They Live?**

Draw a circle around each animal whose home is a plant.

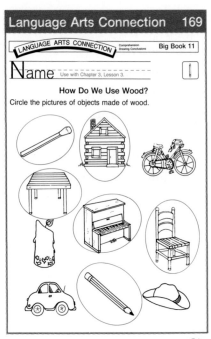

**Language Arts Connection  169**

LANGUAGE ARTS CONNECTION  Comprehension  Drawing Conclusions  Big Book 11

Name  Use with Chapter 3, Lesson 3.

**How Do We Use Wood?**

Circle the pictures of objects made of wood.

# CHAPTER 3

pages 34–49

## Chapter Concepts
- All plants have certain plant parts.
- Plants need animals to perform certain functions.
- Animals use plants in a variety of ways.

## Chapter Background
- There are over 300,000 kinds of plants.
- Plants make food by photosynthesis. They trap light energy of the sun to convert water and carbon dioxide into sugars with the release of oxygen.
- Food and water are passed around the plant through special cells that make up a vascular system in all plant parts.
- Energy needed by all organisms for their life processes comes from the sun.
- The majority of plants are green and supply many land and water animals with food. All organisms that feed on animals obtain their energy indirectly from photosynthesizing organisms.

## Looking Ahead
- You will need peat and loam mix for the activity on page 40.
- You will need a cockleburr for the activity on page 43.
- You will need a honeycomb with honey for the activity on page 47.

## Look for These Symbols
- —Hands-on activity
- —Cooperative learning
- —Overhead transparency
- ◆ —Basic/Reinforcement
- ● —Average/Enrichment
- ▲ —Advanced/Challenge
- SC —Science Center
- —Calculator Practice

SCIENCE
In Your World

34

# CHAPTER 3

# *Plants*

What do you know about plants?

Do you know that trees are plants?

Do you know that some plants have no flowers?

What is your favorite plant?

## Have You Ever...

### Grown a Sweet Potato

1. Place a sweet potato in a jar.

2. Use toothpicks to hold it.

3. Add water.

4. Cover half of the potato.

5. Change the water every day.

What happens to the sweet potato?

35

## PREPLAN

**Time Allotment:** 30 minutes

### Objectives
1. **Relate** that we see many plants in our daily lives.
2. **Observe** what happens when a sweet potato plant is placed in water.

### Setup
If you conduct the activity in the classroom, collect the following materials for each student or **cooperative learning group:**

clear plastic jar    sweet potato
toothpicks    water

## 1   FOCUS

■ Ask students to describe what they see in the picture on page 34. Ask them what kinds of plants are in the picture.

## 2   TEACH

■ Read the chapter title and introductory paragraph.
■ Ask: **What plants do you see around you every day?** Possible answers include: *trees, flowers, grass.*

### Have You Ever . . .
■ Use the activity to point out that plants need water and sunlight to grow.

### Student Responses
The sweet potato grows roots and leaves.

## 3   APPLY

■ Ask students if they have ever eaten a sweet potato. Discuss other plants that are commonly eaten by humans.

### Close
■ Tell students that they will learn more about why people need plants as they read Chapter 3.

## PREPLAN

### Lesson Objectives
1. **Recognize** roots, stems, leaves, and flowers as parts of plants.
2. **Tell** how plants use plant parts.

### Science Background
- Plants need light, water, nutrients, air, and the correct temperature for growth.
- Plants may have fibrous roots like tomatoes, or tap roots like dandelions.
- Stems support leaves and produce buds.
- The main part of a leaf is called the blade. Leaves are usually attached to the stem by a leaf stalk called a petiole.
- Fruits may be either dry, as in a pea pod or a maple samara, or fleshy, as in a blueberry or an orange.

### Lesson Vocabulary
plants    leaves    stems    roots    flowers

**Note:** The activity on student page 41 may be used for guided discovery before you begin this lesson.

## 1  FOCUS

Send a letter home with students asking for them to bring in a small houseplant for the class to adopt for four weeks. Provide a sunny area for the class greenhouse, which should be divided into three sections. Have students form **cooperative groups,** and explain that each group is responsible for one section of the greenhouse. Every day allow a few minutes for pairs of students to examine their group's plants and decide if each one needs watering or not. Each group should make a chart to record their plant care for each day of the four weeks.

# Plant Parts

1. leaves, roots, stems, flowers

**Plants** have parts.

Most plants have leaves.

Most have stems and roots.

Many plants have flowers.

[1]What plant parts do you see?

36

## TEACHER RESOURCE MASTERS

Green plants make their own food.

They make most food in their **leaves.**

[1]How are leaves different?

1. different shapes and sizes

37

## 2  TEACH

■ Arrange for a walk around the school-yard and have students recognize different kinds of plants.

Germinate a bean seed on a damp paper towel to show the young root. Point out the root hairs and explain that the plant takes up water from the soil through these hairs.

### Guided Practice
■ Provide students with paper and have them draw a tree to show all the parts of a plant.
■ If necessary, use the **reteaching strategy** in OPTIONS.

### Independent Practice
■ Use the Teacher Resource Master **Independent Practice,** page 32.

## 3  APPLY

■ Make a plant-part guessing game. Hold up one part of a plant and have students draw what they think the plant it came from looks like. Then show students a picture of the real plant and have them compare it with their own pictures.

### Close
■ Ask each student to draw his/her favorite plant. Discuss and classify the illustrations. Put the pictures in a class book.

## OPTIONS

### Reteaching Strategy
Have students construct a plant from a popsicle stick for the stem, string for roots, green tissue paper for the leaves, and yellow tissue paper for the flowers. Have them glue this onto construction paper and color a line for soil level.

### Resource Options
■ Use Big Book, page 7, "The Grocery Cart," and Teacher Resource Master **Language Connection** page 165.

## TEACHER RESOURCE MASTERS

Independent Practice 1 — 32

INDEPENDENT PRACTICE  Lesson 1  Chapter 3

Name

Use the words in the box to finish each sentence.  obj. 1 & 2

| roots | stems | leaves | seeds | grow |

1. Water moves through tubes in plant stems
2. Green plants make food in their leaves
3. Plants take in water through their roots
4. Plants use food they make to grow
5. Plant flowers make seeds

Draw a line from each word to the plant part it names. obj. 1

6. flower
7. roots
8. stem
9. leaves

# OPTIONS

### LANGUAGE CONNECTION

**Writing:** Have students complete page 29 of the Teacher Resource Package. Then, have students write a story to describe what is happening to the plant. Students should check their stories to be sure that the information included is in the corrected sequential order.

### LANGUAGE CONNECTION

**Writing:** Have students complete page 30 of the Teacher Resource Package. Then, have them write a story about the desert or the forest and why they would like to live in the habitat they chose.

SC ♦ **Reinforcement:** Have students make a collage of dried leaves. Dry leaves between several sheets of newspaper. Place books on top to press leaves flat. Check every few days until they are thoroughly dry. Have students glue their dried leaves to a sheet of white paper to display them.

SC ♦ **Reinforcement:** Make a display of different kinds of seeds such as bean, pea, marigold, corn, and sunflower seeds and label each. Next to the display have a box of mixed seeds. Students should take turns matching a seed in the box with a labeled seed.

### Resource Options

■ Use Big Book, page 8, "The Apple Tree," and Teacher Resource Master **Language Connection** page 166.

---

1. Most water is taken in through the roots and moves to other plant parts.
2. Food made in the leaves of green plants goes to other plant parts, and some of it is stored.

**Stems** of plants carry water and food.

Some plants have stems with tubes.

Water and food go through the tubes.

[1]Where does the water go?

[2]Where does the food go?

38

# TEACHER RESOURCE MASTERS

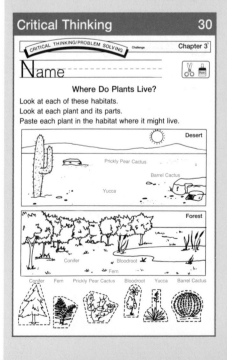

Critical Thinking                    30

CRITICAL THINKING/PROBLEM SOLVING    Challenge          Chapter 3

Name

**Where Do Plants Live?**

Look at each of these habitats.
Look at each plant and its parts.
Paste each plant in the habitat where it might live.

Desert
Prickly Pear Cactus
Barrel Cactus
Yucca

Forest
Conifer       Bloodroot
Fern

Conifer   Fern   Prickly Pear Cactus   Bloodroot   Yucca   Barrel Cactus

Plants use their **roots** to take in water.

Their roots also hold them in the ground.

There are different kinds of roots.

[1]How are these roots different?

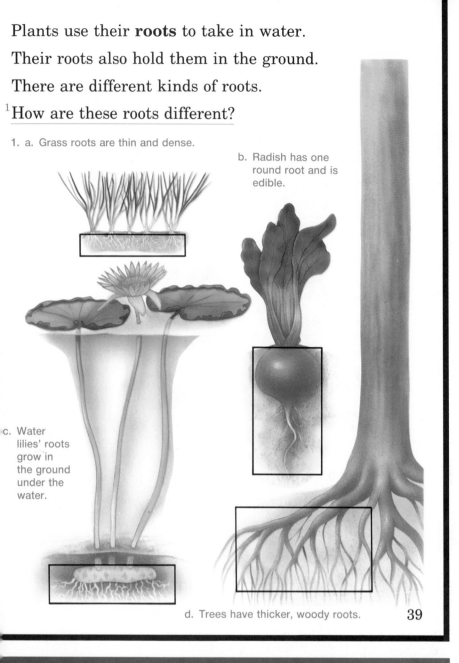

1. a. Grass roots are thin and dense.

b. Radish has one round root and is edible.

c. Water lilies' roots grow in the ground under the water.

d. Trees have thicker, woody roots.

39

## TEACHER RESOURCE MASTERS

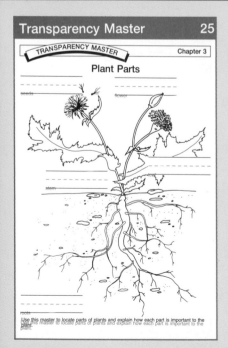

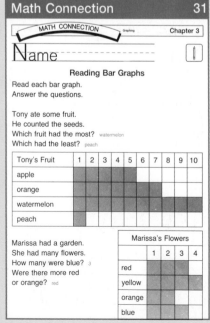

# OPTIONS

● **Enrichment:** Using sprouted seeds, plant one group in dry soil and a second group in damp soil. Have students predict the results. Have them make a chart to record observations. Students should conclude that the mixture of soil and moisture are necessary for plants to grow.

▲ **Challenge:** Gather pictures of familiar seed plants. Ask students to collect and bring to school seeds that would grow into any of the plants pictured. Have them make a display that matches the seeds to the pictures.

## ART CONNECTION

 Ask each student to bring in three differently shaped leaves. Explain that they will be making a class plant book. Provide each student with paper and crayons. Show them how to make leaf rubbings of leaves with prominent veins. Students should cut out leaf rubbings and mount them with glue on two or three large sheets of paper that will be used as pages in the book. Have them label the pages *leaves*.

Add pages to the class plant book by taking students into the schoolyard to make rubbings of tree bark with paper and crayons. Have them label these pages *stems*.

Have students press two or three flowers between newsprint and let them dry under the weight of a heavy book for two or three days. Some of these should be used for the class book by using white glue to stick them to the paper. Have them label these *flowers*.

For the class plant book, bring in a variety of fruits such as orange, apple, cucumber, and green pepper. Slice each fruit in half and have students dip the cut sides into tempera paint and make patterns that show the fruits with their seeds inside. Have them label these pages *fruits*.

# OPTIONS

Show students how to grow ferns. Have students bring in a clean plastic container. Provide them with a peat and loam mix for their miniature "greenhouse." They should press the soil down firmly to about 2 centimeters below the rim of the container. Sprinkle the surface of each with a thin layer of fine gravel or sand. Obtain spores of a fern that grows locally or those of a houseplant. The spores develop as brown dots often on the back of the fronds. A florist may agree to supply you with mature spores from old trimmed leaves. Mature spores will be on older leaves. Spray the surface of each container or pot with a fine mist and have students cover them with a plastic wrap. Keep the small greenhouses in a warm place until the young fern plants develop. They will look like heart-shaped liverworts and after several more weeks will develop small fern leaves. The covering can then be removed and the plants thinned out to watch the ferns grow.

■ Ask students to brainstorm to make a list of fruits and vegetables they eat, and to say which are sweet and which are not. Write these on the chalkboard in two columns under the headings *Sugar* and *Starch*. Explain that many of the plants we eat have other things that are important to our health such as vitamins and vegetable fats that are also made by the plant.

Many plants make **flowers.**

The flowers make seeds.

They make seeds in fruits.

[1]In what fruits can you find seeds?

40

1. oranges, apples, tomatoes, watermelons, and so on

# TEACHER RESOURCE MASTERS

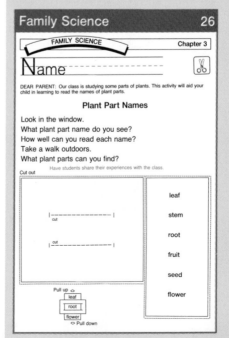

**Family Science** 26

FAMILY SCIENCE                    Chapter 3

Name

DEAR PARENT: Our class is studying some parts of plants. This activity will aid your child in learning to read the names of plant parts.

**Plant Part Names**

Look in the window.
What plant part name do you see?
How well can you read each name?
Take a walk outdoors.
What plant parts can you find?

Have students share their experiences with the class.

Cut out

cut

cut

leaf

stem

root

fruit

seed

flower

Pull up
leaf
root
flower
Pull down

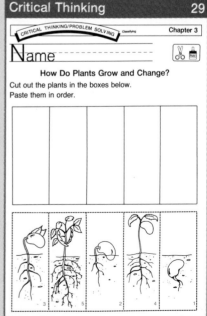

**Critical Thinking** 29

CRITICAL THINKING/PROBLEM SOLVING  Classifying    Chapter 3

Name

**How Do Plants Grow and Change?**

Cut out the plants in the boxes below.
Paste them in order.

# How do seeds grow?

## What you need

| | |
|---|---|
| 2 lima beans | tape |
| a clear cup | soil |
| water | pencil and paper |

## What to do

1. Tape two seeds on the inside of a cup.
2. Fill the cup with soil.
3. Add water to the soil.
4. Put the cup in a warm place.
5. Draw what you see happen.

41

## ACTIVITY RESPONSES

Accept all reasonable student responses to questions during any activity discussion.

## PREPLAN

**Time Allotment:** 20 minutes

**Process Skills:** Observing/Communicating

### Objectives
1. **Set up** an experiment.
2. **Examine** how a seed germinates.
3. **Draw** a germinating seed.

### Setup
Assemble the materials needed for each group of students.

**Cooperative Grouping:** twos—Assign roles as explained on page T24.

## 1 FOCUS

■ Bring in a variety of seed catalogs. Allow students to observe the variety of flowers, trees, and vegetables that can all be grown from seeds.

## 2 TEACH

■ Provide students with the names of the parts that grow as they emerge.
■ Use the Teacher Resource Master **Activity Worksheet,** page 27.

## 3 APPLY

■ Make a class experience chart. Ask students to compare seedlings and record what they did that helped the seeds grow best. Ask them to describe what happened to the tape and have them predict how the plant will continue to grow.

### Close
■ Discuss the activity. Ask students what they observed. Their observations may include the following.
1. Seeds change when given soil, water, and a warm place.
2. The outer coat of seeds breaks open.
3. New plants grow from seeds.

pages 42–43

## PREPLAN

### Lesson Objectives

**3. Identify** ways in which plants need animals.

**4. Recognize** animals that aid plants.

### Science Background

■ Plants that grow by the water may have small dry fruits that are dispersed in the mud on the feet of waterbirds.

■ Pollination in flowering plants occurs when pollen is transferred from the stamens to the pistil. In conifers, pollen is transferred from male to female cones.

■ Bees, butterflies, beetles, ants, flies, wasps, birds, and bats are all important to the pollination of plants.

### Lesson Vocabulary

pollen

## 1   FOCUS

■ Gather several kinds of seeds, cones, and flowers. Have students communicate how animals may aid plants in dispersing seeds, cones, and flowers.

# Plants Need Animals

Animals carry the seeds of some plants.

Some seeds stick to fur.

Some seeds stick to feathers.

[1]Guess what will happen to some of these seeds.

1. Seeds carried by animals may get planted and begin to grow; some might be eaten.

42

Flowers have **pollen.**

Flowers need pollen to make seeds.

Some animals carry pollen.

[1]What animals carry pollen?

1. insects, bats, and birds

43

## TEACHER RESOURCE MASTERS

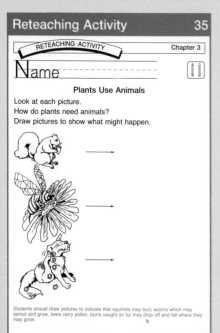

**Reteaching Activity** 35

RETEACHING ACTIVITY — Chapter 3

Name

**Plants Use Animals**

Look at each picture.
How do plants need animals?
Draw pictures to show what might happen.

Students should draw pictures to indicate that squirrels may bury acorns which may sprout and grow, bees carry pollen, burrs caught on fur may drop off and fall where they may grow.

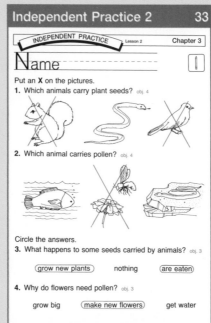

**Independent Practice 2** 33

INDEPENDENT PRACTICE — Lesson 2 — Chapter 3

Name

Put an **X** on the pictures.
1. Which animals carry plant seeds? obj. 4

2. Which animal carries pollen? obj. 4

Circle the answers.
3. What happens to some seeds carried by animals? obj. 3

(grow new plants)   nothing   (are eaten)

4. Why do flowers need pollen? obj. 3

grow big   (make new flowers)   get water

## 2   TEACH

Have students examine a cockleburr with a hand lens. Have them examine a piece of Velcro® with the lens. Explain that the Velcro® sticks together the same way that the cockleburr sticks to clothing or animal fur.

### Guided Practice
■ Have students draw animals carrying seeds intentionally (a squirrel carrying nuts) or unintentionally (burrs on an animal's coat). Have them write sentences telling how animals help plants.
■ If necessary, use the **reteaching strategy** in OPTIONS.

### Independent Practice
■ Use the Teacher Resource Master **Independent Practice,** page 33.

## 3   APPLY

Use examples of dry fruits with hooks that students can observe clinging to fur and fabric. Use teasels, burrs, beggar's ticks, or Queen Anne's lace.

### Close
■ Brush flowers onto a sheet of black paper and have students note the yellow dustlike pollen. Discuss how brightly colored flowers are attractive to insects, birds, and bats.

## OPTIONS

■ **Reteaching Strategy**
Mount pictures of birds, bats, and/or insects. Ask students to describe how these animals aid plants.
■ **Career:** Use "I Want To Know About A Beekeeper," student page 47.

### Resource Options
■ Use Big Book, page 9, "Traveling Seeds," and Teacher Resource Master **Language Arts Connection,** page 167.

## PREPLAN

### Lesson Objectives
**5. Give examples** of plants that we use for food.
**6. Communicate** how animals need plants.
**7. Describe** ways that people use plants.

### Science Background
■ Plants provide us with many natural resources such as rubber, cotton, oils, medicines, paper, houses, and furniture, and many have ornamental value.
■ Of the 350,000 species of plants, only about 6,000 are used by people. Just fifteen species of plants provide us with the bulk of our food crops.
■ Two-thirds of all plants grow in the tropics or subtropical regions.

**Note:** The activity on student page 46 may be used for guided discovery before you begin this lesson.

## 1  FOCUS

Have students make a large oak tree painting. Provide magazine photographs of insects such as caterpillars, and other insect larvae, beetles, flies, spiders and aphids; of birds such as jays, owls, swallows, and bluebirds; and of mammals such as woodmice, squirrels, and chipmunks. Have students cut out and paste these pictures on their tree. If photographs are not available have students draw an animal that they think might live in an oak tree, and paste it on the tree.

### Resource Options
■ Use Activity Book, pages 35 and 36, "Feed the Birds."
■ Use Big Book, page 10, "Quetico Park," and page 11, " Like It or Not."
Use Teacher Resource Masters, **Language Connection,** pages 165–169.

---

# Animals Need Plants

Some animals need plants for food.

You need plants for food.

1. plants grown as vegetables, grains, and fruits

[1]What plants do you like to eat?

**ACTIVITY**

## You Can...
### Be a Science Detective
Spy on animals.
Watch for ways they use plants.
Make a log.

44                                   Use Application Activity on page 217.

## TEACHER RESOURCE MASTERS

Animals use plants for other things, too.

Some animals use trees for homes.

You use wood from trees.

[1]How do you use wood?

1. pencils, paper, chairs, desks, houses, and so on

45

## 2  TEACH

Make a class display. Have students bring in items made from plants or examples of plants people eat.

### Guided Practice
- Use the class display described in the strategy above and add to it items that are not made from plants. Then have students study the display and identify only the items that are made from plants.
- If necessary, use the **reteaching strategy** in OPTIONS.

### Independent Practice
- Use the Teacher Resource Master **Independent Practice,** page 34.

## 3  APPLY

- Use Application Activity, "Feed the Birds," on student page 217.

### Close
- Have students look around the classroom and point out all the things that are made from plants. Make a class list.

## OPTIONS

### YOU CAN . . . BE A SCIENCE DETECTIVE

**Process Skills:** Observing/Communicating

**Objective: Observe** how animals use plants.

### Setup/Teach
With students make sets of "fun" binoculars out of empty paper rolls. Brainstorm how students could use their binoculars to watch animals.
- Decide with students how to organize and record data in their logs.

### Reteaching Strategy
Have students work in **cooperative** groups. Have each group compile a list of the ways animals other than humans use plants.

---

## TEACHER RESOURCE MASTERS

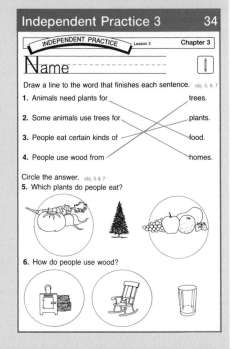

Independent Practice 3    34

INDEPENDENT PRACTICE    Lesson 3    Chapter 3

Name

Draw a line to the word that finishes each sentence.  obj. 5, 6, 7

1. Animals need plants for — trees.
2. Some animals use trees for — plants.
3. People eat certain kinds of — food.
4. People use wood from — homes.

Circle the answer.  obj. 5 & 7
5. Which plants do people eat?

6. How do people use wood?

## PREPLAN

**Time Allotment:** 30 minutes

**Process Skills:** Classifying/Communicating

### Objectives
1. **Collect, record,** and **classify** data.
2. **Communicate** information by interviewing others about their use of plants.

### Setup
■ Prepare a letter for students to use with adults to explain the needs for this activity.

**Cooperative Grouping:** twos—Assign roles as explained on page T24.

## 1 FOCUS

■ Gather some objects made from plants such as cotton clothing articles, wooden objects, processed plant foods, and so on. Discuss how we use these items.

## 2 TEACH

■ Have students brainstorm ideas in a group before interviewing others.
■ Have students illustrate their data, then display logs and illustrations.
■ Use the Teacher Resource Master **Activity Worksheet,** page 28, with this activity.

## 3 APPLY

■ Discuss the class list and compare students' findings. The students may see similar responses on each other's lists.

### Close
■ Show a short film or video about cotton or paper making or other uses of plant products as a culminating activity.

**ACTIVITY**

## How do animals use plants?

### What you need

people to interview     pencil     logs

### What to do

1. Ask some friends how they use plants.

2. Ask dog owners if their dogs use plants.

3. Ask cat owners if their cats use plants.

4. Ask some grown-ups how they use plants.

5. Make a class list.

46

## ACTIVITY RESPONSES

Accept all reasonable student responses to questions during an activity discussion.

# I WANT TO KNOW ABOUT...

## A Beekeeper

Do you like honey?

Lin Yu does.

He raises honeybees.

The bees gather nectar from flowers.

They make honey from the nectar.

Mr. Lin collects the honey from the beehives.

*Career*

47

## TEACHER RESOURCE MASTERS

### Feature Background

■ Worker bees suck nectar from flowers and store it in their stomachs. Chemicals from the bees' stomachs are added to the nectar, changing it to honey. The worker bee places the honey in cells in the honey comb.

■ Bees aid farmers by pollinating crops.

■ Beeswax can be used in candles, lipsticks, polishes, and waterproofing compounds. Young worker bees excrete the wax from their abdomens when it is needed to build or repair the honeycombs.

### Feature Vocabulary

honeybees
nectar
beehive

### Teaching Suggestions

■ Bring a honeycomb with honey to class to show students. Explain that honeybees make the combs and fill them with honey.

■ Bring in foods that contain honey. Ask students if they use honey as a sweetener at home.

■ Make edible honeybees with your class. Mix 1/2 cup of peanut butter and 1 tablespoon of honey. Stir in 1/3 cup of nonfat dry milk powder, 2 tablespoons of sesame seed, and 2 tablespoons of toasted wheat germ until all ingredients are well-mixed. Lay waxed paper on a baking sheet. Using a teaspoon at a time, shape the peanut butter mixture into ovals to look like bees. Put them on the baking sheet. Dip a toothpick in unsweetened cocoa powder and press gently across the top of bees to make stripes. Stick in almonds for wings. Chill for 30 minutes. Makes 28.

■ Remind students that honeybees can sting. Some people are allergic to bee stings.

■ Show a film on how bees make honey. Two films on honeybees are *Secrets of the Bee World,* Walt Disney Films, and *Social Insects—the Honeybee,* Encyclopaedia Britannica Educational Corp.

## CHAPTER 3 REVIEW

pages 48, 49

**Chapter Closure:** Use these pages to review and reinforce chapter concepts.

### What I Learned

Have students read the rebus summary statements aloud to be sure that students interpret the pictures correctly. After each sentence discuss other possible words that would also make the sentences true.

### Words I Know

Use the following suggestions to reinforce the chapter vocabulary. Write each science word or word group on the chalkboard. Ask students to read them. Add the words to the class science list or have students write the words in their individual science word books. Ask students to tell about these words to help you evaluate their comprehension. Have students use each science word or word group in a sentence.

**═══ What I Learned ═══**

- Plants have  ,  , and  .

  leaves    roots    stems

- Many plants have  .

  flowers

- Plants need  .

  animals

- Animals need  .

  plants

Some animals use plants for food.

**═══ Words I Know ═══**

| plants | leaves | stems | roots |
|--------|--------|-------|-------|

flowers    pollen

48

---

## TEACHER RESOURCE MASTERS

Test A                                             36

TEST A                    Recalling Facts        Chapter 3

**Name** Each question is worth 12 points.

Use the words in the box to name each plant part. obj. 1

| leaf | flower | stem | root |
|------|--------|------|------|

1. flower
2. stem
3. leaf
4. root

Use the words in the box to finish each sentence. obj. 3, 4, 6, 7

| fur | food | pollen | houses |
|-----|------|--------|--------|

5. Some seeds stick to fur

6. Bees help carry plant pollen

7. People use wood to make houses

8. Many animals use plants for food

---

## What I Know

*Use the picture to answer the questions.*

1. How do plants use leaves?

2. How do plants use roots?

3. Why do some plants need animals?

4. How do animals use plants?

### What I Know

Have students refer to the picture to answer the questions and extend concepts.

**1.** Plants make food in their leaves.

**2.** Plants use roots to take in water and for support.

**3.** Some plants need animals to carry seeds. Some animals carry pollen that flowers need to make seeds.

**4.** Animals need plants for food and homes. People also use plants for building material, furniture, clothing, rope, medicine, and to build fires.

## OPTIONS

### Resource Options

Use Color Transparencies #3a and #3b.

## TEACHER RESOURCE MASTERS

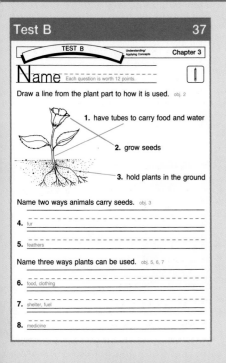

Test B                                    37

TEST B                    Understanding/Applying Concepts        Chapter 3

Name   Each question is worth 12 points.

Draw a line from the plant part to how it is used.  obj. 2

1. have tubes to carry food and water

2. grow seeds

3. hold plants in the ground

Name two ways animals carry seeds.  obj. 3

4. fur

5. feathers

Name three ways plants can be used.  obj. 5, 6, 7

6. food, clothing

7. shelter, fuel

8. medicine

# *The Space Around You*

## Planning Guide

| Lessons | Objectives | Vocabulary |
|---|---|---|
| Chapter Introduction pp. 50, 51 | | |
| Lesson 1 Your space pp. 52–55 | 1. **Identify** personal and shared space or environment. <br> 2. **Identify** who takes care of personal and shared space. <br> 3. **List** what needs to be done to care for our space or environment. | space |
| Lesson 2 Our Space pp. 56–59 | 4. **Identify** the needs of living things in a large, shared environment. <br> 5. **Describe** proper care of larger, shared space. | park |
| Lesson 3 Taking Care of Our World pp. 60–63 | 6. **Identify** Earth as a large, shared space. <br> 7. **Control** litter in our personal and shared environments. <br> 8. **Develop** ideas for practicing conservation in our environment. | world <br> litter |
| Chapter Review pp. 64, 65 | | |
| Unit Review pp. 66, 67 | | |

# Planning Guide

| Text Activities | | Teacher Resource Masters | Other Components |
|---|---|---|---|
| Title/Skill | Materials per Group | | |
| **Have You Ever . . . Made a Tent?** p. 51<br>Observing<br>Time allotment: 30 minutes | 2 chairs or card table<br>1 blanket | | **Activity Center:** "Your Space"; "My Space"; "Too Much Trash" |
| **Who Takes Care of This Space?** p. 55<br>Classifying/Inferring<br>Time Allotment: 30 minutes | yarn<br>pencil and paper | Activity Worksheet, p. 41<br>▲ Critical Thinking, p. 44<br>◆ Reteaching Activity, p. 49<br>Independent Practice, p. 46<br>Language Arts Connection, pp. 170, 171 | Big Book, p. 12<br>Big Book, p. 13 |
| **You Can . . . Plan a Park** p. 59<br>Communicating<br>Time Allotment: 30 minutes<br><br>**Outdoor Spaces,** p. 218<br>Observing/Communicating<br>Time Allotment: 45 minutes | drawing paper<br>crayons<br><br><br>paper<br>pencil<br>crayons | Critical Thinking, p. 43<br>Social Studies Connection, p. 45<br>Independent Practice, p. 47<br>Language Arts Connection, p. 172 | Big Book, p. 14<br>Poster #3 and #4<br>Activity Book, p. 19<br>Activity Book, p. 37 |
| **What Can I Do?** p. 62<br>Observing/Inferring<br>Time Allotment: 30 minutes | litter bag<br>crayons<br>pencil and paper | Transparency Master, p. 39<br>◆ Family Science, p. 40<br>Activity Worksheet, p. 42<br>Independent Practice, p. 48<br>Language Arts Connection, pp. 173, 174 | Big Book, p. 15<br>Big Book, p. 16<br>Activity Book, p. 20 |
| | | Test A, p. 50<br>Test B, p. 51 | Color Transparencies #4a and #4b |
| | | | Unit Test |

◆ Basic / ▲ Advanced / All other masters are for use by all students.

# The Space Around You

## For Exceptional Students

## ESL/LEP

### Chapter 4/Lesson 3, Page 61

Have each ESL student make a set of word cards with the following words: *litter, park, space,* and *world*. Find pictures that illustrate each word. Show students one picture at a time. Ask students to hold the corresponding vocabulary word. Say the word aloud together. Then, have each student fold a large piece of paper into fourths. Use the word cards to label each section. Ask students to draw a picture to illustrate the words.

### Chapter 4/Lesson 1, Page 54

Students may become confused with the two definitions of the word *space*. To help students understand their space, describe a particular space in your classroom. Ask students to guess the space. For example, you might describe the reading corner by saying something about the books, rug, or window that may be nearby. After this ask students to find their own special space in your classroom for independent reading time. Set a specific time for the entire class to read silently.

## Gifted

### Chapter 4/Lesson 3, Page 61

Using two clear plastic shoe boxes, potting soil, grass seeds, and water, have students demonstrate that plants prevent erosion. Plant grass seeds in one box, water carefully, and allow the plants to grow for several weeks in a sunny window. Do not plant any seeds in soil in the second box. When plants in the first box have produced a dense root structure. Pour about 200 milliliters of water into each box at the top of the slope. Compare what happens to the soil.

## Mainstreamed

### Chapter 4/Lesson 1, Page 54

**Visually Impaired:** Direct students to explore the classroom or another room in the building with a partner. Provide the team with a checklist to record what they find such as people, desks, typewriters, tables, telephones, pencil sharpeners, and so on.

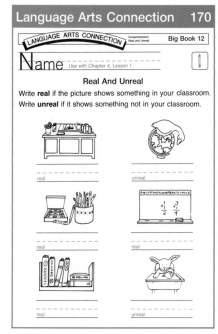

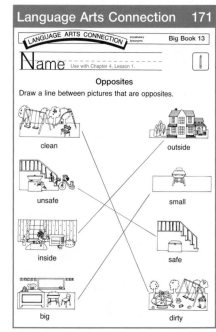

## Whole Class Science Project

Conservation of resources can only occur if people are aware of how much they actually use. How much water does it take to wash hands? To brush teeth? In a basin, catch water used while washing hands. Pour the used water into a measuring cup to find out how much was used. Have students suggest ways that would conserve their use of water. Students should draw a picture titled *Don't Waste Water* to share with their families. Show a picture or drawing of a water meter. Discuss where their water supply comes from and what happens to waste water.

## Science Fair Projects

Individual students could do one of the following projects:

1. Using four different brands of paper towels, find out which one is really the strongest, and which is more absorbent.
2. Make a useful item or a picture using recycled materials.
3. Using resource materials, have student find out what products are made from aluminum and display them on a poster.

**Language Arts Connection    172**

LANGUAGE ARTS CONNECTION   Language Study Skills Observing/Describing   Big Book 14

**N**ame Use with Chapter 4, Lesson 2.

**Our Space**

Draw a circle around the things that are living.
Draw a box around the things that are not living.

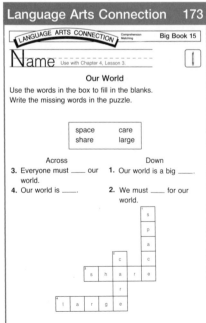

**Language Arts Connection    173**

LANGUAGE ARTS CONNECTION   Comprehension Matching   Big Book 15

**N**ame Use with Chapter 4, Lesson 3.

**Our World**

Use the words in the box to fill in the blanks.
Write the missing words in the puzzle.

| space | care |
| share | large |

Across
3. Everyone must ____ our world.
4. Our world is ____.

Down
1. Our world is a big ____.
2. We must ____ for our world.

**Language Arts Connection    174**

LANGUAGE ARTS CONNECTION   Language Study Skills Finding Details   Big Book 16

**N**ame Use with Chapter 4, Lesson 3.

**Word Search**

The words in the box tell about your world.
Look at each picture.
Circle the word in the puzzle that tells about it.

| clean | living | safe |

# CHAPTER 4

pages 50–65

## Chapter Concepts

■ Each individual has personal space in the environment.
■ People share their space with other living things.
■ Each person is responsible for personal and shared space in the environment.

## Chapter Background

■ Earth is the environment for all people. Satellites and spaceships have made it possible for us to see the entire planet Earth. Your environment provides everything you need for life.
■ Anything that changes one aspect of the physical environment or interferes with the life cycle of a plant or animal species may eventually affect all of us.
■ The meaning of conservation has changed along with the environment. Conservation problems no longer affect only farmers and foresters. Conservationists are concerned with the quality of life for all living things.

## Looking Ahead

■ Plan a visit to a park and/or a discussion with a park ranger to **Close** Lesson 2 on page 57.
■ Find a recycling symbol on a paper product to show the class for the teaching strategy in Lesson 3.

## Look for These Symbols

    —Hands-on activity
    —Cooperative learning
    —Overhead transparency
◆   —Basic/Reinforcement
●   —Average/Enrichment
▲   —Advanced/Challenge
SC  —Science Center
    —Calculator Practice

SCIENCE In Your World

50

# CHAPTER 4

# *The Space Around You*

Can you fly a kite in your space

Can you read a book in your space?

How big is your space?

## Have You Ever...

### Made a Tent?

1. Use two chairs.

2. Place them a few feet apart.

3. Drape a cover over the chairs.

4. Crawl into your tent.

How will you use this space?

51

## PREPLAN

**Time Allotment:** 30 minutes

**Objectives**
1. **Observe** that the whole world is our space.
2. **Observe** that we also have personal space.

**Setup**
If you conduct the activity in the classroom, collect the following materials for each **cooperative learning group:**
2 chairs or 1 card table      1 blanket

## 1   FOCUS

■ Ask students to tell what is going on in the picture on page 50. Observe and discuss how the people in the picture are taking care of their space.

## 2   TEACH

■ Read the chapter title and introductory paragraph.
■ Discuss students' space in the classroom and at home. Encourage them to describe what is in their own personal space.

**Have You Ever . . .**
■ Use this activity to introduce the concept of personal space.

**Student Responses**
■ This space belongs to me, and I can play here with a friend.

## 3   APPLY

■ Have students tell what they consider their own space. Ask them to tell about what parts of that space they share with other living things.

**Close**
■ Tell students they will learn more about sharing and caring for their space as they read Chapter 4.

# PREPLAN

## Lesson Objectives

1. **Identify** personal and shared space or environment.
2. **Identify** who takes care of personal and shared space.
3. **List** what needs to be done to care for our space or environment.

## Science Background

- A person's environment depends on the country, state, city, town, or area in which the person lives.
- Weather and climate are part of a person's environment.

## Lesson Vocabulary

space

**Note:** The activity on student page 55 may be used for guided discovery before you begin this lesson.

# 1 FOCUS

- Ask: **Where is your favorite place?** Make a short list of favorite places. Ask: **Why do you like this place?** Introduce the word *environment*. Define environment as the space around you and all of the things both living and nonliving found in that space. Explain to students that they will learn about different environments and how to take care of them.

# Your Space

Look at the **space** around you.

¹What is in that space?

²Who shares this space?

³Who should take care of it?

1. encourage students to describe themselves, other living things, and objects in the classroom
2. everyone in the classroom
3. same answer as 2

52

# TEACHER RESOURCE MASTERS

**Critical Thinking**                44

CRITICAL THINKING/PROBLEM SOLVING    Challenge    Chapter 4

Name

Taking Care Of My Space

Plan how you will take care of your space.
Write your plan below.
Keep a chart to see how you do.

Answers will vary, but may include organize supplies.

keep trash picked up around my desk, and use paper wisely

**My Plan**

|           |  |  |
|-----------|--|--|
| Monday    |  |  |
| Tuesday   |  |  |
| Wednesday |  |  |
| Thursday  |  |  |
| Friday    |  |  |

Plan can be for home or school. Have students write what they planned at the top of each column.

You have your space at home.

But your space is bigger.

You have space at school.

[1]What is a part of your space at school?

1. classroom, hallways, cafeteria, and so on

53

## TEACHER RESOURCE MASTERS

Independent Practice 1    46

INDEPENDENT PRACTICE    Lesson 1    Chapter 4

Name

Circle the answer.
1. Which is your space? obj. 1

2. Which spaces do you share with others? obj. 1

3. Which space should you take care of by yourself? obj. 2

4. Put an X on the space that has been cared for. obj. 3

## 2 TEACH

■ Ask: **How do you care for your classroom environment?** *keep it clean, orderly, feed the animals, water the plants*
■ Discuss what needs to be done to care for shared areas. Ask: **What would happen to the shared school space if no one took care of it?** *It would be messy, unsafe, and unpleasant.*

### Guided Practice

■ Ask students to draw a picture of a small personal space they use. Have them list things they use in this space and tell how they care for these things.
■ If necessary, use the **reteaching strategy** in OPTIONS.

### Independent Practice

■ Use the Teacher Resource Master **Independent Practice,** page 46.

## 3 APPLY

Have students draw a floor plan of their bedrooms. Lead students to identify how they are responsible for this space.

### Close

Have students make a mural of the school. Identify shared areas. Review who is responsible for shared areas.

## OPTIONS

### Reteaching Strategy

Provide students with maps of small areas they use. Ask students to work in groups to discuss and then explain what is in one of the spaces and how they use and care for it. Examples of such areas may include a classroom library corner, TV space, toy room area, or art supply shelves.

### Resource Options

■ Use Big Book, page 12, "My Space," and Teacher Resource Master **Language Arts Connection,** page 170.

## OPTIONS

### LANGUAGE CONNECTION

**Reading and Writing:** Read *My Back Yard* by Anne and Harlow Rockwell to your students. Have students write a story about their own backyard or another special place in their home.

◆ **Reinforcement:** Have students make a list of ways to care for the classroom such as watering plants, cleaning desktops, and straightening shelves. Have students take turns being responsible for various tasks.

● **Enrichment:** Students may want to bring in postcards or photographs of places they have visited to share with the class. Students should discuss their responsibilities for these public spaces.

▲ **Challenge:** Direct students to develop a plan for constructing a community, and to identify the needs of that community. Have students decide how the need for clean water, clean air, and trash collection will be met.

### Resource Options

■ Use Big Book, page 13, "Sharing Space" and Teacher Resource Master **Language Arts Connection,** page 171.

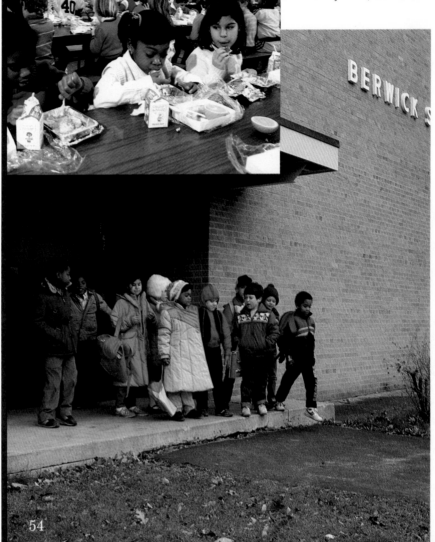

[1]Who should take care of your school?

[2]What can you do?

1. everyone at school
2. keep desk area tidy, replace objects that I use, throw away trash, and so on

54

## TEACHER RESOURCE MASTERS

Reteaching Activity        49

RETEACHING ACTIVITY          Chapter 4

Name

Caring For Your Space

Look at each picture.
Tell how they should care for their space.

Answers should reflect knowledge of the importance of picking up and keeping the environment clean.

# Who takes care of this space?

## What you need

yarn    pencil and paper

## What to do

1. Use yarn to circle your desk.
2. List what is in this space.
3. How do you take care of it?
4. What part of this space do you share?
5. Who takes care of this?

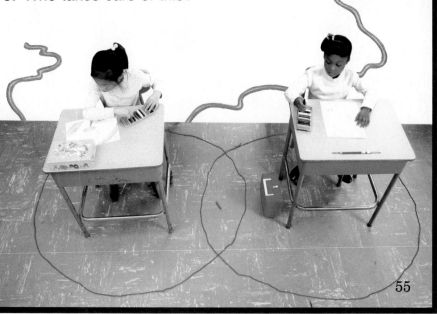

55

## ACTIVITY RESPONSES

Accept all reasonable student responses to questions during any activity discussions.

## PREPLAN

**Time Allotment:** 30 minutes

**Process Skills:** Classifying/Inferring

### Objectives

1. **Identify** personal space and list what is in the space.
2. **Explain** how to take care of space.
3. **Identify** shared space.
4. **Relate** who cares for shared space.

### Setup

Cut lengths of yarn long enough to make a circle about 1 meter in diameter.

**Cooperative Grouping:** twos—Assign roles as explained on page T24.

## 1  FOCUS

■ Show students how to place the yarn in a circle on the floor around a student's desk. Do this with several adjacent desks so the circles overlap in the aisle between desks.

## 2  TEACH

■ Have students identify space that is shared. Ask: **How can we take care of the shared space?** *Keep shared areas clean. Respect the rights of others.*

■ Use Teacher Resource Master 41, **Activity Worksheet,** for "Who takes care of this space?"

## 3  APPLY

■ Describe personal and shared environments at home: bedroom, kitchen, living room. Have students identify who cares for these areas. Discuss how families take responsibility for home care.

### Close

■ Ask students what they observe about their environment.

# PREPLAN

## Lesson Objectives
**4. Identify** the needs of living things in a large, shared environment.
**5. Describe** proper care of larger, shared space.

## Science Background
■ The National Park Service was founded in 1916. Its job is to protect the wild lands of the national parks.
■ A wildlife refuge is an area of land or water that is set aside and managed for the protection and preservation of native plants and animals. Theodore Roosevelt established the first national refuge in 1903.
■ Organizations have been established to care for the environment. These organizations vary in their environmental interests. The Wilderness Society is concerned with saving wild areas. The National Audubon Society, Sierra Club, and National Wildlife Federation are some other active environmental organizations.

## Lesson Vocabulary
park

# 1　FOCUS

■ Remind students that environment is the space around you and all the things, both living and nonliving, found in that space. Ask: **What places can you name that are used by everyone?** *parks, forests, lakes, movie theaters, shopping centers, playgrounds*

**Science and Technology:** Use "I WANT TO KNOW ABOUT . . . Animals in Danger," student page 63, with this lesson.

## Our Space

We use land to build homes and plant food.

We use water to drink and to swim.

We use air to breathe and blow bubbles.

56

# TEACHER RESOURCE MASTERS

Other living things use the space around us.
We share this space with other animals.
We share this space with plants.

57

## 2   TEACH

■ Discuss how pets share our space. Have students share experiences caring for a pet. Discuss why it is important for us to care for the space our pet uses in shared environments such as neighborhoods, parks, and so on.

### Guided Practice

Have students work in **cooperative groups** and role-play to demonstrate proper care of living and nonliving things in the environment. The role-playing may include people having a picnic in the park and cleaning up after themselves; visiting a zoo and following rules about not feeding animals; a family camping and being responsible for how they use the land.

■ If necessary, use the **reteaching strategy** in OPTIONS.

### Independent Practice

■ Use the Teacher Resource Master **Independent Practice,** page 47.

## 3   APPLY

■ Use Application Activity, "Outdoor Spaces," on student page 218.

### Close

■ Plan a picnic for your students at a local park. Show them how to clean up their litter. Ask the park ranger to speak to your class.

## OPTIONS

### Reteaching Strategy

Provide each student with a cut-out picture of an animal. Ask students to draw the space this animal might use. Ask them to describe other living things that might share that space.

### Resource Options

■ Use Big Book, page 14, "The Park" and Teacher Resource Master **Language Arts Connection,** page 172.

## TEACHER RESOURCE MASTERS

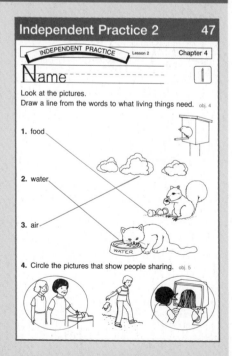

Independent Practice 2          47

INDEPENDENT PRACTICE    Lesson 2    Chapter 4

Name

Look at the pictures.
Draw a line from the words to what living things need.   obj. 4

1. food

2. water

3. air

4. Circle the pictures that show people sharing.   obj. 5

# OPTIONS

## YOU CAN . . . PLAN A PARK

**Process Skills:** Communicating/Inferring

**Objective: Describe** features of a shared environment and **infer** how to care for them.

**Setup/Teach**

Give each student a 12″ × 18″ sheet of manila paper. Students can use one or more mediums such as paint, crayons, colored chalk, cut-out pictures, or construction paper to make their parks more interesting. Show students how to use folded bits of paper to make some park features stand out. Students can **work cooperatively** in groups to make one larger mural.

## LANGUAGE CONNECTION

**Reading and Writing:** Read *The Trek* by Ann Jonas to your students. Have students decide whether the story is fact or fantasy and discuss how they know. Ask students to describe the setting to you. Have students use their own personal lives and write an imaginary story.

## Resource Options

■ Use Poster #3, "Rabbit Ears" and Poster #4, "Where Is Central Park?"
■ Use Activity Book, page 19, "Communicating."
■ Use Activity Book, pages 37 and 38, "Outdoor Spaces."

Think about this **park.**

1. living things
2. fish, birds, trees, and so on
3. fish, play, walk, and so on

¹Who shares this space?

²Who needs this space to live?

³How do you use this space?

58

# TEACHER RESOURCE MASTERS

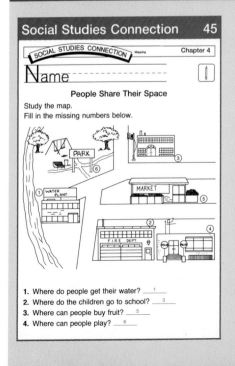

Social Studies Connection    45

SOCIAL STUDIES CONNECTION    Mapping    Chapter 4

Name

**People Share Their Space**

Study the map.
Fill in the missing numbers below.

1. Where do people get their water? ___1___
2. Where do the children go to school? ___3___
3. Where can people buy fruit? ___5___
4. Where can people play? ___6___

The space around us is important.

We need to care for everything around us.

[1]What will you do?

1. pick up litter, report broken equipment to park authorities, and so on

**ACTIVITY**

# You Can...

## Plan a Park

Plan how you could make a park.
Make a poster to show your park.
How can others care for your park?

Use Application Activity on page 218.

59

# OPTIONS

◆ **Reinforcement:** Have students make a collage of places that are shared areas within your neighborhood, city, county, or state.

● **Enrichment:** Arrange a field trip to a local park. Look for evidence of good care as well as signs of neglect. Explain that the environment is more enjoyable when it is well cared for and that it will last longer for others to enjoy.

▲ **Challenge:** Have students make a booklet with pictures and rules showing how to care for a pet. Have students explain how caring for a pet contributes to the care of the environment.

# TEACHER RESOURCE MASTERS

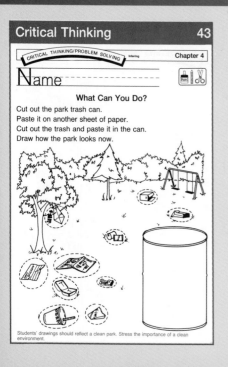

**Critical Thinking** 43

CRITICAL THINKING/PROBLEM SOLVING · Inferring · Chapter 4

Name

**What Can You Do?**

Cut out the park trash can.
Paste it on another sheet of paper.
Cut out the trash and paste it in the can.
Draw how the park looks now.

Students' drawings should reflect a clean park. Stress the importance of a clean environment.

## PREPLAN

### Lesson Objectives

**6. Identify** Earth as a large, shared space.

**7. Control** litter in our personal and shared environments.

**8. Develop** ideas for practicing conservation in our environment.

### Science Background

■ There are natural sources of pollution. Volcanoes, forest fires, dust storms, and plants release contaminants.

■ Air pollution is a serious national and international problem. The leading cause of pollutants in the air is motor vehicles. The second leading cause of air pollution is industrial smoke and fumes.

■ Water is polluted by solid wastes, sewage, chemicals, and heat from power plants.

■ One ton of recycled newsprint saves 17 trees.

### Lesson Vocabulary

world          litter

**Note:** The activity on student page 62 may be used for guided discovery before you begin this lesson.

## 1  FOCUS

■ Bring in newspaper or magazine articles dealing with pollution or conservation. Define the term pollution—air, water, noise, or land that is not clean or safe.

■ If possible, have students visit a recycling plant. Review items that can be recycled and predict how they may be used.

# Taking Care of Our World

We are part of the **world.**

Our world is big.

We all share it.

60

## TEACHER RESOURCE MASTERS

Transparency Master          39

TRANSPARENCY MASTER          Chapter 4

Clean Air Or Water?

FACTORY

Use this master to discuss problems with pollution.

Some of us do not keep our world clean.

Some of us **litter.**

What happens if we do not care for our world?

How can you help?

1. Explain to students about pollution.
2. Discuss conservation.

61

## 2 TEACH

■ Discuss the term *recycling*. List materials that can be recycled.
■ Bring in products that display the recycle symbol. Explain that paper is recycled to save trees and land and to reduce litter.

### Guided Practice

■ After discussing different ways to help our environment, have students complete an "I learned" statement. For example, "I learned that litter is _____."
■ If necessary, use the **reteaching strategy** in OPTIONS.

### Independent Practice

■ Use the Teacher Resource Master **Independent Practice,** page 48.

## 3 APPLY

Plan a "Save Our World" campaign. Have students **work cooperatively** in small groups and design buttons, banners, and posters to illustrate conservation practices.

### Close

■ Direct the class to write a letter to an environmental agency to question their role in caring for the environment.

## OPTIONS

### Reteaching Strategy

■ Ask an upper class student to come into your classroom to litter. When the older student leaves ask the class how they felt about what happened.

### Resource Options

■ Use Activity Book, page 20, "Taking Care of Our World."
■ Use Big Book, page 15, "What Can You See" and page 16, "Part of This World." Use Teacher Resource Masters, **Language Arts Connection,** pages 170–174.

## TEACHER RESOURCE MASTERS

**Family Science**      40

FAMILY SCIENCE      Chapter 4

**N**ame

DEAR PARENT: We are learning about taking care of our world. Find ways to use containers or other objects more wisely. Help your child learn more about conservation.

**Using Things Wisely**

Every year our dumps get larger.
Some things people use could be used again.
Save paper, aluminum, or plastic.
Find places that collect these things.
Find people who can use some of these things again.

**1.** What did you save?

_Answers may include plastic containers, newspapers, aluminum cans, or foil._

**2.** Who uses some of these things again?

_schools, paper recycling companies, aluminum can companies_

**3.** How could paper, plastic, or aluminum be used again?

_art projects, storage, recycled stationary, new aluminum cans_

**Independent Practice 3**      48

INDEPENDENT PRACTICE  Lesson 3   Chapter 4

**N**ame

Circle the answers.
**1.** Which must all people share? obj. 6

**2.** How do we help take care of our world? obj. 7

**3.** Which shows people not taking care of our world? obj. 8

## PREPLAN

**Time Allotment:** 30 minutes
**Process Skills:** Observing/Inferring

### Objectives
1. **Identify** an environmental need.
2. **Describe** steps to take to meet the environmental need.

### Setup
Collect pictures of environments that show signs of neglect.

**Cooperative Grouping:** fours—Assign roles as explained on page T24.

## 1 FOCUS

■ Show students pictures of neglected environments. Have students identify what is wrong in each picture and explain what needs to be done to correct it.

## 2 TEACH

■ Discuss with students where they will be going on the walk.
■ Predict some of the problems they may see, such as litter or broken playground equipment. Have groups of students collect litter, then discuss what they found.
■ Use Teacher Resource Master 42, **Activity Worksheet,** for "What can I do?"

## 3 APPLY

Have students go for a walk with parent volunteers in a larger environment, such as a park or neighborhood, and identify problems in the environment.

### Close
■ Make a list of the students' observations. Discuss how the various problems may have been avoided. Help students develop a plan of action for dealing with the identified problems.

### ACTIVITY

## What can I do?

### What you need
litter bag      crayons      pencil and paper

### What to do
1. Go for a walk with your class.
2. What does your part of the world need?
3. What can be done?
4. Make a list of jobs your class can do.
5. What job will you do?

## ACTIVITY RESPONSES
Accept all reasonable student responses to questions during any activity discussion.

# I WANT TO KNOW ABOUT...

## Animals in Danger

Some kinds of falcons are in danger.
They cannot stay alive without help.
This zookeeper is feeding a baby falcon.
The puppet looks like the falcon's mother.
Someday this bird will be set free.
It will not depend on people to feed it.

*Science and Technology*

63

## TEACHER RESOURCE MASTERS

### Feature Background

■ The bird in this picture is a peregrine falcon. Peregrine falcons are on the endangered species list. Insecticides have made the eggs of the peregrine falcon very thin-shelled. Scientists have experimented with incubating some of these eggs and have carefully raised the young birds, eventually releasing them back into their natural environment. For additional information, refer to *Ranger Rick*, June, 1985.

### Feature Vocabulary

zookeeper
puppet

### Teaching Suggestions

■ Discuss with students the importance of protecting rare animals. Tell students that scientists raise many types of animals to make sure that the young are protected and have a chance to mature.
■ Have a speaker from your local zoo come to your class. Ask the speaker to discuss other programs to breed and raise animals.
■ Have students make animal puppets out of socks or brown lunch sacks.

**Chapter Closure:** Use the summary statements under What I Learned to discuss with students concept ideas related to each statement.

## What I Learned

Have students read the rebus summary statements aloud to be sure that students interpret the pictures correctly. After each sentence is read, discuss other words that might make the sentence true.

## Words I Know

Use any or all of the following suggestions to reinforce the chapter vocabulary.

Write each science word or word group on the chalkboard. Ask students to read them. Add the words to the class science list or have students write the words in their individual science word books. Ask students to tell about these words to help you evaluate their comprehension. Have students use each science word or word group in a sentence.

**CHAPTER REVIEW**

**4**

━━━━━ **What I Learned** ━━━━━

- Your  home and your  school are a part of your space.

- You share your space with  plants and other  animals .

- You should take care of your space.

  We should help keep our 🌍 world clean.

━━━━━ **Words I Know** ━━━━━

space    park    world    litter

64

## TEACHER RESOURCE MASTERS

**Test A**                               **50**

## What I Know

*Use the picture to answer the questions.*

**1.** How do we share our space?

**2.** How can we care for our space?

**3.** Why do we need to care for our world?

**4.** How can we care for our world?

65

### What I Know

Have students refer to the picture to answer the questions and extend concepts.

**1.** We share our space with other living things.

**2.** We can care for our space at home and at school by keeping it clean, putting things back in their place, and being thoughtful of other living things and their needs.

**3.** We need to care for our world because everyone shares it. If we do not care for it, it may change so much that we will not have what we need to live.

**4.** We should be responsible for taking care of our world. We should be careful about campfires, leaving places we **visit** in good condition, and being thoughtful of other living things and their needs.

## OPTIONS

### Resource Options

Use Color Transparencies #4a and #4b.

## TEACHER RESOURCE MASTERS

Test B     51

pages 66, 67

## The Writing Connection

Help students get started by reviewing the animals in the chapter. Talk about the different body coverings and habitats of animals. As a variation, students can pretend they are a favorite plant.

## Other Ideas

Read "Sarah Cynthia Sylvia Stout Would Not Take the Garbage Out" from *Where the Sidewalk Ends* by Shel Silverstein. Have students make a list of the ways they could keep their world clean. Students can write letters to Sarah with helpful clean-up suggestions. Letters may also be written to the mayor or a local newspaper.

Students can design an imaginary special space on a piece of paper. Then have students write a story to tell about their space. Have them include their reason for choosing the space.

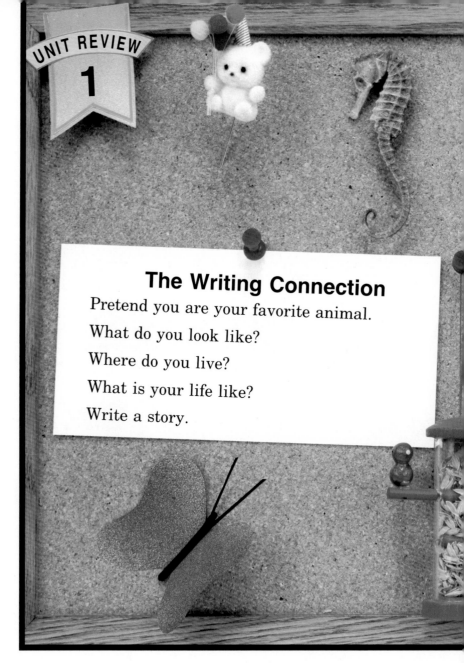

UNIT REVIEW 1

## The Writing Connection

Pretend you are your favorite animal.

What do you look like?

Where do you live?

What is your life like?

Write a story.

## Something To Do

Draw some faces on eggshell halves.

Fill the shells with soil.

Plant some rye grass seeds.

Goldfish may
turn white
if kept in a
dark room.

## Books To Read

**A Snake Is Totally Tail** by Judi Barrett

**This Year's Garden** by Cynthia Rylant

**The Trek** by Ann Jonas

### Something to Do

This activity will allow students to watch the growth of plants. You might encourage some students to allow the plants to grow without trimming them, to allow seeds to form.

### Would You Believe?

When goldfish are in the dark, they are unable to get sunlight. The ultraviolet radiation in sunlight can stimulate the synthesis of melanin. Melanin is the principle pigment that makes goldfish gold. People also have melanin. Compare for students the darkening of the skin, or tan, they may get from being in the sun. In highly pigmented skin, a large portion of ultraviolet light is absorbed by melanin and thus does not reach the underlying tissues.

### Books to Read

♦ **This Year's Garden** by Cynthia Rylant, New York: Bradbury Press, 1984. Grades K-3. A family plans, plants, cares for, and harvests a garden.

● **A Snake Is Totally Tail** by Judi Barrett, New York: Macmillan Publishing Co., Inc., 1983. Grades K-2. Each page of the book names and describes a new animal. The animal characteristics are done in alliteration.

▲ **The Trek** by Ann Jonas, New York: Greenwillow Books, 1985. Grades K-3. On her way to school, a young girl walks through an imaginary jungle and desert inhabited by hidden animals.

# Earth Science

## Classroom Centers

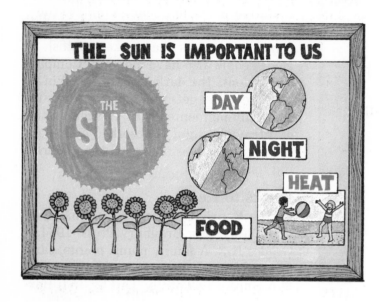

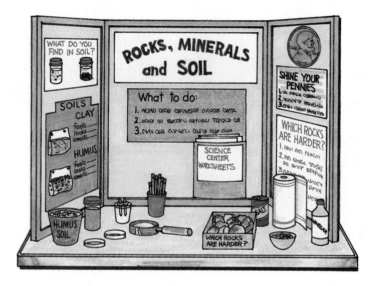

## Bulletin Board

**Goals:** The purpose of this bulletin board is to show that the sun plays a vital role in life on Earth.

**Materials:** construction paper
illustrations or photographs of growing plants and people enjoying themselves on a hot day
illustrations of Earth showing day and night

**Procedure:** Arrange the bulletin board to reflect the influence of the sun on life on Earth. Encourage students to bring in photographs or other evidence of the presence and importance of the sun. These can be placed on the bulletin board.

## SC Science Center

**Goals:** Students will be able to reinforce information learned in the unit and extend their knowledge of rocks, minerals, and soil through simple experimentation. You may find other suggestions in the margin material suitable for additional science center activities.

**Materials:** construction paper      clay soil
paper towels      humus
quart jar of water with lid      hand lens
pencil and paper      vinegar
rocks of various sizes      salt
   and colors      petri dishes
pennies

**Procedure:** Students can mix small amounts of water and humus and water and clay and use a hand lens to observe components. Students can shine pennies by dropping a small amount of vinegar and salt on them and rubbing them with a paper towel. Students can test the hardness of rocks by scratching them with a penny and observing them with a hand lens. Have students complete a science center worksheet when they have finished these activities. A science center worksheet can be found on page 205 in the Teacher Resource Package.

## Field Trip Ideas

Arrange a trip to a park, river, or creek to observe any natural or artificial changes.

Visit a nearby planetarium. Often one is located at a college or university and a tour and show can be arranged.

## Speakers and Visitors

Have a local fossil collector speak about his or her collection and discuss how fossils form.

Have a local collector share samples of rocks, minerals, and gems with students. The visitor should also show tools used for taking rock samples.

## Audiovisuals for the Students

 ## Films and Filmstrips

*Dinosaur,* 16 mm, 14 min., color, Pyramid Films & Video.
*Exploring the Earth Around Us,* five filmstrips with sound, 11–13 min., color, National Geographic Educational Services.

 ## Videotapes

*Dinosaurs,* 85 min., color, New World Video.
*Prehistoric Magic,* 15 min., color, Agency for Instructional Technology.
*Environment,* 5 min., color, Encyclopaedia Britannica Educational Corp.

 ## Computer Software

*Dinosaur Dig*   One introduction and four games teach students about specific dinosaurs, times in which certain dinosaurs lived and their relative sizes and weights.
Type: Tutorial, Games
Hardware: Apple II+, IIe, Commodore 64, IBM PC, PCjr
Supplier: Mindscape
*Earth and Its Composition*   An introduction to components that make up Earth; water, mountains, air, and volcanoes are also explained.
Type: Tutorial
Hardware: Apple II+, IIe, PET, Commodore 64
Supplier: Right On Programs

## Resources for the Teacher

 ## Materials at Little/No Cost

Dino Productions
P.O. Box 3004
Englewood, CO 80155
Send for a catalog that includes many items on dinosaurs.
NASA, Educational Affairs Division
400 Maryland Avenue, SW
Washington, DC 20546

 ## Resource Books

Asimov, Isaac. *Exploring the Earth and the Cosmos.* New York: Crown Publishing, Inc., 1982.
Fagan, Brian M. *Prehistoric Times.* New York: W. H. Freeman, 1983.
Glut, D. F. *The Dinosaur Dictionary.* New York: Outlet Books Co., 1985.
Hurlburt, Cornelius, S., editor. *The Planet We Live On.* New York: Harry N. Abrams, Inc., 1976.

# UNIT 2

## Earth Science

### UNIT CONCEPTS

**Chapter 5**
■ Earth and its life forms have changed over time.
■ Dinosaurs differed in size, shape, diet, habitat, and mode of locomotion.
■ Dinosaurs became extinct although fossils that are studied indicate when and where they existed.

**Chapter 6**
■ Earth's rocks and minerals can be identified by physical properties.
■ Earth's land is also covered by soil and is an important resource.

**Chapter 7**
■ The sun provides Earth's heat and light.
■ Earth's rotation causes day and night.
■ People explore space.

# Earth Science

68

Firelight and shadows

dancing on the wall.

Look at my shadow

    TEN FEET TALL!

"Look"
Charlotte Zolotow

69

## CONNECTING LITERATURE TO SCIENCE

### Understanding the Selection

- Discuss what a shadow is by asking students to tell when they have seen their shadows.
- Read the poem aloud. Then have students read the poem aloud with you.
- Ask: **What is ten feet tall in the poem?** *the shadow* Ask: **What caused the shadow?** *the blocked light*

### Relating the Selection to Unit Concepts

- Ask students if only animals can cast shadows. Through discussion, make the point that all things can cast a shadow if light is present.
- Tell students they will be learning about dinosaurs in this unit.
- Ask: **Do you think dinosaurs were able to cast a shadow?** *yes* **How would the size of your shadow compare with the size of a dinosaur's shadow?** *My shadow would be much smaller than a dinosaur's shadow.*

### Relating the Selection to the Student's World

- Have students look at the photograph and tell what they see. *a rollerskate casting a shadow*
- Have students look outside and tell about the shadows they see.

## ACTIVITY CENTER

For fun, hands-on, independent activities that integrate reading, writing, math, and technology with the chapters in this unit, have students complete some or all of the Activity Center Activities below. Look for specific chapter references in the Lesson Planning Guides.

**Reading: 5** What's Wrong? **6** Sign of the Times **7** Rock Fun
**Writing: 5** A Dinosaur's Day, **6** Rock On, **7** First Kid in Space
**Math: 5** A Whatchamacallit! **6** Rock Drop, **7** Out of This World!
**Technology: 5** Let's Study Prints, **6** Sandy Paper, **7** Making Shadows

# Life Long Ago

## Planning Guide

| Lessons | Objectives | Vocabulary |
|---|---|---|
| **Chapter Introduction** pp. 70, 71 | | |
| **Lesson 1 Earth Long Ago** pp. 72, 73 | 1. **Compare** Earth in the past and today. 2. **Compare** animals and plants of the past and today. | Earth |
| **Lesson 2 Dinosaurs** pp. 74–79 | 3. **Compare** dinosaurs by size. 4. **Explain** that some dinosaurs ate plants and some ate other animals. 5. **Infer** how dinosaurs may have moved. 6. **Recognize** that some dinosaurs laid eggs. | dinosaurs |
| **Lesson 3 How Do We Know?** pp. 80–83 | 7. **Explain** that people have never seen live dinosaurs. 8. **Describe** how scientists have learned about dinosaurs. | prints |
| **Chapter Review** pp. 84, 85 | | |

# Planning Guide

| Text Activities | | Teacher Resource Masters | Other Components |
|---|---|---|---|
| **Title/Skill** | **Materials per Group** | | |
| **Have You Ever . . . Found a Fossil?** p. 71<br>Observing<br>Time Allotment: 30 minutes | limestone rocks with fossils | | **Activity Center:** "What's Wrong"; "Sign of the Times"; "A Dinosaur's Day"; "A Whatchamacallit?"; "Let's Study Prints" |
| | | ◆ Reteaching Activity, p. 63<br>Independent Practice, p. 60<br>Language Arts Connection, p. 175 | Big Book, p. 17 |
| **You Can . . . Make a Graph,** p. 76<br>Classifying/Communicating<br>Time Allotment: 20 minutes | drawing paper<br>crayons | Transparency Master, p. 53<br>◆ Family Science, p. 54<br>Activity Worksheet, p. 55<br>Critical Thinking, p. 57<br>Math Connection, p. 59<br>Independent Practice, p. 61<br>Language Arts Connection, p. 176 | Activity Book, pp. 21, 22<br>Big Book, p. 18<br>Activity Book, pp. 39, 40 |
| **What Made These Tracks?** p. 79<br>Classifying/Inferring<br>Time Allotment: 20 minutes | transparent overlays<br>markers | | |
| **How Are Prints Made?** p. 83<br>Constructing a Model<br>Time Allotment: 30 minutes | clay<br>plastic leaf<br>penny<br>key<br>shell<br>hard lens | Activity Worksheet, p. 56<br>▲ Critical Thinking, p. 58<br>Independent Practice, p. 62<br>Language Arts Connection, p. 177 | Activity Book, p. 23<br>Big Book, p. 19 |
| | | Test A, p. 64<br>Test B, p. 65 | Color Transparencies #5a and #5b |

◆ **Basic** / ▲ **Advanced** / All other masters are for use by all students.

# CHAPTER 5

# *Life Long Ago*

## For Exceptional Students

### ESL/LEP

**Chapter 5/Lesson 2, Page 78**
Write the word *dinosaur* on the chalkboard and pronounce it for students. Have each student find a picture of a dinosaur in the textbook. Help students realize the actual size of various dinosaurs. Take the students and a ball of twine, yarn, or heavy string to the playground or hallway. Measure the twine and mark the lengths that show students how large the dinosaurs actually were. You may want to have students estimate the lengths before measuring.

**Chapter 5/Lesson 2, Page 78**
Use the song as a starting point for students to gain more information about three specific types of dinosaurs. Read each stanza for the class to make sure they can pronounce the words before beginning the song. Have your class record the song on a cassette tape to listen to individually or share with families.

### Gifted

**Chapter 5/Lesson 2, Page 78**
Have students choose a book to read about dinosaurs. Tell them to read the story carefully. After they've closed the book, students should perform the following tasks:
**1.** Draw a picture of the dinosaur.
**2.** Write three facts about the dinosaur under the picture.
**3.** Share the picture and information with the class.

### Mainstreamed

**Chapter 5/Lesson 3, Page 83**
**Hearing Impaired:** Identify ten objects found in the student's environment, such as pencil, paper clip, or key. Make a clay impression of the objects. Ask the student to identify each object by observing the impression. Repeat using different objects, such as a silver dollar, cork screw, bottle opener, or nail.

## Song of the Dinosaurs

1. Long a - go in steam-y swamps,
2. Bront-o-saur-us ver-y tall,
3. Steg - o-saur-us, fun-ny pack,
4. Tyran-no-saur-us was the King,

Din - o saurs made heav- y stomps.
Side to side looked like a wall.
Bon - y plates all o'er his back.
Not a - fraid of an - y - thing.

Some were large and ver-y slow,
Not too smart or ver-y fast,
Had two brains that you could find,
Big as house with teeth and claws,

Oth - ers quick and on the go.
Might be why he did not last.
One in front and one be-hind.
Oth - ers were a - fraid of jaws!

# Whole Class Science Project

Divide the class into two groups, assigning one group meat-eating dinosaurs and the other group plant-eating dinosaurs. Each group should list names of dinosaurs in their category. They should find out the following information about each dinosaur in their category: length, weight, how many years ago it lived, and what type of food it ate. The students should draw a picture of each one. The two groups could display their pictures around the room, labeling the picture with the name of the dinosaur and writing other information below the picture. Each group could write a creative story involving the dinosaurs they read about. In order to make the story more interesting, they could add a dinosaur that ate both meat and plants (omnivore). Each group should share its story with the class.

# Science Fair Projects

Individual students could do one of the following projects:

1. Using models of dinosaurs, students will explain how scientists can tell which ones ate plants and which ones ate meat.
2. Display actual fossils, label each by name, and supply pictures or drawings of what the plant or animal actually looked like.
3. Use models of dinosaurs to set up a display using cards to give pertinent information about each dinosaur.
4. Use pieces of soft coal, separate into layers by tapping them with a hammer, and discover if layers contain leaf imprints or other signs of plants. Report how imprints were formed in coal.

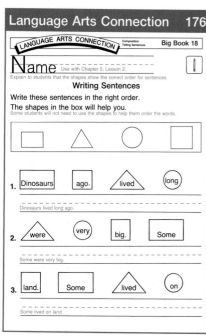

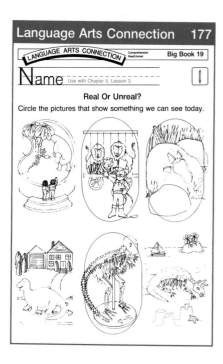

# CHAPTER
## 5

pages 70–85

## Chapter Concepts

■ Earth and its life forms have changed over time.

■ Dinosaurs differed in size, shape, diet, habitat, and mode of locomotion.

■ Dinosaurs became extinct although fossils that are studied indicate when and where they existed.

## Chapter Background

■ Since its formation 4.5 billion years ago, Earth has changed. Mountains have been built and eroded. Ocean basins have opened and closed. The continents have shifted their positions. Glaciers have covered parts of Earth in the past. All these changes affected Earth's climate.

## Looking Ahead

■ You will need *The Dinosaur Who Lived in My Backyard* by B. G. Hennessy to **Close** Lesson 2.

## Look for These Symbols

　—Hands-on activity

　—Cooperative learning

　—Overhead transparency

◆ —Basic/Reinforcement

● —Average/Enrichment

▲ —Advanced/Challenge

　—Science Center

　—Calculator Practice

SCIENCE
In Your World

70

# CHAPTER 5

# *Life Long Ago*

Long ago, Earth was quite different.

Huge dinosaurs roamed the world.

Some were as big as five elephants in a row.

How do you think we know?

**ACTIVITY**

## Have You Ever...

### Found a Fossil?

**1.** Look for fossils.

**2.** Look at rocks near home.

**3.** Look at rocks in other places.

**4.** Guess what your fossil is.

What do fossils look like?

71

## PREPLAN

**Time Allotment:** 30 minutes

### Objectives
**1. Understand** that dinosaurs lived long ago.
**2. Observe** fossils found in rocks.

### Setup
To conduct the activity collect the following materials for each student or **cooperative learning group:**
limestone rocks with fossils

## 1    FOCUS

■ Discuss the fact that although the dinosaurs died off millions of years ago, we know about them from fossils. Define fossils for students.

## 2    TEACH

■ Read the chapter title and introductory paragraph.
■ Ask students to describe the dinosaur skeleton and tell how they think skeletons are put together.

### Have You Ever . . .
■ Have students infer how animals or plants might have become fossils.

### Student Responses
■ Fossils are prints of dead plants or animals.

## 3    APPLY

■ Display and discuss any students' fossil collections.
■ Ask a collector or people from a local museum to share fossils they might have.

### Close
■ Tell students they will learn more about dinosaurs as they read Chapter 5.

# PREPLAN

## Lesson Objectives

1. **Compare** Earth in the past and today.
2. **Compare** animals and plants of the past and today.

## Science Background

■ Fossilized plants and animals preserved in Earth's rocks are indicative of the environments in which they lived. Coal, for example, forms in swampy, tropical areas. When scientists find coal beds they can hypothesize that the area that now contains the coal was once a swampy, humid region.

## Lesson Vocabulary

Earth

# 1 FOCUS

■ Bring in historic and recent pictures of your community or another. Discuss changes that happen over time. Relate this information to the illustration on these student pages.

[W] [SC] Show students a world map. Point out the parts on the map that are land and water. Tell students that at one time all of the land on Earth was touching. Then, like pieces of a giant puzzle, two big pieces broke away (top and bottom) and then they broke apart from each other. Make a puzzle of continent pieces to illustrate this.

# Earth Long Ago

What do you think Earth was like long ago?

[1]How do you think it was different?

1. Encourage students to compare the plants and animals in the illustration with today's environment.

Shansisuchus
(shan see SEW kus)

Plesiosaur
(PLEE see uh Sawr)

72

# TEACHER RESOURCE MASTERS

**Earth** was warmer long ago.

Animals and plants were different.

There were no people.

Fabrosaurus
(fuh broh SAWR us)

Coelophysis
(see LOF uh sus)

73

## TEACHER RESOURCE MASTERS

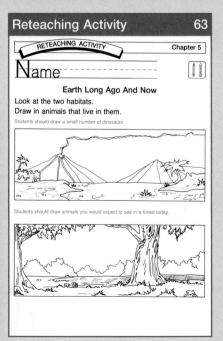

Reteaching Activity 63

RETEACHING ACTIVITY Chapter 5

Name

**Earth Long Ago And Now**

Look at the two habitats.
Draw in animals that live in them.

Students should draw a small number of dinosaurs.

Students should draw animals you would expect to see in a forest today.

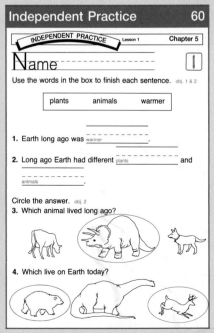

Independent Practice 60

INDEPENDENT PRACTICE Lesson 1 Chapter 5

Name

Use the words in the box to finish each sentence. obj. 1 & 2

plants    animals    warmer

1. Earth long ago was warmer _____.

2. Long ago Earth had different plants _____ and _____ animals

Circle the answer. obj. 2

3. Which animal lived long ago?

4. Which live on Earth today?

## 2  TEACH

■ Discuss how different Earth was long ago. Explain to students that at one time there were no flowers and that much of Earth was covered with oceans that were not very deep.

### Guided Practice

■ Have students use a large sheet of manila paper to draw and color Earth as they imagined it was like long ago. Ask them not to include any animals. Save these illustrations to use with the next lesson.

■ If necessary, use the **reteaching strategy** in OPTIONS.

### Independent Practice

■ Use the Teacher Resource Master **Independent Practice,** page 60.

## 3  APPLY

■ Ask students to define *change*. Make a list of things that change over time. Students may name people, trees, the fashions people wear and so on. Discuss how long some changes take.

### Close

■ Have students imagine that they traveled in a time machine and visited Earth of long ago. Ask students to draw and write a post card to send to friends.

## OPTIONS

### Reteaching Strategy

■ Collect pictures of animals, including dinosaurs. Make two groups on the bulletin board—"Now" and "Long Ago." Have students put pictures into the right group.

### Resource Options

■ Use Big Book, page 17, "Winter's Here" and Teacher Resource Master **Language Arts Connection,** page 175.

## PREPLAN

### Lesson Objectives

3. **Compare** dinosaurs by size.
4. **Explain** that some dinosaurs ate plants and some ate other animals.
5. **Infer** how dinosaurs may have moved.
6. **Recognize** that some dinosaurs laid eggs.

### Science Background

■ Dinosaurs belong to two (or perhaps three) separate orders of reptiles. One group of dinosaurs is called the lizard or reptilepelvis type. The other dinosaur order is characterized by a birdlike pelvis.

■ Mass extinction occurred at the close of the Mesozoic Era 65 to 70 million years before the present. Scientists hypothesize that changes in climate, food chains, and environments contributed to the dinosaur extinctions.

### Lesson Vocabulary

dinosaurs

**Note:** The activity on student page 79 may be used for guided discovery before you begin this lesson.

## 1 FOCUS

■ Ask: **How were dinosaurs different from each other?** Students should draw upon prior knowledge that dinosaurs differed in size, shape, what they ate, how they moved, and so on.

# Dinosaurs

**Dinosaurs** lived long ago.
[1]What do you know about dinosaurs?

1. Encourage students to exchange information about dinosaurs.

Brachiosaurus
(brak ee oh SAWR us)

Coelophysis
(see LOF uh sis)

74

## TEACHER RESOURCE MASTERS

Some dinosaurs were as little as birds.

Some were as big as a school bus.

Many were much bigger than you.

Iguanodon
(uh GWAHN uh dahn)

75

## 2 TEACH

■ Ask students to bring in any models or other dinosaur paraphernalia they have collected. Make a class display.
■ Ask: **How does the shape of your front teeth compare to the shape of your back teeth?** *Front are sharp and back are flat.* **Which teeth do you use to bite off a piece of chicken?** *front* **Which teeth do you use to chew your food?** *back* Inform students that scientists can tell what kind of food dinosaurs ate by the shape of their teeth.

### Guided Practice

Have students make construction paper dinosaurs and glue them onto the environment illustrations they made in the activity on page 73.
■ If necessary, use the **reteaching strategy** in OPTIONS.

### Independent Practice

■ Use the Teacher Resource Master **Independent Practice,** page 61.

## 3 APPLY

■ Make a chart on the chalkboard with the headings *Big, Small, Plant Eater, Meat Eater, Moved on Two Legs, Moved on Four Legs.* Have students group dinosaurs into these categories.

### Close

■ Read *The Dinosaur Who Lived in My Backyard* by B. G. Hennessy.

## OPTIONS

### Reteaching Strategy

Have student groups **work cooperatively** and use library books to look up a particular dinosaur. Determine what data should be gathered.

### Resource Options

■ Use Activity Book, pages 21 and 22, "Measuring."

## TEACHER RESOURCE MASTERS

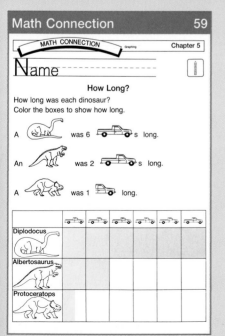

Math Connection    59

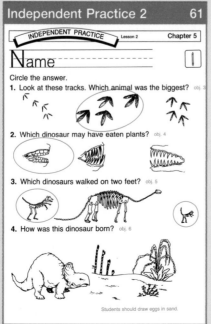

Independent Practice 2    61

# OPTIONS

## YOU CAN . . . MAKE A GRAPH

**Process Skills:** Classifying/Communicating

**Objective: Construct** a graph to **compare** meat-eating and plant-eating dinosaurs.

**Setup/Teach**

**Cooperative Grouping: twos**—Assign roles as explained on page T24.

Help students make a graph like the one below. Determine with the class which dinosaurs ate meat and which ate plants. Have students color in the boxes.

| Dinosaurs | P | M |
|---|---|---|
| Apatosaurus | ▨ | |
| Triceratops | ▨ | |
| T. Rex | | ▨ |
| | | |

## Resource Options

■ Use Big Book, page 18, "Animals of Long Ago" and Teacher Resource Master **Language Arts Connection** page 176.

■ Use Activity Book, pages 39 and 40, "Which Dinosaur Is Next?"

Dinosaurs had to find food to live.

Some dinosaurs ate plants.

Some ate other animals.

Parasaurolophus
(par uh sawr oh LOH fus)

### ACTIVITY

## You Can...

### Make a Graph

Which dinosaurs ate plants?
Which ones ate other animals?
Color a graph to show how many.

76

# TEACHER RESOURCE MASTERS

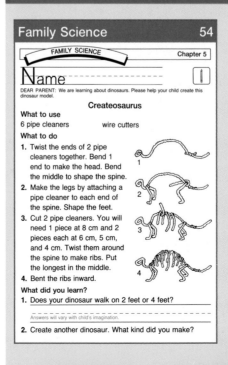

Family Science                54

FAMILY SCIENCE                    Chapter 5

Name _____                    ✐

DEAR PARENT: We are learning about dinosaurs. Please help your child create this dinosaur model.

**Createosaurus**

**What to use**

6 pipe cleaners          wire cutters

**What to do**

1. Twist the ends of 2 pipe cleaners together. Bend 1 end to make the head. Bend the middle to shape the spine.

2. Make the legs by attaching a pipe cleaner to each end of the spine. Shape the feet.

3. Cut 2 pipe cleaners. You will need 1 piece at 8 cm and 2 pieces each at 6 cm, 5 cm, and 4 cm. Twist them around the spine to make ribs. Put the longest in the middle.

4. Bent the ribs inward.

**What did you learn?**

1. Does your dinosaur walk on 2 feet or 4 feet?

_____

Answers will vary with child's imagination.

2. Create another dinosaur. What kind did you make?

Some dinosaurs lived on land.

Some lived on land and in water.

[1]How did some dinosaurs move? <u>1. walk on two legs, walk on four legs, and swim</u>

Tyrannosaurus rex
(ti RAN nuh SAWR us · REKS)

## TEACHER RESOURCE MASTERS

Transparency Master          53

TRANSPARENCY MASTER          Chapter 5

**Where Did They Live?**

Provide students with large sheets of paper so they can create dinosaur habitats. Use the transparency for discussion.

Critical Thinking          57

CRITICAL THINKING/PROBLEM SOLVING   Classifying   Chapter 5

Name

**How Did They Move?**

Cut out the dinosaur boxes below.
Paste them where they belong.
Write how each animal moved.

Evaluate students' ability to see and match shapes.

two feet

four feet

fly

swim

## OPTIONS

◆ **Reinforcement:** Make several black or blue construction paper dinosaurs. Cut each dinosaur into three parts. Ask students to put the correct parts of the dinosaurs together. Laminate the puzzle pieces and store them in a large brown envelope.

● **Enrichment:** Ask students to **work cooperatively** in groups of two to prepare shoe-box dioramas of dinosaur scenes. Have them form clay models of a meat eater and a plant eater. Plants can be drawn on paper, cut out, and glued to the back of the shoe box. Leave a tab on some of the plant drawings when cutting them out. Put glue on the tab to attach these to the foreground of the scene. Fold at the tab to make them stand up. Small stones, moss, and aluminum foil "water" will add realism to the scene.

▲ **Challenge:** To help students understand average temperatures, have them prepare a temperature chart. They can use local news broadcasts or newspapers as an information source. They should record the high, low, and average temperatures for a week. Ask students what might happen if the temperatures suddenly stayed much lower than average. Tell them that a drop of only a few degrees in the average temperature for ten years would affect the whole Earth. The growing season would be shorter. Animals and people would have a hard time finding food. This might have happened during the days of the dinosaurs.

# OPTIONS

## LANGUAGE CONNECTION

**Writing:** Have students write a story as if they lived during the days when dinosaurs roamed Earth. Tell students that this writing is just to be a first draft and that they should concentrate on getting their ideas down on paper.

## MATH CONNECTION

Remind students that Earth was warmer long ago. Tell students you are going to write some numbers that represent temperatures on a number line. See if students can tell which number is missing.

72  73  74  75  76  77  **78**  79  80

---

A mother dinosaur laid these eggs.

She buried her eggs in the sand.

These baby dinosaurs came from the eggs.

These babies could care for themselves.

[1] Who do you think the babies look like?

1. The dinosaur babies look like the parent dinosaur; these babies were Protoceratops.

Protoceratops
(pro toh SER uh taphs)

78

# TEACHER RESOURCE MASTERS

## What made these tracks?

### What you need

clear plastic sheet          marker

### What to do

**1.** Match these tracks.

**2.** Match these dinosaur tracks.

79

## ACTIVITY RESPONSES

Accept all reasonable student responses to questions during any activity discussion.

## PREPLAN

**Time Allotment:** 20 minutes
**Process Skills:** Classifying/Inferring

### Objectives
**1. Match** tracks of modern animals with their pictures.
**2. Match** dinosaur tracks with a picture of the appropriate dinosaur.

### Setup
transparent overlays and watercolor markers for each student

## 1  FOCUS

■ Make some footprints or tracks and display them for students. Discuss how they can infer who or what made the tracks.
■ Ask how many students have made footprints in snow, beach sand, or mud. Ask: **How are your tracks different from the tracks of an adult?** *Student tracks are smaller and closer together. The kind of shoes worn may cause different tracks as well.*

## 2  TEACH

■ Inform students that some animals' tails leave tracks. Ask students why some animals do not leave tracks with their tails.
■ Use the Teacher Resource Master **Activity Worksheet,** page 55, with this activity.

## 3  APPLY

Use tempera paint and long sheets of narrow paper and allow students to make tracks of their bare feet. Compare tracks.

### Close
■ Discuss differences between tracks made by small and large animals; walking and running; and 2-legged and 4-legged animals.

## PREPLAN

### Lesson Objectives

**7. Explain** that people have never seen live dinosaurs.

**8. Describe** how scientists have learned about dinosaurs.

### Science Background

■ Dinosaurs roamed Earth between 225 and 136 million years ago. The oldest known *Homo sapien* fossils are about 300,000 years old.

■ Scientists who study fossils are called paleontologists.

■ Mass extinction at the close of the Mesozoic Era affected both land and marine organisms. Hypotheses to explain these extinctions include biological, physical, and climatic changes. Currently, one widely accepted hypothesis involves the impact of Earth with a meteorite. The impact produced enough heat that massive fires destroyed most vegetation. The soot from this fire entered the atmosphere and produced a greenhouse effect that caused drastic changes in Earth's climate.

### Lesson Vocabulary

prints

**Note:** The activity on student page 83 may be used for guided discovery before you begin this lesson.

## 1 FOCUS

■ Ask students to name their favorite dinosaur. Make a chalkboard list. Ask: **How do you know what your favorite dinosaur looked like?** *Emphasize that no one has ever seen a live dinosaur.* Ask: **What kind of clues help us understand what dinosaurs may have looked like?** *bones, prints, teeth*

# How Do We Know?

Dinosaurs do not live today.

People never saw them.

Dinosaurs died before people lived on Earth.

80

## TEACHER RESOURCE MASTERS

How do we know about animals of long ago?

We find their **prints** and bones in rock.

We study the prints and bones.

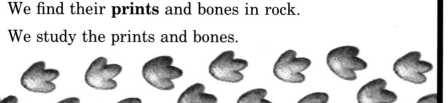

81

## TEACHER RESOURCE MASTERS

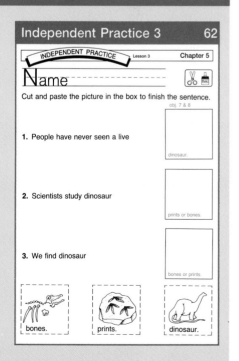

Independent Practice 3 — 62

INDEPENDENT PRACTICE — Lesson 3 — Chapter 5

Name

Cut and paste the picture in the box to finish the sentence.
obj. 7 & 8

1. People have never seen a live
_____ dinosaur.

2. Scientists study dinosaur
_____ prints or bones.

3. We find dinosaur
_____ bones or prints.

bones. | prints. | dinosaur.

## 2 TEACH

■ **Problem Solving:** Pose the following problem: Suppose there were a group of little animals that could eat only apples. These little animals lived in an apple orchard. One winter all of the apple trees froze and there were no more apples. Ask **what would happen to the animals?** Compare the story with what may have happened to dinosaurs.

### Guided Practice

Ask students to draw the answers to the following questions.
1. **How do we know how some dinosaurs were born?** *fossil eggs* 2. **What might tell us how big a dinosaur was?** *bones* 3. **What might tell us where a dinosaur walked?** *footprints* 4. **Why do you think no dinosaur lives today?** *Accept reasonable answers.*
■ If necessary, use the **reteaching strategy** in OPTIONS.

### Independent Practice

■ Use the Teacher Resource Master **Independent Practice,** page 62.

## 3 APPLY

■ Ask students to find out what other animals have become extinct.

### Close

■ "Adopt" an animal that is in danger of becoming extinct. Write letters or otherwise find ways to protect that animal.

## OPTIONS

### Reteaching Strategy

Ask a parent volunteer to make a dish with four layers of jello, placing fruit in one layer. Explain how prints and bones get buried in rock layers.

### Resource Options

■ Use Activity Book, page 23 "Communicating."

# OPTIONS

## LANGUAGE CONNECTION

**Writing:** Bring in some fossil prints for students to observe. Have students choose a fossil and write a story to describe what type of animal made the print. Encourage students to begin with a first draft and then edit their stories, refining them by elaborating on their ideas.

♦ **Reinforcement:** Suggest that students go with their parents to look around their neighborhoods for fossils. Stone walls and buildings, beside streams, stone roads or rock outcroppings by highways are good places to look. Some students may find fossils to share with the class.

● **Enrichment:** Obtain toy dinosaur skeletons from a local toy store or museum of natural history. Some of your students may already have these models. Ask them to display the model skeleton and explain the dinosaur it represents.

▲ **Challenge:** Ask students to gather information about reptiles that live on Earth today. They should tell what kinds these are, where they live, and some of the special characteristics of reptiles. Students may wish to concentrate their research on reptiles that live only in the United States or on rare and unusual reptiles.

We are trying to find out why dinosaurs died.

Maybe they could not find enough food.

[1] Why do you think dinosaurs no longer live?

1. Accept any reasonable answer.

Triceratops
(trī SER uh tops)

82

# TEACHER RESOURCE MASTERS

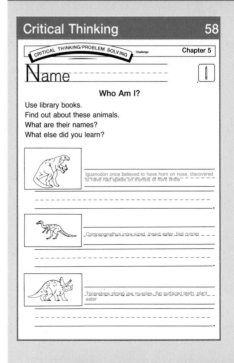

Critical Thinking          58

CRITICAL THINKING/PROBLEM SOLVING    Challenge    Chapter 5

Name

**Who Am I?**

Use library books.
Find out about these animals.
What are their names?
What else did you learn?

Iguanodon once believed to have horn on nose, discovered to have had spikes on thumbs of front limbs

Compsognathus crow-sized, insect eater, fast runner

Triceratops strong jaw muscles, flat surfaced teeth, plant eater

# How are prints made?

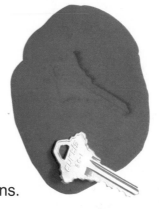

## What you need

clay     plastic leaf     shell

penny     key        hand lens

## What to do

1. Roll the clay into four balls.

2. Press each ball of clay flat.

3. Push something into the clay.

4. Look at your prints with a hand lens.

83

## ACTIVITY RESPONSES

Accept all reasonable student responses to questions during any activity discussion.

## PREPLAN

**Time Allotment:** 30 minutes

**Process Skill:** Constructing a Model

### Objectives

1. **Compare** the shapes of different objects and the prints they make in clay.

2. **Identify** an object from its clay print.

### Setup

Gather a group of small objects such as plastic leaves, keys, coins, or bottle caps to be used in making clay prints.

■ Check your modeling clay to make sure it is moist and pliable.

**Cooperative Grouping:** twos—Assign roles as explained on T24.

## 1   FOCUS

■ Make a clay print of an object. Show the print to students and ask how many can identify the object that made the print. Make a different print with the same object placed on its edge or end. Discuss how the same object can make different prints.

## 2   TEACH

■ Encourage students to examine their prints closely with a hand lens.

■ Use the Teacher Resource Master **Activity Worksheet,** page 56.

## 3   APPLY

■ Demonstrate how prints can be made using other mediums. Use tempera paint to imprint leaves or other objects.

### Close

■ Compare this activity with how scientists interpret dinosaur prints. Tell how footprints are made in mud or sand that become buried under more mud and sand and slowly is changed to rock.

**Chapter Closure:** Use the pages to review and reinforce chapter concepts.

## What I Learned

Have students read the rebus summary statements aloud to be sure that they interpret the pictures correctly. After each sentence is read, discuss other words that would also make the sentence true.

## Words I Know

Use any or all of the following suggestions to reinforce the chapter vocabulary.

Write each science word or word group on the chalkboard. Ask students to read them. Add the words to the class science list or have students write the words in their individual science word books. Ask students to tell about these words to help you evaluate their comprehension. Have students use each science word or word group in a sentence.

---

**CHAPTER REVIEW**

**5**

### ▬▬▬ What I Learned ▬▬▬

- Earth was different long ago.

   and  were different.

  Animals       plants

- Some  ate  and some ate other

  dinosaurs       plants

  animals

- We know about  from  and  .

  dinosaurs       prints       bones

### ▬▬▬ Words I Know ▬▬▬

**Earth     dinosaurs     prints**

84

---

## TEACHER RESOURCE MASTERS

## What I Know

*Use the picture to answer the questions.*

1. What was Earth like long ago?

2. What kinds of dinosaurs lived long ago?

3. How did dinosaurs move?

4. Where did mother dinosaurs lay their eggs?

5. How do we know about life long ago?

85

### What I Know

Have students refer to the picture to answer the questions and extend concepts.

**1.** It was warmer and there were no people. Some plants and animals were different.

**2.** Many kinds of dinosaurs lived on Earth long ago. Some were little, some were big; some ate plants, some ate animals; some lived on land; and some lived on land and in water.

**3.** Some walked or ran on two feet, some on four feet, some were able to swim, and others flew.

**4.** Some mother dinosaurs laid their eggs in the sand.

**5.** Scientists study prints and bones in rock to find out abut life long ago.

## OPTIONS

### Resource Options

⬚ Use Color Transparencies #5a and #5b.

## TEACHER RESOURCE MASTERS

Test B      65

TEST B    Understanding/Applying Concepts    Chapter 5

Name — Each question is worth 20 points.

Use the words in the box to finish each sentence. obj. 1, 7, 8

| warmer | dinosaurs | people | bones |
|---|---|---|---|

1. When dinosaurs lived there were no people

2. We learn about dinosaurs from their bones

3. Long ago Earth was warmer.

4. Today there are no live dinosaurs

5. Draw pictures of a large and a small dinosaur. obj. 3

Answers may include Tyrannosaurus rex, Apatosaurus, and so on.

Compsognathus, or by comparison a dinosaur smaller in recorded history than one drawn in previous box.

a large dinosaur      a smaller dinosaur

# Land Around Us

## Planning Guide

| Lessons | Objectives | Vocabulary |
|---|---|---|
| Chapter Introduction pp. 86, 87 | | |
| Lesson 1 Rocks and Minerals pp. 88–93 | 1. **State** and **show** that land is made of rocks and soil. <br> 2. **Identify** properties of rocks. <br> 3. **Identify** some properties of minerals such as color, luster, and hardness. <br> 4. **Identify** ways rocks change with time. | rocks <br> minerals |
| Lesson 2 Soil pp. 94–99 | 5. **State** and **show** that land is made of soil. <br> 6. **Describe** the properties of soil. <br> 7. **Explain** why soil is important. | soil |
| Chapter Review pp. 100, 101 | | |

# Planning Guide

| Text Activities | | Teacher Resource Masters | Other Components |
|---|---|---|---|
| **Title/Skill** | **Materials per Group** | | |
| **Have You Ever . . . Made a Rock Drawing?** p. 87<br>Observing/Inferring<br>Time Allotment: 30 minutes | colored chalk<br>white drawing paper<br>matte spray | | **Activity Center:** "Rock Fun"; "Rock On"; "Rock Drop"; "Sandy Paper" |
| **How Are Rocks Different?** p. 93<br>Observing/Classifying<br>Time Allotment: 30 minutes | 10 different rocks<br>    (examples might<br>    include granite,<br>    limestone, marble,<br>    obsidian, pumice,<br>    shale)<br>hand lens<br>pencil and paper | Transparency Master,<br>    p. 67<br>Activity Worksheet,<br>    p. 69<br>▲ Critical Thinking, p. 72<br>◆ Reteaching Activity,<br>    p. 76<br>Independent Practice,<br>    p. 74<br>Language Arts<br>    Connection,<br>    pp. 178, 179 | Poster #3<br>Big Book, p. 20<br>Big Book, p. 21<br>Activity Book, p. 24 |
| **You Can . . . Be a Researcher,** p. 97<br>Inferring<br>Time Allotment: 30 minutes | books<br>pencil and paper | ◆ Family Science, p. 68<br>Activity Worksheet,<br>    p. 70<br>Critical Thinking, p. 71<br>Math Connection,<br>    p. 73<br>Independent Practice,<br>    p. 75<br>Language Arts<br>    Connection,<br>    pp. 180, 181, 182 | Big Book, p. 22<br>Big Book, p. 23<br>Big Book, p. 24<br>Activity Book, pp. 41, 42 |
| **How Are Soils Different?** p. 98<br>Observing/Classifying<br>Time Allotment: 30 minutes | soil: clay, humus, sandy<br>hand lens<br>newsprint<br>pencil and paper | | |
| **Making a Land Map,** p. 219<br>Communicating<br>Time Allotment: 30 minutes | paper<br>crayons | | |
| | | Test A, p. 77<br>Test B, p. 78 | Color Transparencies<br>#6a and #6b |

◆ **Basic** / ▲ **Advanced** / All other masters are for use by all students.

## For Exceptional Students

### ESL/LEP

**Chapter 6/Lesson 1, Page 92**
Write the word *rock* on the chalkboard and pronounce it for students. Give each student a cupful of rocks and glue or paste. Have students copy the word with glue on a piece of heavy paper. Then students can place the rocks on the glue to spell the word rock. You may want to do a similar activity for the words *soil* and *mineral*.

**Chapter 6/Lesson 1, Page 92**
Lay out a group of rocks. Ask students to work with a partner. Students take turns describing a rock while their partner tries to locate the same rock. Have students bring in a special rock they have found. Ask each student to share with the class why they chose that particular rock. Have students write a story about the rock they found.

### Gifted

**Chapter 6/Lesson 1, Page 92**
Have motivated students find out about rocks that were used as tools. These should include arrowheads, axes, and hoes. Students might use references, resource persons, or a local museum to find out how the tools were made, who used them, and how these stone tools made a difference in people's lives.

### Mainstreamed

**Chapter 6/Lesson 1, Page 92**

**Learning Disabled:** Place a sample of small rocks in front of the student. Ask the student to divide the rocks into 2 or 3 groups according to a physical property, such as color, size, or smoothness. Repeat using other properties. Ask the students to speculate on how that particular property was created.

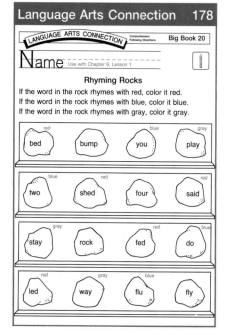

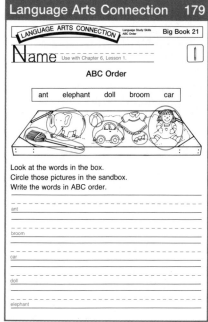

# Whole Class Science Project

Have students set up three different plastic shoebox-sized containers, each containing a different growth medium, one with small stones, one with sand, and the third with humus. Provide students with the same type of seed to plant in each of the boxes. Water each after planting the seeds. Allow seedlings to grow. Do not fertilize or transplant. Have students observe: (1) how well seeds germinate, (2) overall health of the seedlings, and (3) how well the roots develop. Allow seedlings to develop for several weeks and have students construct a pictorial report booklet telling which growth medium provided the best materials for the development of the seedlings.

# Science Fair Projects

Individual students could do one of the following projects:

1. Using rocks from a local stream or farm, have student make a collection and classify the rocks according to color.
2. Using references, have students learn the layers of materials that are used for making a road. Layers should be diagrammed in a poster and some materials displayed.
3. Using samples, have students learn about different types of coal and display them on a board.
4. Using references and samples have students find out what materials are used in bricks and how they are made.

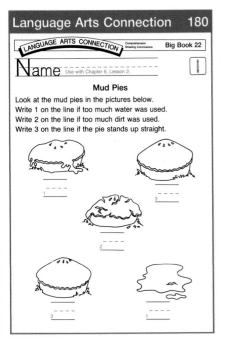

**LANGUAGE ARTS CONNECTION** — Comprehension Drawing Conclusions — Big Book 22

**Name** Use with Chapter 6, Lesson 2.

**Mud Pies**

Look at the mud pies in the pictures below.
Write 1 on the line if too much water was used.
Write 2 on the line if too much dirt was used.
Write 3 on the line if the pie stands up straight.

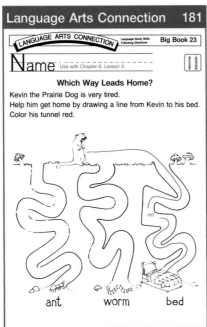

**LANGUAGE ARTS CONNECTION** — Language Study Skills Following Directions — Big Book 23

**Name** Use with Chapter 6, Lesson 2.

**Which Way Leads Home?**

Kevin the Prairie Dog is very tired.
Help him get home by drawing a line from Kevin to his bed.
Color his tunnel red.

ant    worm    bed

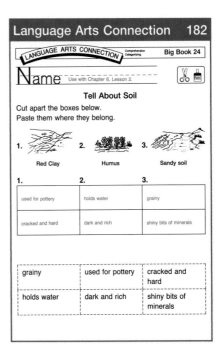

**LANGUAGE ARTS CONNECTION** — Comprehension Categorizing — Big Book 24

**Name** Use with Chapter 6, Lesson 2.

**Tell About Soil**

Cut apart the boxes below.
Paste them where they belong.

1. Red Clay    2. Humus    3. Sandy soil

| 1. | 2. | 3. |
| --- | --- | --- |
| used for pottery | holds water | grainy |
| cracked and hard | dark and rich | shiny bits of minerals |

| grainy | used for pottery | cracked and hard |
| --- | --- | --- |
| holds water | dark and rich | shiny bits of minerals |

## Chapter Concepts

- Earth's rocks and minerals can be identified by physical properties.
- Earth's land is also covered by soil and is an important resource.

## Chapter Background

- Rocks are divided into three groups. Igneous rocks are formed when melted Earth material cools. Sedimentary rocks form when particles are cemented together. Metamorphic rocks form as a result of temperature and pressure changes.
- Earth's rocks are always changing. Earthquakes and volcanic eruptions happen relatively quickly. Other changes such as weathering are slow.
- Erosion is the transport of weathered material by wind, water, and ice. Weathering and erosion are Earth processes that produce soil.

## Looking Ahead

- Gather rocks such as shale, limestone, granite, basalt, and gneiss from a rock hound or hobby shop to use in **Teach** Lesson 1.
- Invite a person from the County Extension office to discuss how to sample soil to **Close** Lesson 2.

## Look for These Symbols

- —Hands-on activity
- —Cooperative learning
- —Overhead transparency
- ◆ —Basic/Reinforcement
- ● —Average/Enrichment
- ▲ —Advanced/Challenge
- SC —Science Center
- —Calculator Practice

SCIENCE
In Your World

86

# CHAPTER 6

# *Land Around Us*

Do you live in the city?

Do you live in the mountains?

Wherever you live, there is land.

Some land is very rocky.

Some rocks are very useful.

## ACTIVITY

## Have You Ever...

### Made a Rock Drawing?

**1.** Chalk comes from rock.

**2.** Draw a picture.

**3.** Use colored chalk and paper.

Is your picture a rock drawing?

87

---

## PREPLAN

**Time Allotment:** 30 minutes

**Objectives**
1. **Observe** that we live on land.
2. **Infer** how rocks can be useful.

**Setup**
To conduct the activity collect the following materials for each student or **cooperative learning group:**
colored chalk      white drawing paper
matte spray

## 1   FOCUS

■ Ask students to describe what they see in the picture on page 86.
■ Encourage students to tell about experiences they may have had climbing on rocks or walking along rocky paths.

## 2   TEACH

■ Read the chapter title and introductory paragraph.

### Have You Ever . . .
■ Use this activity as an introduction to the use of minerals.
■ Chalk is calcium carbonate, a form of the mineral calcite.

**Student Responses**
My picture is a rock drawing because I used chalk to make it and chalk is a rock.

## 3   APPLY

■ Have students tell about experiences they may have had using rocks such as limestone to draw on asphalt or concrete surfaces.

**Close**
■ Tell students they will learn more about rocks as they read Chapter 6.

## PREPLAN

### Lesson Objectives
1. **State** and **show** that land is made of rocks and soil.
2. **Identify** properties of rocks.
3. **Identify** some properties of minerals such as color, luster, and hardness.
4. **Identify** ways rocks change with time.

### Science Background
■ Minerals are identified by their physical properties. These properties include hardness, luster, streak, cleavage, color, form, and specific gravity. About 2,000 minerals have been identified.

■ Mohs' mineral scale has ten minerals with each successive mineral harder than the one before it.

■ Luster refers to the way in which light bounces off a mineral's surface. Minerals are metallic (shiny) or nonmetallic (dull).

■ Weathering is the changes that rocks undergo at or near Earth's surface. Mechanical weathering breaks rocks into smaller pieces. Plant roots and ice can cause mechanical weathering. Chemical weathering changes the chemical composition of rocks. Water and acid rain cause chemical weathering.

### Lesson Vocabulary
rocks        minerals

**Note:** The activity on student page 93 may be used for guided discovery before you begin this lesson.

## 1 FOCUS

■ Ask: **Where do you find rocks?** *Answers may include mountains, parks, around flower beds, and underground.* Show students pictures of layers of rock. Explain that there are rocks we cannot see buried beneath thick layers of soil.

---

# Rocks and Minerals

Much of our land is made of **rocks.**

[1]Where have you found rocks?

[2]How are rocks different?

1. in the park, around the school, in the country, at the beach, and so on
2. color, size, texture

granite

conglomerate

sandstone

obsidian

88

---

## TEACHER RESOURCE MASTERS

Some rocks are one color.

Some have many colors. 1. white, black, gray, pink

[1]What colors do you see in these rocks?

pumice

limestone

coal

granite

diorite

marble

89

## 2 TEACH

■ Have students observe rock samples. Have them describe these rocks using the properties of hard, soft, light, dark, rough, and smooth.

### Guided Practice
■ Review the properties used to describe rocks. Have students number a paper from 1–10. Ask them to write a word to describe each of ten rocks you display.
■ If necessary, use the **reteaching strategy** in OPTIONS.

### Independent Practice
■ Use the Teacher Resource Master **Independent Practice,** page 74.

## 3 APPLY

**Problem Solving:** Ask: **How does water change rocks?** Inform students that sugar cubes are not rocks or minerals but they can be used to show how rocks change. Have students examine sugar cubes. Point out their sharp edges. Place four sugar cubes in a small plastic container with a lid. Have a student shake the container briskly for one minute. Examine the sugar cubes. Ask students to describe any changes. Ask: **What caused the sugar cubes to change?** *They bumped into each other.* Explain that rocks change in the same way, but it usually takes a long time.

### Close
■ Read *Sylvester and the Magic Pebble* by William Steig to your class.

## OPTIONS

**Reteaching Strategy**
Make word cards for *light, dark, hard, soft, rough, smooth.* Ask students to find examples of each property and place a rock sample beside the word card that labels that property.

## TEACHER RESOURCE MASTERS

**Transparency Master** 67

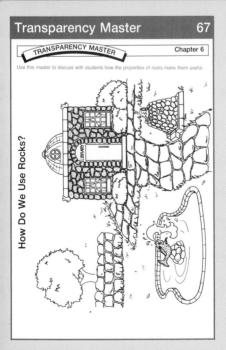

TRANSPARENCY MASTER Chapter 6

Use this master to discuss with students how the properties of rocks make them useful.

How Do We Use Rocks?

**Independent Practice 1** 74

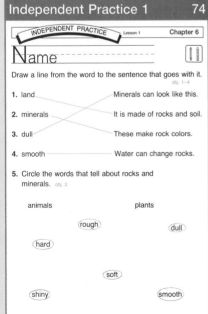

INDEPENDENT PRACTICE Lesson 1 Chapter 6

Name

Draw a line from the word to the sentence that goes with it. obj. 1–4

1. land — Minerals can look like this.
2. minerals — It is made of rocks and soil.
3. dull — These make rock colors.
4. smooth — Water can change rocks.

5. Circle the words that tell about rocks and minerals. obj. 3

animals    plants
rough    dull
hard
soft
shiny    smooth

# OPTIONS

### LANGUAGE CONNECTION

**Writing:** Have students choose something made from a mineral and describe it in words. Students should use action words and adjectives to describe the object without using the name of the object. Students should then read their descriptions aloud so that the class can identify the object. Point out to students that the more precise information they include, the better. The class should be able to pick out the object from the descriptions if the writing is effective.

### 🖩 MATH CONNECTION

Have students complete page 69 of the Teacher Resource Masters. Have students write the numbers for each group of rocks in order from least to greatest.

♦ **Reinforcement:** Concrete sidewalks are not rocks but they can be used to illustrate the effects of weathering. Take students on a walk. Look for evidence of changes in concrete: cracks, pits, stains, flaking, worn spots. Point out that these changes are slow and similar to changes that occur in rocks.

**Resource Options**
■ Use Big Book, page 20, "Rocky M. G. Rye" and Teacher Resource Master **Language Arts Connection,** page 178.
■ Use Big Book, page 21, "Please Don't Ask" and Teacher Resource Master **Language Arts Connection,** page 179.
■ Use Activity Book, page 24, "Observing."
■ Use Poster #3, "Rabbit Ears."

pyrite     galena     specular hematite

talc     earthy hematite

agate     cinnabar

**Minerals** make the colors of rocks.

Some minerals are shiny.

Some are dull.

90

# TEACHER RESOURCE MASTERS

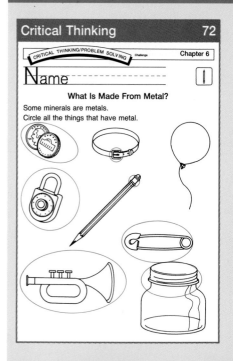

Critical Thinking    72

CRITICAL THINKING/PROBLEM SOLVING   Challenge    Chapter 6

Name

**What Is Made From Metal?**

Some minerals are metals.
Circle all the things that have metal.

Some minerals are hard.

Others are soft.

[1]What can you guess about these minerals?

1. useful as many household items; have students name the uses

talc, soft–powder

graphite, soft–pencil lead

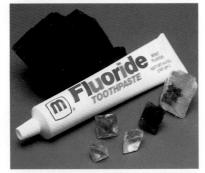

fluorite, soft–toothpaste

corundum, hard red rubies, blue sapphires

quartz, hard sandpaper

91

## OPTIONS

● **Enrichment:** Discover something about the rocks in the school area. How were they formed? How are they used? Plan a walk to an area near the school where rocks may be observed.

▲ **Challenge:** Have students use library books to find out the properties of moon rocks.

▲ **Challenge:** Have students discover how rocks and minerals are used every day. A poster can be made with photos from old magazines showing how rocks and minerals are an important part of the environment.

**Career:** Use "I WANT TO KNOW ABOUT . . . A Jeweler," student page 99, with this lesson.

## TEACHER RESOURCE MASTERS

## OPTIONS

■ Ask: **What rock do we use often in the classroom? Hint: It is very soft. It can be used to write on the chalkboard. What is it?** *chalk* Display a photograph of chalk cliffs. Explain that the chalk in the photograph contains tiny shells and crystals.

Obtain some sandy soil samples. Have students use sifters to separate the sand from other material in the soil. Encourage them to define sand as being made from pieces of larger rocks and minerals.

Most rocks were made before dinosaurs lived.

But rocks change.

Water can change rocks.

Water can make rocks smooth.

Water can make rocks small.

92

## TEACHER RESOURCE MASTERS

Reteaching Activity 76

RETEACHING ACTIVITY Chapter 6

Name

**How Are Rocks Different?**
Color the shiny rocks yellow.
Color the smooth rocks black.
Color the rough rocks brown.

# How are rocks different?

## What you need

10 different rocks    hand lens    pencil and paper

## What to do

1. Look at different rocks.

2. How can you group them?

3. Make two groups.

4. Tell about each group.

93

## ACTIVITY RESPONSES

Accept all reasonable student responses to questions during any activity discussion.

## PREPLAN

**Time Allotment:** 30 minutes
**Process Skills:** Observing/Classifying

### Objectives
1. **Describe** the properties of rocks.
2. **Group** the rocks into two piles by using properties.

### Setup
Gather rock samples. Samples may include shale, marble, granite, basalt, pumice, limestone, and obsidian.

**Cooperative Grouping:** twos—Assign roles as explained on page T24.

## 1    FOCUS

■ Make a list of properties on the board.
■ Demonstrate how to use a hand lens to study a rock.

## 2    TEACH

■ **Trouble Shooting:** Caution students not to touch the rocks with their hand lenses. Many rocks are harder than glass and will scratch the lens.
■ Ask students to classify rocks in two piles that have a common property—either hard and soft, light and dark, or rough and smooth. Have students tell how they divided their rocks into groups.
■ Use the Teacher Resource Master **Activity Worksheet,** page 69, with this activity.

## 3    APPLY

Have students make two piles again, using different properties. Have students explain how the groups are different.

### Close
■ Ask students what properties of rocks they were able to observe.

## PREPLAN

### Lesson Objectives
5. **State** and **show** that land is made of soil.
6. **Describe** the properties of soil.
7. **Explain** why soil is important.

### Science Background
■ Almost all land organisms depend on soil.

■ Soil that is rich in organic materials forms a community teeming with activity.

■ There are many different kinds of soils. The properties of soils are determined by climate, topography, the rocks from which they are formed, biological process, and age.

■ Topsoil provides the nutrients that plants need in order to grow.

■ Soil is always forming on Earth. It takes about 300 years for one centimeter of soil to form in some areas.

### Lesson Vocabulary
soil

**Note:** The activity on student page 98 may be used for guided discovery before you begin this lesson.

## 1 FOCUS

■ Have students close their eyes and imagine what Earth would look like if the land had no soil. Ask them to describe how it would look. Students should realize that there would be no flowers, no trees, no lawns or gardens.

# Soil

Much of our land is covered with **soil.**

Soil is made from rocks and minerals.

Soil has water and air.

It has dead plants and animals, too.

94

## TEACHER RESOURCE MASTERS

cotton fields

red clay

sandy soil

humus

purple prickly cactus

plant seedlings

There are different kinds of soil.

¹What can you guess about these soils?

²What is the soil like where you live?

1. soils have different colors, textures, and uses
2. Encourage students to describe soil observations about color, texture, and plant growth.

95

## 2　TEACH

**Problem Solving:** Allow students to squeeze soil to determine soil quality. If the soil compacts very tightly it is rich in clay. Sandy soil will not compact and will sift through fingers. Humus will compact together but not as tightly as a clay-rich soil. Ask: **Which of these soils is best for growing most house plants?** Help students realize that humus is the best type because it allows air and water needed by plants to get into the soil. Sandy soils allow this also, but lack organic matter found in humus. Clay-rich soils do not have good drainage.

### Guided Practice

■ Ask students to describe the properties of soils. Include color, texture, odor, and content.
■ If necessary, use the **reteaching strategy** in OPTIONS.

### Independent Practice

■ Use the Teacher Resource Master **Independent Practice,** page 75.

## 3　APPLY

■ Use Application Activity, "Making a Land Map," on student page 219.
■ Have students sift an example of soil found near the school and identify some of the soil contents: small rocks, insects, leaves, twigs, roots, and so on.

### Close

■ Contact your local County Extension Service and ask someone to come and demonstrate how they take soil samples and why taking soil samples is important. Ask the speaker to tell how soil can be made better for growing living things.

## OPTIONS

**Reteaching Strategy**
Have students experiment with growing lima beans in three soil types. Ask them to record plant behavior.

## TEACHER RESOURCE MASTERS

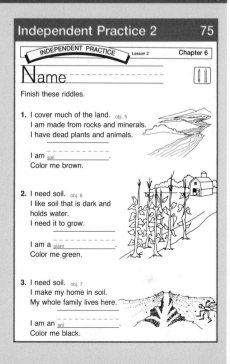

Independent Practice 2　75

INDEPENDENT PRACTICE　Lesson 2　Chapter 6

Name

Finish these riddles.

1. I cover much of the land.　obj. 5
   I am made from rocks and minerals.
   I have dead plants and animals.

   I am ___soil___
   Color me brown.

2. I need soil.　obj. 6
   I like soil that is dark and holds water.
   I need it to grow.

   I am a ___plant___.
   Color me green.

3. I need soil.　obj. 7
   I make my home in soil.
   My whole family lives here.

   I am an ___ant___
   Color me black.

# OPTIONS

## YOU CAN . . . BE A RESEARCHER

**Process Skills:** Communicating/Inferring

**Objective: Infer** how animals need soil and tell about it.

**Setup/Teach**

■ Get library books that inform students about animals that use soil for shelter, to grow and store food, and for protection.

## LANGUAGE CONNECTION

**Writing:** Write and send class letters to schools in coastal towns or cities. Ask students there to send a sample of sand so that you may compare sands from different locations. Offer to send them something of special interest from your area. After the letters have been written, read them again to see if details are in the proper order. Students can read the letters aloud to find any corrections they may need to make in their first drafts.

## LANGUAGE CONNECTION

**Reading:** Read *Mud Puddle* by Robert Munsch to your students. Ask students to recall the facts of the story.

**Resource Options**

■ Use Big Book, page 22, "Friends and Mud Pies" and Teacher Resource Master **Language Arts Connection,** page 180.

■ Use Big Book, page 23, "Ten Little Prairie Dogs" and Teacher Resource Master **Language Arts Connection,** page 181.

■ Use Big Book, page 24, "Springtime on the Farm" and Teacher Resource Master **Language Arts Connection,** page 182.

■ Use Activity Book, pages 41 and 42, "Making a Land Map."

Plants need soil.

Some plants grow best in one kind of soil.

[1]What plants grow best in sandy soil?

[2]What plants like dark soil that holds water?

1. beach grasses, cactus, and so on
2. vegetables, fruits, flowers, and so on

96

# TEACHER RESOURCE MASTERS

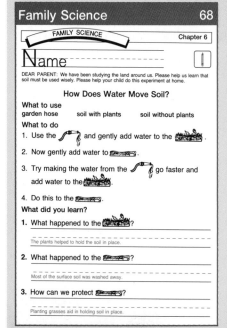

**Family Science**     68

FAMILY SCIENCE    Chapter 6

Name

DEAR PARENT: We have been studying the land around us. Please help us learn that soil must be used wisely. Please help your child do this experiment at home.

**How Does Water Move Soil?**

**What to use**

garden hose    soil with plants    soil without plants

**What to do**

1. Use the and gently add water to the .

2. Now gently add water to .

3. Try making the water from the go faster and add water to the

4. Do this to the .

**What did you learn?**

1. What happened to the ?

The plants helped to hold the soil in place.

2. What happened to the ?

Most of the surface soil was washed away.

3. How can we protect ?

Planting grasses aid in holding soil in place.

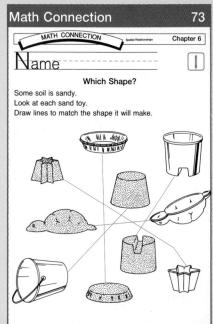

**Math Connection**     73

MATH CONNECTION   Spatial Relationships   Chapter 6

Name

**Which Shape?**

Some soil is sandy.
Look at each sand toy.
Draw lines to match the shape it will make.

Other living things use soil.
[1]Can you think of ways they use it?

1. homes, burying objects, burrowing, and so on,

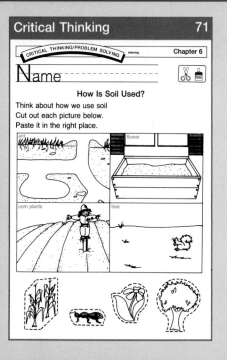

ACTIVITY

## You Can...

### Be a Researcher

Find out about burrows.
What animals use them?
Draw a picture.

Use Application Activity on page 219.

97

# OPTIONS

◆ **Reinforcement:** Have students collect photos from old magazines that show different ways soils are used. Have students paste the photos onto poster board and write a sentence explaining why soil is important.

● **Enrichment:** Have a farmer, gardener, or park superintendent visit the class. Ask this person to tell how to take care of the soil. The person could show pictures of the farm, garden, or park.

▲ **Challenge:** Grow some plant seedlings. Plant the seedlings in different kinds of soil such as sand, clay, humus, and potting soil. Find out in which soil type the plant grows best.

### ART CONNECTION

Allow students to make an object from clay. If a kiln is available, have it fired. If no kiln is available, use clay that will harden well without firing.

# TEACHER RESOURCE MASTERS

**Critical Thinking**     71

CRITICAL THINKING/PROBLEM SOLVING   Inferring    Chapter 6

Name

**How Is Soil Used?**

Think about how we use soil
Cut out each picture below.
Paste it in the right place.

## PREPLAN

**Time Allotment:** 30 minutes
**Process Skills:** Observing/Classifying

### Objectives
1. **Observe** three kinds of soil.
2. **Describe** soil properties.

### Setup
■ Gather three kinds of soil: sandy soil; a clay-like variety; and humus. Fill three shoe boxes each with a different soil type. Provide scoops and large sheets of newsprint for each group. Obtain one sifter.

🗝 **Cooperative Grouping:** threes—Assign roles as explained on page T24.

## 1  FOCUS

■ Use the sifter to demonstrate certain properties of some kinds of soil. Discuss *fine* and *loose.* List properties on the chalkboard.

## 2  TEACH

🗝 Ask student groups to scoop soil samples onto their newsprint. Show how to examine samples with a hand lens.
■ Use the Teacher Resource Master **Activity Worksheet,** page 70.

## 3  APPLY

After students have described soil properties, ask them to use the labels A, B, or C and predict what kinds of plants or animals use each soil type.

### Close
■ Appoint one class researcher from each **cooperative group** to go to the library and find out which living things prefer which soil type. Choose a day for the researchers to report to their groups on their findings.

---

## ACTIVITY

## How are soils different?

### What you need

3 kinds of soil      newsprint

hand lens      pencil and paper

### What to do

1. Use a hand lens to look at kinds of soil.

2. What color is each soil?

3. How does each feel?

4. Which soil sticks together?

5. Which are good for growing food? Why?

98

## ACTIVITY RESPONSES

Accept all reasonable student responses to questions during any activity discussion.

# I WANT TO KNOW ABOUT...

## A Jeweler

Todd Running is a jeweler.
He cuts and polishes gems.
Gems are rocks or minerals.
The gems are used to make jewelry.
[1] What gems do you like best?

1. Encourage students to describe properties of diamonds, emeralds, rubies, and so on.

*Career*

99

**TEACHER RESOURCE MASTERS**

## Feature Background

■ *Lapidary* is the cutting and polishing of gems.

■ Jewelers must have knowledge of geology and chemistry to identify gems and understand their characteristics. They must also know the crystal structure of different minerals so they can cut the gems correctly.

■ Rubies and sapphires are forms of corundum. Impurities and different crystal structures cause the red or blue color.

■ An emerald is a crystal of the mineral beryl.

## Feature Vocabulary

jeweler
gems
jewelry

## Teaching Suggestions

■ Discuss the meaning of the word *gem*. Ask students to name any gems they know. Ask students to describe the gem.

■ Make a display or bulletin board that shows different birthstones. List each student's name next to his or her birthstone.

■ Have a jeweler speak to your class about cutting and polishing gems. Ask the jeweler to show the tools used for cutting and polishing.

■ Put a world map on the bulletin board. Tag the areas of the world where different gems are mined. Refer to an encyclopedia for information on the mining of different gems.

**Chapter Closure:** Use these pages to re-view and reinforce chapter concepts.

## What I Learned

Have students read the rebus summary statements aloud to be sure they inter-pret the pictures correctly. After each sentence is read, discuss other words that would also make the sentence true.

## Words I Know

Use any or all of the following sugges-tions to reinforce the chapter vocabulary.

Write each science word or word group on the chalkboard. Ask students to read them. Add the words to the class science list or have students write the words in their individual science word books. Ask students to tell about these words to help you evaluate their comprehension. Have students use each science word or word group in a sentence.

---

**CHAPTER REVIEW**

**6**

═══ **What I Learned** ═══

• Land is made up of  and  .

       rocks        soil

• Minerals in rocks make them  or dull.

       shiny

• Rocks can change.

   can make  smooth.

  Water           rocks

• Living things use  .

      soil

═══ **Words I Know** ═══

**rocks    minerals    soil**

100

---

# TEACHER RESOURCE MASTERS

**Test A**          **77**

TEST A     Recalling Facts     Chapter 6

Name   Each question is worth 16 points.

Use the words in the box to finish each sentence. obj. 3 & 4

| now | minerals | smooth | old |

1. Some rocks are very old _____.

2. Other rocks are being made now _____.

3. Water can make rocks small and smooth _____.

4. Rock colors are made by minerals _____.

Draw a line from each sentence to its picture. obj. 3, 7

5. Plants need soil.

6. Minerals can be hard or soft.

## What I Know

*Use the picture to answer the questions.*

1. Where can you find rocks?

2. How are rocks different?

3. How do rocks change?

4. How do living things use soil?

101

### What I Know

Have students refer to the pictures to answer the questions and extend concepts.
1. Land is made of rocks. Mountains are made of rocks. Rocks can be found at beaches, in fields, and in streams.
2. Rocks have different minerals. Minerals make the colors and textures of rocks.
3. Water can make rocks smooth and small. Over time, water can erode rocks into particles of sand.
4. Plants use soil to grow. Other living things tunnel into soil to build homes or store food.

## OPTIONS

### Resource Options
Use Color Transparencies #6a and #6b.

## TEACHER RESOURCE MASTERS

**Test B** 78

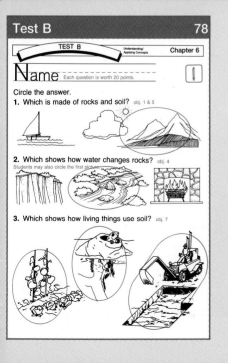

# CHAPTER 7

# Earth and Space

## Planning Guide

| Lessons | Objectives | Vocabulary |
|---------|------------|------------|
| **Chapter Introduction** pp. 102, 103 | | |
| **Lesson 1 Earth and the Sun** pp. 104–107 | 1. **Compare** the relative sizes of Earth and the sun. <br> 2. **Observe** changes in the shadows at different times of the day. | |
| **Lesson 2 The Sun** pp. 108–111 | 3. **Demonstrate** what causes day and night using a light and a globe. <br> 4. **Infer** that the apparent movement of the sun is caused by Earth's rotation. | |
| **Lesson 3 Space Travel** pp. 112–115 | 5. **Define** astronaut. <br> 6. **Describe** how astronauts travel in space. <br> 7. **Explain** activities astronauts do in space. | astronaut |
| **Chapter Review** pp. 116, 117 | | |
| **Unit Review** pp. 118,119 | | |

# Planning Guide

| Text Activities | | Teacher Resource Masters | Other Components |
|---|---|---|---|
| **Title/Skill** | **Materials per Group** | | |
| **Have You Ever . . . Seen Your Shadow?** p. 103<br>Inferring<br>Time Allotment: 30 minutes | flashlight | | **Activity Center:** "First Kid in Space"; "Out of This World"; "Making Shadows" |
| **How Do Shadows Change?** p. 107<br>Measuring/Inferring<br>Time Allotment: 3/10 minute periods in one day | chalk<br>string<br>pencil and paper | ♦ Family Science, p. 80<br>Activity Worksheet, p.81<br>▲ Critical Thinking, p. 84<br>Math Connection, p. 85<br>Independent Practice, p. 86<br>Language Arts Connection, pp. 183, 184 | Big Book, p. 25<br>Big Book, p. 26<br>Activity Book, p. 25 |
| **What Makes Day and Night?** p. 111<br>Using a Model/Predicting<br>Time Allotment: 15 minutes<br><br>**Sun's Up! Get Up!** p. 220<br>Observing/Using Numbers/Predicting/Inferring<br>Time Allotment: 3/10 minute periods | sun poster<br>Earth poster<br>flashlight<br>pencil<br><br>pencil<br>newspaper | Transparency Master, p. 79<br>Activity Worksheet, p.82<br>Critical Thinking, p. 83<br>Independent Practice, p. 87<br>Language Arts Connection, p. 185 | Big Book, p. 27<br>Activity Book, p. 26<br>Activity Book, pp. 43, 44 |
| **You Can . . . Test Space Foods,** p. 114<br>Observing<br>Time Allotment: 20 minutes<br><br>**Space Kids,** p. 221<br>Communicating/Inferring<br>Time Allotment: 40 minutes | dried fruits<br>instant foods and beverages<br><br>paper<br>pencil | ♦ Reteaching Activity, p. 89<br>Independent Practice, p. 88<br>Language Arts Connection, p. 186 | Big Book, p. 28<br>Activity Book, pp. 45, 46 |
| | | Test A, p. 90<br>Test B, p. 91 | Color Transparencies #7a and #7b |
| | | | Unit Test |

♦ **Basic** / ▲ **Advanced** / All other masters are for use by all students.

# Earth and Space

## For Exceptional Students

### ESL/LEP

**Chapter 7/Lesson 2, Page 110**
Discuss the differences between day and night with students. Ask each student to fold a large piece of paper in half. Label the left side with the word *day* and the right side with the word *night*. Students should draw a picture illustrating each word. Have students share their pictures with the class.

**Chapter 7/Lesson 3, Page 114**
Make two sets of cards, one with words and the other with pictures. Be sure to include the words *sun, shadows,* and *astronaut*. Use the cards to play a game similar to Concentration, matching the word with its picture. As each match is made, students should say the word aloud.

### Gifted

**Chapter 7/Lesson 2, Page 110**
Interested students may describe the difference between stars and planets. Student may choose a planet and share something about the choice with the class. An illustration of the planet should accompany the description.

### Mainstreamed

**Chapter 7/Lesson 3, Page 114**
**Mild Behavior Disorders:** Arrange two student seats in tandem fashion. Print a sign that says "Astronaut Express" and place it next to the seats. Tell the students that you are a news reporter sent by your editor to get their feelings about their space ride. Ask students to tell you where they are going and how they intend to get there. Record students' responses on a tape recorder.

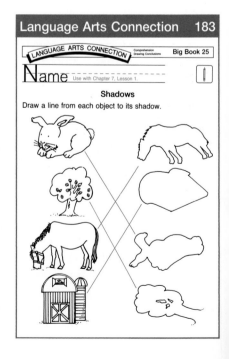

Language Arts Connection 183

LANGUAGE ARTS CONNECTION | Comprehension Drawing Conclusions | Big Book 25

Name _____ Use with Chapter 7, Lesson 1.

**Shadows**
Draw a line from each object to its shadow.

## Whole Class Science Project

Have students learn about the effect of solar energy by using water in canning jars with lids and tape. Have students work in small groups. Measure equal amounts of water in jars of the same size so each jar is about one-half full. Use masking tape to mark the level of water in both jars. Place lids securely on both jars. Mark one *C* for control and place it in a shaded area in the room. Place the second jar, marked *T* for test, in bright sunlight or under a lamp for two hours. At the end of that time, have students hold both jars to note temperature differences. Students should give suggestions for any differences.

## Science Fair Projects

Individual students could do one of the following projects:
1. Using a drawing or photograph, demonstrate a favorite constellation, give its name, and explain how it got its name.
2. Using a diagram, find out the parts of a comet.
3. Using a model, learn the parts of a rocket.
4. Using an old dark-colored umbrella and stick-on stars, demonstrate the configuration of some constellations.

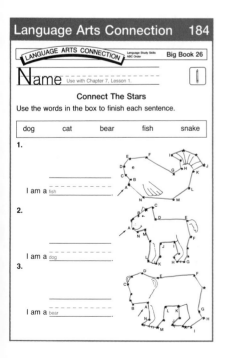

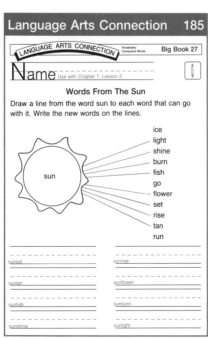

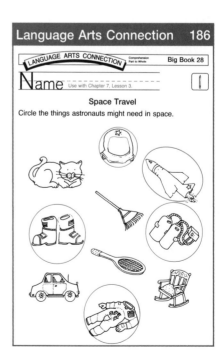

# CHAPTER 7

pages 102–117

## Chapter Concepts
- The sun provides Earth's heat and light.
- Earth's rotation causes day and night.
- People explore space.

## Chapter Background
- Earth is the third planet from the sun. Earth, along with the other eight known planets, their satellites, and other space bodies, make up the solar system.
- Earth's atmosphere extends from Earth's surface into interplanetary space. It is composed mostly of nitrogen, oxygen, argon, carbon dioxide, and water vapor.

## Looking Ahead
- You will need photographs that show objects or people with shadows to complete the chapter opening lesson.
- You will need dehydrated foods such as dried fruits and instant foods to complete the activity on page 114.

## Look for These Symbols
- —Hands-on activity
- —Cooperative learning
- —Overhead transparency
- ◆ —Basic/Reinforcement
- ● —Average/Enrichment
- ▲ —Advanced/Challenge
- SC —Science Center
- —Calculator Practice

SCIENCE
In Your World

102

# CHAPTER
## 7

# Earth and Space

Earth and the sun are far apart.

We live on Earth.

We get light and heat from the sun.

## Have You Ever...

### Seen Your Shadow?

1. Stand in front of a wall.
2. Hold out your hand.
3. Shine a flashlight on your hand.
4. What do you see on the wall?
5. Make other shadow shapes.

How are shadows made?

103

## PREPLAN

**Time Allotment:** 30 minutes

### Objectives
1. **Recognize** that the sun provides light for Earth.
2. **Infer** that light must be present for shadows to occur.

### Setup
To conduct the activity, collect the following materials for each student or **cooperative learning group.**
flashlight          darkened area
blank wall/screen

## 1   FOCUS

■ Discuss the picture of Earth on page 102.

## 2   TEACH

■ Read the chapter title and introductory paragraph.
■ Ask: **How does Earth get its light?** *from the sun*
■ Ask: **How is a flashlight like the sun?** *A flashlight gives light like the sun.*

**Have You Ever . . .**
Use this activity as an introduction to creating shadows.

### Student Responses
■ Shadows can be made when light is blocked by an object.

## 3   APPLY

■ Allow students to experiment making shadows using classroom objects.

### Close
■ Share with students that they will learn more about shadows as they read Chapter 7.

## PREPLAN

### Lesson Objectives
1. **Compare** the relative sizes of Earth and the sun.
2. **Observe** changes in the shadows at different times of the day.

### Science Background
■ Our sun is one of the many billions of stars that make up the Milky Way. Scientists believe the sun and other stars formed from a huge mass of gases (mostly hydrogen) called a nebula. Gravity gradually compressed the gases, causing the temperature to increase. The interior temperature and pressure became great enough to trigger a nuclear fusion or thermonuclear reaction. During nuclear fusion in the sun, matter is converted into energy.

■ The closest star to Earth is the sun.

■ Earth revolves about the sun once every 365¼ days. It rotates on its axis once every 24 hours.

### Lesson Vocabulary
sun    shadows

**Note:** The activity on student page 107 may be used for guided discovery before you begin this lesson.

## 1  FOCUS

■ Ask: **What do you like to do on the first really warm, bright day in spring?** *run outside to play* Ask: **What makes you feel so good?** *warm, bright sunshiny air* Ask: **Why is the sun important to Earth?** *It gives us both light and heat.*

■ Place a large globe in the front of the room. Have volunteers point to land areas and oceans, and show where the air would be.

# Earth and the Sun

We live on Earth.

Earth is in **space.**

Earth moves through space.

104

## TEACHER RESOURCE MASTERS

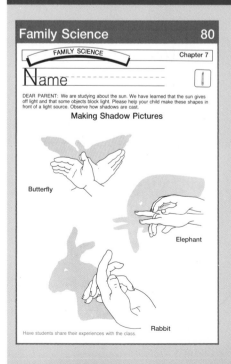

Family Science                                      80

FAMILY SCIENCE                          Chapter 7

Name

DEAR PARENT: We are studying about the sun. We have learned that the sun gives off light and that some objects block light. Please help your child make these shapes in front of a light source. Observe how shadows are cast.

**Making Shadow Pictures**

Butterfly

Elephant

Rabbit

Have students share their experiences with the class.

The **sun** is in space, too.

It is far away from Earth.

The sun is much bigger than Earth.

We see the sun, but it looks very small.

[1]Why does the sun look so small?

1. because it is so far away; 93,000,000 miles

105

## TEACHER RESOURCE MASTERS

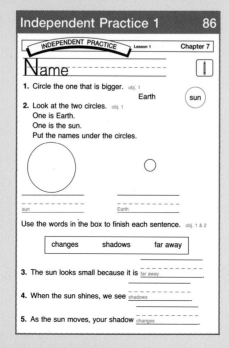

Independent Practice 1    86

INDEPENDENT PRACTICE   Lesson 1    Chapter 7

Name

**1.** Circle the one that is bigger. obj. 1

Earth    (sun)

**2.** Look at the two circles. obj. 1
One is Earth.
One is the sun.
Put the names under the circles.

sun           Earth

Use the words in the box to finish each sentence. obj. 1 & 2

| changes | shadows | far away |

**3.** The sun looks small because it is far away

**4.** When the sun shines, we see shadows

**5.** As the sun moves, your shadow changes

## 2   TEACH

Set up a thermometer in a warm sunny place. Measure the temperature during the day several times. Make a class graph for one week. Discuss how heat from the sun warms Earth.

Push a straight pin through a small piece of black paper so the pinhead is visible. Hold it up beside a basketball. Point out if the sun were the size of the basketball, Earth would be no bigger than the head of a pin.

### Guided Practice

■ Have students think of other examples where very large objects look small or where small objects look bigger relative to the observer.

■ If necessary, use the **reteaching strategy** in OPTIONS.

### Independent Practice

■ Use the Teacher Resource Master **Independent Practice,** page 86.

## 3   APPLY

■ Inform students that it would take just over 100 Earths on a string (like a string of beads) to stretch across the sun. Ask students why, if the sun is so much larger, it looks so small.

### Close

■ Students should be able to understand that when a large object is far away, it will appear smaller. Students should also be able to say that shadows appear on sunny days and describe how shadows change throughout the day.

## OPTIONS

### Reteaching Strategy

■ Obtain a softball and a basketball. Arrange the balls so the basketball appears smaller than the softball. Ask: **Which ball looks larger?** *softball* Stress that because the sun is so far from Earth, it appears much smaller.

# OPTIONS

### LANGUAGE CONNECTION

**Writing:** Have students write a story entitled "The Day Earth Stopped Moving." Before students begin writing, remind them that the sun gives light and heat, which are both important for life on Earth. Students should write a first draft and then edit it to polish and correct their work.

▲**Reinforcement:** Review with students how the sun gives light and warmth, which makes it possible for plants to grow and for us to get food to eat. Experiment with two plants. Provide light to one and no light to the other to show students how the lack of light could affect plants.

●**Enrichment:** Use the Teacher Resource **Appendix** page 204 to have students make a thermometer. Discuss how temperature is measured.

▲**Challenge:** Have students make a sundial. A short pencil should be placed in a lump of clay on a blank paper located in a windowsill that receives sunlight all day. The clay can be covered with aluminum foil to avoid it getting sticky. The pencil's shadow can be traced each hour and marked with the time. The sundial can then be used to tell time.

### Resource Options

■ Use Big Book, page 25, "The Shadow Shaker" and Teacher Resource Master **Language Arts Connection** page 183.
■ Use Big Book, page 26, "The Star Blanket" and Teacher Resource Master **Language Arts Connection** page 184.
■ Activity Book, page 25, "Inferring."

## When the sun shines, we see **shadows**.

[1]**How do shadows change?**

1. The length and shape of shadows change because of the angle of the rays of the sun at certain times of the day.

106

# TEACHER RESOURCE MASTERS

### Critical Thinking                    84

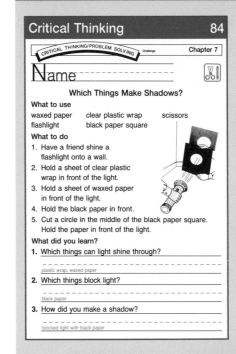

CRITICAL THINKING/PROBLEM SOLVING   Challenge   Chapter 7

# Name

**Which Things Make Shadows?**

**What to use**

| waxed paper | clear plastic wrap | scissors |
| flashlight | black paper square | |

**What to do**

1. Have a friend shine a flashlight onto a wall.
2. Hold a sheet of clear plastic wrap in front of the light.
3. Hold a sheet of waxed paper in front of the light.
4. Hold the black paper in front.
5. Cut a circle in the middle of the black paper square. Hold the paper in front of the light.

**What did you learn?**

1. Which things can light shine through?

   plastic wrap, waxed paper

2. Which things block light?

   black paper

3. How did you make a shadow?

   blocked light with black paper

### Math Connection                    85

MATH CONNECTION   Recognizing a Pattern   Chapter 7

# Name

**Which Shadow Next?**

Look at the shadow patterns.
Think about what comes next.
Paste it in place.

child running

child crouching

child doing jumping jacks

## How do shadows change?

**What you need**

chalk

string

pencil and paper

**What to do**

1. Have a friend stand in one spot.

2. Trace your friend's shadow.

3. Do this again later in the day.

4. Measure the shadows with a string.

5. How did the shadows change?

107

## ACTIVITY RESPONSES

Accept all reasonable student responses to questions during any activity discussion.

## PREPLAN

**Time Allotment:** Allow 3 ten-minute periods during one sunny day.

**Process Skills:** Measuring/Inferring

**Objectives**

1. **Measure** the length of a shadow.
2. **Compare** shadow lengths at different times of the day.
3. **Infer** why shadows change.

**Setup**

■ Choose an asphalt or concrete area on the south side of your building.

Cooperative Grouping: twos—Assign roles as explained on page T24.

## 1 FOCUS

■ Demonstrate how to outline a person's shadow. Use chalk on asphalt or concrete. Trace with a stick on a dirt or gravel surface.

## 2 TEACH

Label the string lengths with tape. Put the person's name and time of day on the label. Save each string length for comparison at the end of the activity.

■ Have students making the shadow always stand in the same place.

■ Use the Teacher Resource Master **Activity Worksheet,** page 81.

## 3 APPLY

■ Place the labeled string lengths side by side for comparison. Have students note the changes in length and in direction with time of day.

**Close**

■ Ask: **How did the shadows change?** *The shadows became shorter as the sun appeared higher in the sky.*

## PREPLAN

### Lesson Objectives
3. **Demonstrate** what causes day and night using a light and a globe.
4. **Infer** that the apparent movement of the sun is caused by Earth's rotation.

### Science Background
■ The sun is a typical star midway through its life cycle. Its average surface temperature is over 5,000°C.
■ The sun is almost the only source of energy in the solar system. The light from other stars is negligible compared with that from the sun.
■ Earth turns on its axis from west to east once a day.

**Note:** The activity on student page 111 may be used for guided discovery before you begin this lesson.

## 1  FOCUS

Have a student hold a volleyball in front of the classroom. Darken the room and shine a flashlight on the ball. Point out that one half of the ball is lighted while the other half is dark. Ask: **If the volleyball were Earth and the light were the sun, where is it day and where is it night?** *The lighted portion represents day.* Place a piece of tape in the middle of the lighted side. Mark an X on the tape. Ask the student holding the ball to slowly turn it. Have other students observe what happens to the tape marker.

# The Sun

The sun seems to rise.

A new day begins.

The sun gives off light.

This light reaches part of Earth.

108

## TEACHER RESOURCE MASTERS

The sun seems to set at the end of the day.

Then part of Earth has night.

[1]What happens to the sun at night?

1. The sun shines on the other half of Earth.

## 2 TEACH

■ Take students outside the building and have the class come to a consensus about where the sun first appears in the morning and where it seems to set. Explain the directions East and West.

✋ Use a globe to explain that as Earth moves, it spins (rotates). Discuss that it takes Earth 24 hours to make one complete turn.

### Guided Practice

■ Ask students to fold a paper in half. On one half, ask them to draw a picture of the sun, Earth, and where they would be on Earth during the day. Then have them show where they would be at night.

■ If necessary, use the **reteaching strategy** in OPTIONS.

### Independent Practice

■ Use the Teacher Resource Master **Independent Practice,** page 87.

## 3 APPLY

■ Use Application Activity, "Sun's Up! Get Up!," on student page 220.

### Close

■ Students should be able to spin a globe slowly with a light source and explain why day and night occurs.

## OPTIONS

### Reteaching Strategy

■ Have each student make a small flag attached to a toothpick and insert it into a small ball of clay. Then have a student place the flag on a globe. Have students follow the flag as it moves away from and again toward the sun as the student rotates the globe. Have others repeat the demonstration.

### Resource Options

■ Use Big Book, page 27, "Day and Night" and Teacher Resource Master **Language Connection,** page 185.

## TEACHER RESOURCE MASTERS

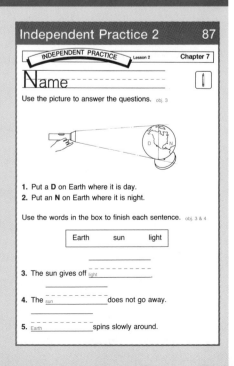

Independent Practice 2     87

INDEPENDENT PRACTICE    Lesson 2    Chapter 7

**N**ame

Use the picture to answer the questions. obj. 3

1. Put a **D** on Earth where it is day.
2. Put an **N** on Earth where it is night.

Use the words in the box to finish each sentence. obj. 3 & 4

| Earth | sun | light |

3. The sun gives off ____ light ____.

4. The ____ sun ____ does not go away.

5. ____ Earth ____ spins slowly around.

# OPTIONS

### LANGUAGE CONNECTION

**Writing:** Help students determine what part of Earth is having daylight while they are having night. Have students write a story telling what they think people are doing during the day while the students sleep. Students should write a first draft, then edit it to correct spelling and elaborate on their ideas.

### LANGUAGE CONNECTION

**Writing:** Have students complete a poem that begins with "When the sun is shining down on me . . ." Have students concentrate on including their personal experiences in the poem.

♦ **Reinforcement:** Do a brainstorming exercise with students. Write their ideas on the chalkboard without correcting any of their information. Have them list things that would happen if the sun lost its light and heat.

● **Enrichment:** Point out that like the globe, Earth is tilted. Lead students to see how the temperature at the North and South Poles could be different than at the middle of Earth.

▲ **Challenge:** Have students propose that Earth could speed up and spin faster. Ask: **How would this change the length of day and night?** *They would be shorter.* **What would happen if Earth slowed down?** *Days would be longer than 24 hours.*

### Resource Options
■ Use Activity Book, page 26, "Observing."
■ Use Activity Book, pages 43 and 44, "Sun's Up! Get Up!".

The sun does not go away.

Earth spins slowly around.

Part of Earth has day.

Another part of Earth has night.

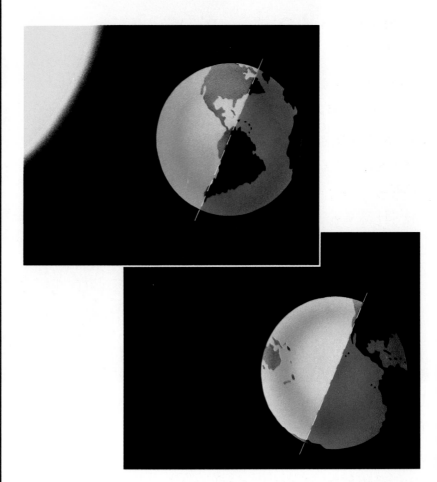

Use Application Activity on page 220.

# TEACHER RESOURCE MASTERS

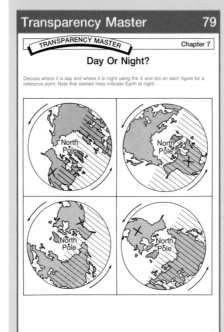

**Transparency Master** 79

TRANSPARENCY MASTER — Chapter 7

**Day Or Night?**

Discuss where it is day and where it is night using the X and dot on each figure for a reference point. Note that slanted lines indicate Earth at night.

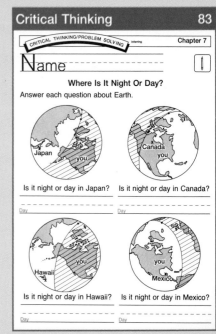

**Critical Thinking** 83

CRITICAL THINKING/PROBLEM SOLVING — Inferring — Chapter 7

**N**ame

**Where Is It Night Or Day?**
Answer each question about Earth.

Is it night or day in Japan? _Day_

Is it night or day in Canada? _Day_

Is it night or day in Hawaii? _Day_

Is it night or day in Mexico? _Day_

# What makes day and night?

## What you need

sun poster    Earth poster    flashlight    pencil

## What to do

1. Suppose you are the sun.
2. Have a friend be Earth.
3. Shine light on your friend.
4. What part of your friend is day?
5. What part of your friend is night?

111

## ACTIVITY RESPONSES

Accept all reasonable student responses to questions during any activity discussion.

## PREPLAN

**Time Allotment:** 15 minutes
**Process Skills:** Using a model/Predicting

### Objectives

1. **Demonstrate** day and night using a flashlight "sun" and a person to represent Earth.
2. **Identify** daylight areas and night areas on the model Earth.

### Setup

■ Make "day" and "night" signs to tape on the student representing Earth.
■ Check flashlight batteries for freshness.
■ **Cooperative Grouping:** threes—Assign roles as explained on page T24.

## 1    FOCUS

■ Use student volunteers to demonstrate the sun-Earth model before student groups try it on their own.

## 2    TEACH

■ **Safety Considerations:** Caution students not to shine the light into other students' eyes. Light should be directed at the signs.
■ Have "Earth" slowly turn counterclockwise. Have students note which part of the person is lighted by the "sun" and which part is in the dark.
■ Use the Teacher Resource Master **Activity Worksheet,** page 82.

## 3    APPLY

■ Use a globe and a flashlight and ask volunteers to demonstrate day and night to the class. Repeat several times.

### Close

■ Discuss what causes day and night. Make sure students understand that it is Earth that moves rather than the sun.

## PREPLAN

### Lesson Objectives
**5. Define** astronaut.
**6. Describe** how astronauts travel in space.
**7. Explain** activities astronauts do in space.

### Science Background
■ Thrust is the force that propels a rocket forward. Rockets launch spacecraft into space.

■ The Apollo program was a series of space flights that culminated in placing an astronaut on the moon. Neil Armstrong was the first man to walk on the moon's surface.

■ A space shuttle is a reusable craft designed to transport astronauts, materials, and satellites to and from space. The shuttle system has four major elements: the orbiter, liquid fuel rocket engines, an external liquid fuel tank, and two solid fuel rocket booster engines.

■ A space station has living quarters, work space, and all the equipment and support systems necessary for astronauts to live and work in space.

■ Astronauts are either pilots or mission specialists.

### Lesson Vocabulary
astronaut

## 1 FOCUS

▨ Have two students role-play astronauts in space and one student pretend to be in the control center on Earth. Have the astronauts relay what is seen in space to the control center. Ask: **What does an astronaut do? Where do astronauts work?** *Accept all reasonable answers.* Encourage imaginative answers.

# Space Travel

1. Encourage imaginative answers.
2. rockets, space shuttle

Suppose you could go into space.

You would be an **astronaut.**

[1]Where would you go?

[2]How would you get there?

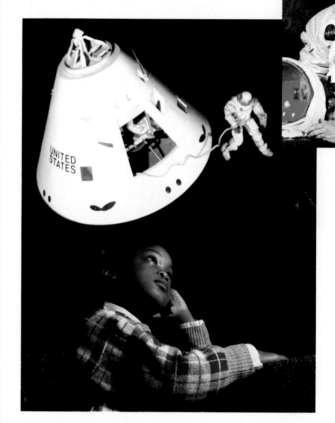

112

## TEACHER RESOURCE MASTERS

Astronauts travel in space.

They ride in special ships.

Rockets boost them into space.

Astronauts are brave!

113

## 2 TEACH

■ **Problem Solving:** Ask: **What kind of suit does an astronaut need?** Inform students that conditions in space are much different than those on Earth. Have students design and sketch a space suit. The suits should include features for air, means for eating and drinking, heating and cooling systems, and so on.

### Guided Practice

Have students **work cooperatively in groups** and plan a space mission. Ask each group to plan how they will get into space, what they will eat, what they will do and what tools they will use. Ask student groups to think about the training their space group will need.

■ If necessary, use the **reteaching strategy** in OPTIONS.

### Independent Practice

■ Use the Teacher Resource Master **Independent Practice,** page 88.

## 3 APPLY

■ Use Application Activity, "Space Kids," on student page 221.

Make a time line indicating important dates in space history. Write about specific space events including the dates on sentence strips. Have students match the order of the sentence strips to the time line. Discuss how planning for space travel has changed.

### Close

■ Students should be able to relate that astronauts work in space under conditions that are very different from Earth.

### Reteaching Strategy

Have students find out what the inside of a space shuttle is like. Have students explain why space travel might be difficult.

### Resource Options

■ Use Big Book, page 28, "Countdown" and Teacher Resource Master **Language Arts Connection,** page 186.

## TEACHER RESOURCE MASTERS

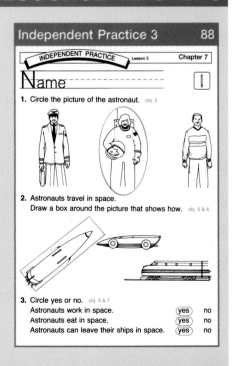

Independent Practice 3   88

INDEPENDENT PRACTICE   Lesson 3   Chapter 7

Name

1. Circle the picture of the astronaut. obj. 5

2. Astronauts travel in space.
Draw a box around the picture that shows how. obj. 5 & 6

3. Circle yes or no. obj. 5 & 7
Astronauts work in space. (yes) no
Astronauts eat in space. (yes) no
Astronauts can leave their ships in space. (yes) no

# OPTIONS

## YOU CAN . . . TEST SPACE FOODS

**Process Skill:** Observing

**Objective: Observe** what kinds of foods must be eaten in space.

### Setup/Teach

Gather dehydrated foods from camping supply or grocery stores. Or, collect a variety of instant foods and beverages. Demonstrate for students how to add hot or cold water to some of these foods. Have a "space" lunch.

## LANGUAGE CONNECTION

**Reading:** Read *Alister In Outer Space* by Marilyn Sadler. Ask students to re-call the details of the story. What happened first, second, third? What happened at the end of the story? Ask students where they think Alister has landed. Ask them to predict what will happen next. Ask students to tell you if the story is fact or fantasy.

## MATH CONNECTION

Pose the following problem to your students. **Three astronauts were going to share 9 cookies in space.** Have students model the situation to tell you how many cookies each astronaut will get if they share them equally. *Each astronaut will get 3 cookies.*

**Science and Technology:** Use "I WANT TO KNOW ABOUT . . . Space Suits," student page 115, with this lesson.

## Resource Options

■ Use Activity Book, pages 45 and 46, "Space Kids".

---

Astronauts travel around Earth.

They can work in space.

Then they come back to Earth.

[1] What do they learn about space?

[2] What do they learn about Earth?

## You Can...

### Test Space Foods

Eat foods like astronauts eat.

Try some dried fruits.

Try some instant foods.

Why are these used in space?

114

Use Application Activity on page 221.

# TEACHER RESOURCE MASTERS

**Reteaching Activity**    89

RETEACHING ACTIVITY    Chapter 7

Name

**What Is In Space?**

Color the things you find in space.
Cut them out.
Paste them onto black paper.

Students should cut out sun, moon, Earth, and spacecraft. Encourage them to paste the objects showing their relationship in space.

# I WANT TO KNOW ABOUT...

## Space Suits

Space is different from Earth.

Astronauts must be prepared.

They must wear special suits.

The suits help them breathe in space.

The suits also help them move.

[1] Would you like to wear a space suit?

1. Discuss with students the advantages and limitations of wearing a space suit in space.

*Science and Technology*

115

## TEACHER RESOURCE MASTERS

### Feature Background

■ Astronauts wear hard suits during any extra-vehicular activity (EVA). The suits are designed to fit the nature of the mission. Factors such as length of stay, atmospheric conditions, and distance from Earth must be considered.

■ Hard suits may be made of a variety of materials, such as aluminum alloys or stainless steel. These materials protect against puncturing and radiation exposure. Future suits could be coated with a very thin layer of gold. Gold is very corrosion-resistant. The suits must be pressurized and allow for mobility.

■ The back-pack on the space suit contains the life-support system.

### Feature Vocabulary

astronaut

breathe

### Teaching Suggestions

■ Discuss with students what living things need. Explain that these needs must be met in space as well.

■ Have students role-play a day in space. Encourage them to be practical in their activities. Have students consider such activities as cooking, washing dishes, cleaning clothes, working outdoors, and taking care of an injury.

■ Have students describe some of the special tools that a person working or traveling in space might need. Allow students to draw their own space tools.

**Chapter Closure:** Use these pages to review and reinforce chapter concepts.

## What I Learned

Have students read the rebus summary statements aloud to be sure that they interpret the pictures correctly. After each sentence, discuss other words that would also make the sentences true.

## Words I Know

Use any or all of the following suggestions to reinforce the chapter vocabulary.

Write each science word or word group on the chalkboard. Ask students to read them. Add the words to the class science list or have students write the words in their individual science word books. Ask students to tell about these words to help you evaluate their comprehension. Have students use each science word or word group in a sentence.

---

# CHAPTER REVIEW
# 7

## What I Learned

- The  is bigger than  .
  sun      Earth

- When the  shines, we see  .
  sun      shadows

- We have  and  because Earth spins.
  day      night

- Astronauts travel in  .
  special ships

## Words I Know

space     sun     shadows     astronaut

116

---

# TEACHER RESOURCE MASTERS

| Test A | 90 |

TEST A     Recalling Facts     Chapter 7

**N**ame   Each question is worth 14 points.

Use the words in the box to finish each sentence. obj. 1–4

| bigger | Earth | day | space |

1. Both Earth and sun move in space _____

2. The sun is bigger _____ than Earth.

3. The sun is far away from Earth _____.

4. Where sunlight shines on Earth it is day _____

Circle the answer. obj. 1, 3, 5
5. Which give off light?
   Earth    (sun)    ball

6. Which travels in space?
   fireman    chef    (astronaut)

7. Which is smaller?
   Sun    (Earth)

## What I Know

*Use the picture to answer the questions.*

1. Why does the sun look small from Earth?

2. Why do we see shadows?

3. Why do we have day and night?

4. What can astronauts do in space?

5. How could you travel in space?

117

**What I Know**

Have students refer to the picture to answer the questions and extend concepts.

**1.** The sun looks smaller because it is so far away from Earth.

**2.** When the sun shines, we see shadows.

**3.** Earth spins slowly around. When one part of Earth has day, another part of Earth has night.

**4.** Astronauts can work in space to learn more about Earth and find out about what happens in space.

**5.** Rockets and space shuttles are used for space travel.

## OPTIONS

**Resource Options**

Use Color Transparencies #7a and #7b.

## TEACHER RESOURCE MASTERS

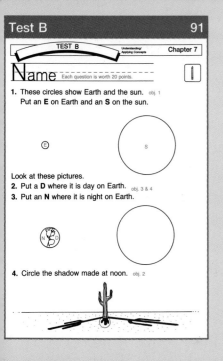

Test B      91

TEST B    Understanding/Applying Concepts    Chapter 7

Name   Each question is worth 20 points.

1. These circles show Earth and the sun. obj. 1
Put an **E** on Earth and an **S** on the sun.

Look at these pictures.
2. Put a **D** where it is day on Earth. obj. 3 & 4
3. Put an **N** where it is night on Earth.

4. Circle the shadow made at noon. obj. 2

pages 118, 119

## The Writing Connection

Before they write, have students talk about what they know about space. They may want to include the sun and Earth in their stories. Students should think about what it would feel like in space.

Students can also write about the actual blast-off of their ship. They may tell what their ship looks like and how they feel when the ship blasts off.

## Other Ideas

Have students pretend they are selling a new kind of pet rock. Students should write an advertisement describing the rock. They should try to convince people that their rock is the one to buy.

Have students keep a journal about their first week in space as an astronaut.

Have students write a story about what it would be like to be a dinosaur that has come to live in our world today.

Have students write a story about a mysterious shadow that has been following them. Students may want to write stories that give clues about a specific shadow for other students to read and guess. For example, they may describe their little brother's shadow.

Students may enjoy writing a story about finding a cave. They might tell where and how they found the cave and what it is like inside the cave.

**UNIT REVIEW**

**2**

## The Writing Connection

You have blasted off into space.

Where do you go?

What do you see?

Write a story.

**Something To Do**

Read about a dinosaur that lived long ago.
Make a model of that dinosaur out of clay.
Write a story about your dinosaur.

*Would You*
**Believe?**

You can't
pour water in
space.

**Books To Read**

**My Visit to the Dinosaurs** by Aliki
**Moon Man** by Tomi Ungerer
**Under the Ground** by Eugene Booth

**Something to Do**

Using the salt dough recipe and the directions below, suggest that students create a three-dimensional environment for displaying their animal models.

30 cm × 30 cm cardboard squares for each student
paint, brushes, water containers, and paint smocks
newspaper to cover the students' work area
large mixing bowl
8 cups of flour
measuring cup
4 cups each of salt and warm water

Cover the work area with newspaper. Have students use cardboard squares as a base. Make four batches of salt-and-flour dough by dissolving one cup of salt in one cup of warm water. Stir. Add two cups of flour and mix well. Extra flour may be needed to eliminate excess stickiness. Give students enough dough to create mountains, hills, plains, or deserts. Students may need to use a form to help shape mountains. After the landforms have dried, have students paint them.

**Would You Believe?**

On Earth, gravity is the force that pulls objects. Gravity is the force that pulls water downward to allow us to pour water out of a glass. In space, there is no force to pull water downward. In fact, water poured in space will form into balls and float.

**Books to Read**

◆ **Moon Man** by Tomi Ungerer, New York: Harper & Row Junior Books, 1984. Grades K–2. This story recounts a surprise visit to Earth by the man in the moon.

● **Under the Ground** by Eugene Booth, Milwaukee, WI: Raintree Publishers, 1985. Grades K–3. Pictures are used to illustrate animals, tunnels, and people underground.

▲ **My Visit to the Dinosaurs** by Aliki, New York: Harper, Thomas Y. Crowell Junior Books, 1985. Grades 2–3. This story is an account of a child's visit to a museum.

# Physical Science

## Classroom Centers

## Bulletin Board

**Goals:** This bulletin board can be used to illustrate the various pushes and pulls used during play.

**Materials:** construction paper    letters
scissors    light cardboard
crayons    thumbtacks

**Procedure:** Construct the bulletin board as follows: Cover the entire board with construction paper. Decide where you want each of eight figures placed. Cut two parallel slits, three centimeters apart, beneath each figure.

Draw and color each child on light cardboard, including a six-centimeter extension at the bottom of each figure. Cut out figures and insert the extension through one pair of slits on the board. Make sure figures slide freely but fit snugly. You may want to position thumbtacks at each end of the parallel slits to keep the construction paper tight. Have students move the figures within each slot as you discuss the type of force required for each activity. If students note that certain activities, such as running with the kite, contain both pushes and pulls (pulling of kite on string, pushing of feet against ground), praise them for their observations.

## SC Science Center

**Goals:** Students will identify the properties of objects and identify objects by their properties. You may find other suggestions in the margin material suitable for additional science center activities.

**Materials:** objects to study    pencils

**Procedure:** Prepare a worksheet for students. Provide a list of opposite properties as shown below. Properties may include hard/soft, solid/liquid, wet/dry, big/small, heavy/light, cold/hot, smooth/rough, thin/thick, and any other pairs of opposite properties that apply to the objects you use. Students should complete one worksheet for each object. When students have completed the activity, discuss their responses. Then place a different group of objects in the science center. Allow students to match the objects to their worksheets as an evaluation.

| Object _____ | | |
|---|---|---|
| Hard | | Soft |
| Liquid | | Solid |
| Heavy | | Light |

## Places to Go, People to See

### Field Trip Ideas

Take students to a factory that sorts and resells scrap metal. Have the students observe the use of large electromagnets to lift and then release heavy iron objects.

### Speakers and Visitors

Arrange for an electrical appliance repair person to speak to the class. Ask the speaker to demonstrate the use of magnets in the operation of electrical motors.

## Audiovisuals for the Students

 ### Films and Filmstrips

*Things Change: Solids, Liquids, Gases,* 10 min., 16 mm, color, Encyclopaedia Britannica Educational Corp.

*Magnets, the Dragon's Secret,* 16 mm, 15 min., color, Encyclopaedia Britannica Educational Corp.

 ### Videotapes

*Things Change: Solids, Liquids, Gases,* 10 min., color, Encyclopaedia Britannica Educational Corp.

*Magnetism,* 7 min., color, International Film Bureau.

 ### Computer Software

*The Five Senses Series*   Includes four program disks: The Eyes Have It; Now Hear This; Smell and Tell; A Touchy Subject

Type: Tutorial, Simulation, Quiz

Hardware: Apple II +, IIe

Supplier: Marshware

*How Things Work*   A series of graphic simulations that teach students how simple machines work.

Type: Tutorial, Simulation

Hardware: Apple II +, IIe, IIc, IBM PCjr

Supplier: World Book Discovery

## Resources for the Teacher

 ### Materials at Little/No Cost

American Gas Association
Educational Programs
1515 Wilson Blvd.
Arlington, VA 22209
"What is a Gas?" is an activity book designed to help students discover the gaseous state of matter.

Edmund Scientific Co.
Dept. 6101, EE09 Edscorp Bldg.
Barrington, NJ 08007
Send $3.95 for a set of colorful magnetic marbles. The order number is EE34968 for 20 marbles.

 ### Resource Books

Hoyt, Marie A. *Magnet Magic.* New York: Educational Services Press, 1983.

Lee, E. W. *Magnetism: An Introductory Survey.* New York: Dover Publications, 1984.

Lobb, Nancy. *The Five Senses.* Hayward, CA: Janus Books, 1982.

Walton, Alan J. *Three Phases of Matter,* 2nd Edition. New York: Clarendon Press, 1983.

# Physical Science

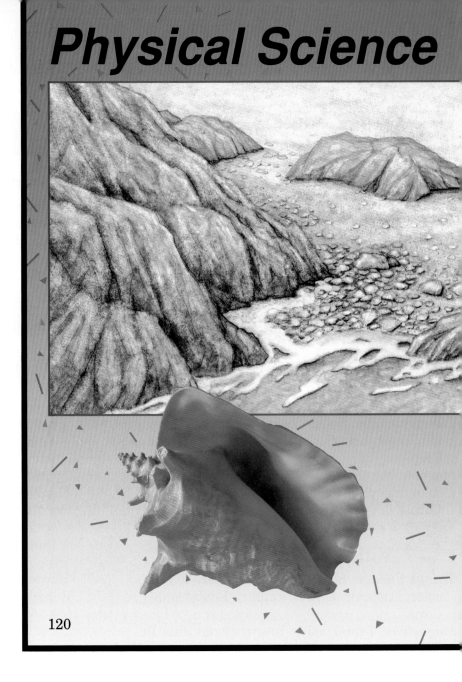

## UNIT CONCEPTS

### Chapter 8
■ We observe by using our senses.
■ Objects are characterized by their properties.
■ We identify solids, liquids, and gases by observing their physical characteristics.

### Chapter 9
■ Objects can move certain distances at various speeds and in different directions.
■ Pushes and pulls are forces that can cause objects to move.
■ People use machines to exert pushes and pulls to do work.

### Chapter 10
■ Magnets can pull or attract some metals such as iron.
■ Magnets can push or repel when the ends or poles are alike.
■ Magnets can have different shapes and sizes and are used in many ways because of their ability to attract and repel.

120

Big rocks into pebbles,

pebbles into sand.

I really hold a million million rocks here in my hand.

"Rocks"
Florence Parry Heide

121

# ACTIVITY CENTER

For fun, hands-on, independent activities that integrate reading, writing, math, and technology with the chapters in this unit, have students complete some or all of the Activity Center Activities below. Look for specific chapter references in the Lesson Planning Guides.

**Reading:** 8 Where Am I? 9 Rhyme Time, 10 Push and Pull
**Writing:** 8 Wet and Wild, 9 Can I Play? 10 Magnet Magic
**Math:** 8 Penny Toss, 9 Crayon Machine, 10 Go Fishing
**Technology:** 8 Cracking Crackers, 9 Wind Up, 10 Magnet Fun

## CONNECTING LITERATURE TO SCIENCE

### Understanding the Selection

■ Ask students to tell about their experiences playing in sand at the beach or in a sandbox.
■ Have students speculate on how sand is formed.
■ Read the poem aloud. Then have students read the poem aloud with you.
■ Ask: **What does the poet say happens to rocks?** *Big rocks become pebbles; pebbles become sand.*
■ Ask: **What might cause a rock to become pebbles?** Lead students in a discussion of what they have observed about rocks that physical forces such as wind and water have changed.

### Relating the Selection to Unit Concepts

■ Ask students what the difference is between the rocks discussed in the poem and the water shown in the illustration. Lead students to discover that rocks are solids and water is a liquid.
■ Draw two cluster diagrams on the board and ask students to look around the classroom or think about things at home and name other things that are solids like rocks and liquids like water. See the example below.

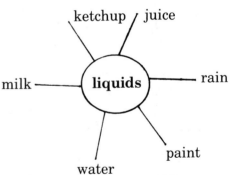

### Relating the Selection to the Student's World

■ Have students identify the small photograph and ask if they have ever collected shells.
■ Help students understand that shells, like rocks, are solids that can break into smaller pieces. Inform students that some sand on beaches is made from shells.
■ Ask students to bring in shells they have collected. Ask them to observe how shells are different and to describe shells by color, size, shape, and so on.

# CHAPTER 8

# *Learning to Observe*

## Planning Guide

| Lessons | Objectives | Vocabulary |
|---|---|---|
| **Chapter Introduction** pp. 122, 123 | | |
| **Lesson 1 Using Your Senses** pp. 124–127 | 1. **Recognize** that our senses allow us to observe objects. <br> 2. **Identify** how our senses react to enable us to make observations. | |
| **Lesson 2 How Are Things Different?** pp. 128–129 | 3. **Observe** and **compare** properties that are opposite. | |
| **Lesson 3 Solid, Liquid or Gas?** pp. 130–135 | 4. **Identify** and **classify** some solids, liquids, and gases. <br> 5. **Describe** some properties of solids, liquids, and gases. | solid <br> liquid <br> gas |
| **Chapter Review** pp. 136, 137 | | |

# Planning Guide

| Text Activities | | Teacher Resource Masters | Other Components |
|---|---|---|---|
| **Title/Skill** | **Materials per Group** | | |
| **Have You Ever . . . Tried Taste Tests?** p. 123<br>Inferring<br>Time Allotment: 30 minutes | milk<br>apple juice<br>saltine crackers<br>3 oz. paper cups | | Activity Center: "Where Am I?"; "Rhyme Time"; "Wet and Wild"; "Penny Toss" |
| **What Is It?** p. 127<br>Classifying/Inferring<br>Time Allotment: 20 minutes<br><br>**What's the Sense?** p. 222<br>Observing/Classifying/Communicating<br>Time Allotment: 30 minutes | mystery bags<br>pencil and paper<br>  (Include items such as<br>  an antique object, a<br>  pineapple, a rolling<br>  pin, and so on)<br><br>paper bag<br>paper<br>crayons<br>yarn | ♦ Family Science, p. 94<br>Activity Worksheet,<br>  p. 95<br>♦ Reteaching Activity,<br>  p. 103<br>Independent Practice,<br>  p. 100<br>Language Arts<br>  Connection,<br>  p. 187, 188, 189 | Poster #5<br>Big Book, p. 29<br>Big Book, p. 30<br>Big Book, p. 31<br>Activity Book, pp. 47, 48 |
| **You Can . . . Do An Experiment,** p. 129<br>Predicting<br>Time Allotment: 20 minutes | dishpan<br>water<br>objects to test<br>(examples include cork,<br>toothpick, clothespin,<br>soap, button, and so on)<br>penicl and paper | ▲ Critical Thinking, p. 98<br>Math Connection, p. 99<br>Independent Practice,<br>  p. 101 | Activity Book, pp. 27, 28 |
| **Is Air There?** p. 134<br>Observing/Communicating<br>Time Allotment: 25 minutes<br><br><br><br>**A Drink of Water,** p. 223<br>Observing/Communicating/Inferring<br>Time Allotment: 30 minutes | a pattern<br>construction paper<br>scissors<br>paper clip<br>pencil<br><br>drinking cup<br>paper<br>pencil | Transparency Master,<br>  p. 93<br>ActivityWorksheet,p.96<br>Critical Thinking, p. 97<br>Independent Practice,<br>  p. 102<br>Language Arts<br>  Connection, p. 190 | Activity Book, pp. 29, 30<br>Big Book, p. 32<br>Activity Book, pp. 49, 50 |
| | | Test A, p. 104<br>Test B, p. 105 | Color Transparencies<br>#8a and #8b<br>Software: "What Will Happen?" |

♦ Basic / ▲ Advanced / All other masters are for use by all students.

# Learning to Observe

## For Exceptional Students

## ESL/LEP

### Chapter 8/Lesson 3, Page 133

Have each student make two sets of word cards using the following vocabulary words: *observe, liquid, solid,* and *gas.* Mix up the cards, then see if students can find matching pairs. As each match is made, students should say the word aloud.

### Chapter 8/Lesson 3, Page 133

Bring in a number of items, both liquid and solid. Have students sort the items on a table. Label one half of the table *solids* and the other *liquids.* You may want to make a class list of the solids and liquids you sort. Ask students to tell how they decided whether an item is a solid or liquid.

## Gifted

### Chapter 8/Lesson 1, Page 127

Try an experiment. Bring in a lemon, an orange, and an onion. Cut each in half. Put each into a separate closed container. Punch holes in the container. Have a simple chart prepared:

| Student | Lemon | Orange | Onion |
|---------|-------|--------|-------|
| 1       |       |        |       |
| 2       |       |        |       |
| 3       |       |        |       |

Ask each student to select three friends on which to try the experiment. Each student will ask the friends to identify the objects by their odors. Then have students record their results. Ask the following questions.
1. How many of your group could name what was inside?
2. Why do you think they could?
3. Which, in your opinion, was the most pleasant smell?
4. What other kinds of things could you use for this experiment? Why would you choose these?

## Mainstreamed

### Chapter 8/Lesson 2, Page 129

**Visually Impaired:** Provide students with clay. Have them form several shapes (square, circle, cube, cylinder) from the same piece of clay. Ask them to describe the features of each figure.

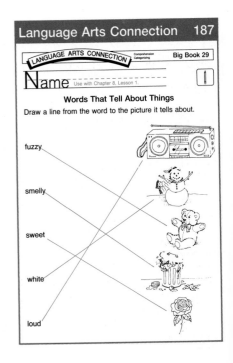

## Whole Class Science Project

Exhibit to students pairs of objects, materials, or pictures of objects and ask them to tell: 1) ways in which the objects are alike; 2) ways in which the objects are different; and 3) whether they think both objects are really the same but changed in some way. Select objects that have many similarities as well as objects that have opposite characteristics. When appropriate, have students handle and examine the objects. Some possible pairs are ice and water, tree seedling and large tree, clean steel and rusty steel, sand and salt, dough and baked bread, cotton balls and cotton cloth, styrene plastic foam and styrene plastic toy, empty and inflated balloon, new candle and burned candle, pictures of a dog and a bear, and a tadpole and a frog. After completing the activity, challenge students to bring in objects that are the same material but in different forms. Be sure to notify parents and invite their help in selecting safe and appropriate materials.

## Science Fair Projects

Individual students could do one of the following projects:

1. Take a lump of clay and experiment with different shapes to test its ability to float. Place objects such as washers inside the "boat." Find a shape that will keep the most washers afloat.
2. Closely observe samples of molded gelatin and/or peanut butter. Make a chart telling how each material is like both a solid and a liquid.
3. Give students the opportunity to mix primary paint colors to make secondary colors.

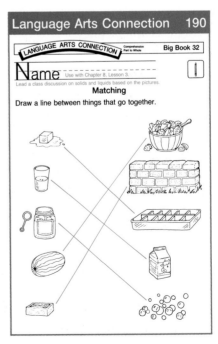

# CHAPTER

## 8

pages 122–137

## Chapter Concepts

■ We observe by using our senses.
■ We identify solids, liquids, and gases by observing their physical characteristics.

## Chapter Background

■ The scientific method is a method used by scientists to find an answer or to solve a problem. The steps of the scientific method include (a) stating the problem, (b) predicting an answer, (c) experimenting, (d) recording observations, and (e) forming a conclusion.
■ Scientists use all of their senses to gather information. This process is called making observations. A scientist's notes about his/her observations are called data.

## Looking Ahead

■ Ask a high school chemistry student or otherwise skilled person to do some safe, exciting experiments with matter to **Close** Lesson 3.

## Look for These Symbols

    —Hands-on activity
    —Cooperative learning
    —Overhead transparency
◆  —Basic/Reinforcement
●  —Average/Enrichment
▲  —Advanced/Challenge
SC —Science Center
    —Calculator Practice

SCIENCE
In Your World

122

# CHAPTER 8

# *Learning to Observe*

Have you ever been to the beach?

Have you ever walked in the city?

What did your senses tell you?

## ACTIVITY
## Have You Ever...

### Tried Taste Tests?

**1.** Do a taste test.

**2.** First taste milk.

**3.** Now taste a cracker.

**4.** Try some juice.

What can you tell about each food?

123

## PREPLAN

**Time Allotment:** 30 minutes

### Objectives
**1. Recognize** how to use senses to make observations.
**2. Infer** that different foods can be identified using the sense of taste.

### Setup
To conduct the activity, collect the following materials for each student or **cooperative learning group:**

| | |
|---|---|
| milk | saltine crackers |
| apple juice | 3 oz. paper cups |

## 1   FOCUS

■ Discuss the pictures on pages 122, 123.

## 2   TEACH

■ Read the chapter title and introductory paragraph.
■ Encourage students to describe places they have visited and explain how they use their senses to make observations.

### Have You Ever . . .
■ **Trouble Shooting:** To save time and to avoid spills, you may want to set up cups with small amounts of juice and milk before you begin this activity.

### Student Responses
■ The milk was cold; the juice was sour; the cracker was salty.

## 3   APPLY

■ Ask students what other senses they could use to learn about milk, juice, and crackers. Invite students to compare what they learn by using each sense.

### Close
■ Tell students that you will be learning about other senses you use to observe as you do Chapter 8.

## PREPLAN

### Lesson Objectives

**1. Recognize** that our senses allow us to observe objects.

**2. Identify** how our senses react to enable us to make observations.

### Science Background

■ The purpose of this lesson is not to teach the senses but rather to show that we describe the properties of the world and the things in it by using the senses.

■ Scientists describe the world in terms of what they learn through the senses. Even instruments that sense and measure must communicate their results to the human senses.

■ The senses discussed are seeing, hearing, feeling (tactile), tasting, and smelling (olfactory). Other senses include heat, pain, pressure, balance, and the sense of position of body parts (kinesthetic sense).

### Lesson Vocabulary

observe

**Note:** The activity on student page 127 may be used for guided discovery before you begin this lesson.

## 1   FOCUS

■ Gather some common objects such as a plastic cup, drinking straw, a wet sponge, wadded paper, piece of fruit, metal spoon, shoelace, balloon, or rubber ball. Hold up the objects one at a time. Ask students to give words that describe the object. Write the words on the chalkboard. Guide student participation with questions such as: What would it feel like? What sounds does it make? Try to get a list of words that include using each of the senses to describe properties.

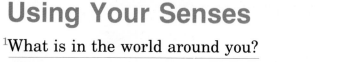

# Using Your Senses

[1]What is in the world around you?

[2]How can you find out?

1. Have students discuss people, places, and objects they find in their environment
2. Lead students to discover how their senses play a major role in learning about the environment.

124

## TEACHER RESOURCE MASTERS

You find out when you **observe.**

You observe with your eyes and your ears.

You observe with your nose and your tongue.

You observe with your hands.
1. seeing, hearing, touching, tasting, and smelling

[1]How could you observe things at the beach?

125

## TEACHER RESOURCE MASTERS

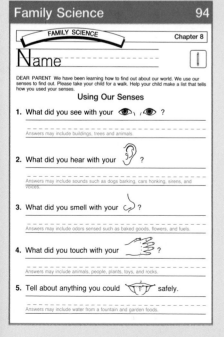

| Family Science | 94 |
|---|---|

**DEAR PARENT** We have been learning how to find out about our world. We use our senses to find out. Please take your child for a walk. Help your child make a list that tells how you used your senses.

**Using Our Senses**

1. What did you see with your 👁 , 👁 ?

Answers may include buildings, trees and animals.

2. What did you hear with your 👂 ?

Answers may include sounds such as dogs barking, cars honking, sirens, and voices.

3. What did you smell with your 👃 ?

Answers may include odors sensed such as baked goods, flowers, and fuels.

4. What did you touch with your ✋ ?

Answers may include animals, people, plants, toys, and rocks.

5. Tell about anything you could 👅 safely.

Answers may include water from a fountain and garden foods.

| Independent Practice 1 | 100 |
|---|---|

1. Write the words where they belong.  obj. 1 & 2

see  smell  hear  taste  feel

hear

see

smell

taste

feel

2. Draw a picture of something you like to smell.

Drawings will vary. Accept all reasonable answers.

3. Draw a picture of something you like to taste.  obj. 2

## 2 TEACH

■ Ask students to pretend that they must tell someone who has never seen an orange what peeling and eating one is like.
🖐 Display several balls that differ in size, color, surface texture, firmness, or weight. List the properties of each ball.

### Guided Practice
🖐 Choose a few students and have them put on a blindfold or close their eyes. Place several objects on their desks. Ask them to use their sense of touch to place the objects into groups.
■ If necessary, use the **reteaching strategy** in OPTIONS.

### Independent Practice
■ Use the Teacher Resource Master **Independent Practice,** page 100.

## 3 APPLY

■ Use Application Activity, "What's the Sense?," on student page 222.

### Close
🖐 🆂🅲 Allow students to collect some natural objects they find and share them with the class. Have the class describe each object by its properties.

## OPTIONS

### Reteaching Strategy
🖐 Write the words *smell, taste, feel, see,* and *hear* on the chalkboard. Present an object and point to one of the senses on the board. Ask students to describe one thing about the object by using that sense. You may want to point to more than one sense for a given object. Choose objects with obvious properties such as fruit, vegetables, a file, something that makes music or noise, and so on.

### Resource Options
■ Use Poster #5, "The Birthday Piñata."

# OPTIONS

## LANGUAGE CONNECTION

**Writing:** Read *The Look Book* by Jane Belk Moncure to your students. Have students write a story about their favorite thing to see. Students should capture their ideas in the first draft, then elaborate on their ideas in subsequent drafts.

## MATH CONNECTION

Use pattern blocks to make a simple pattern. Have a student continue the pattern by adding a block with the next shape. Say the pattern aloud to check. Repeat, using other patterns.

▲ **Reinforcement:** Place an object in a "feely" box or bag. Have students take turns giving one word at a time that describes what they observe when they handle the object.

● **Enrichment:** Introduce ways to use two or more properties to describe objects. Place several objects in a large paper bag. Without looking, have students take turns putting their hands in the bag and identifying each object by two propertie .

## Resource Options

■ Use Big Book, page 29, "Did You Ever Taste a Raisin" and Teacher Resource Master **Language Arts Connection,** page 187.
■ Use Big Book, page 30, "Colors Can Change" and Teacher Resource Master **Language Arts Connection,** page 188.
■ Use Big Book, page 31, "Casey, The Curious Kitten" and Teacher Resource Master **Language Arts Connection,** page 189.
■ Use Activity Book, pages 47 and 48, "What's the Sense?"

Suppose you could touch and smell this orange. Pretend you could taste it.

1. the rough texture of the oran  peeling, the soft pulp, the stick  juice, the sweet/sour taste

[1]What would your senses observe?

126

Use Application Activity on page 222.

# TEACHER RESOURCE MASTERS

Reteaching Activity                103

RETEACHING ACTIVITY            Chapter 8

Name

Which Sense?

What sense are these children using?
Write see, hear, smell, taste, or touch.

see

taste (smell)

touch

smell

hear

# What is it?

ACTIVITY

## What you need

mystery bags

pencil and paper

## What to do

1. Feel and shake each bag.

2. Shake each bag and listen.

3. What do you observe?

4. What do you find out?

127

## ACTIVITY RESPONSES

Accept all reasonable student responses to questions during any activity discussion.

## PREPLAN

**Time Allotment:** 20 minutes

**Process Skills:** Classifying/Inferring

### Objectives

1. **Observe** objects using the senses.

2. **Draw conclusions** about properties of objects based on observations.

### Setup

Gather some objects that have relatively simple characteristics. Place the objects in paper bags.

**Cooperative Grouping:** fours—Assign roles as explained on page T24.

## 1  FOCUS

■ In full view of students, place a familiar object into a paper bag. Ask students to pretend they do not know what is in the bag. Have different students handle the bag with the object and tell something they find out about the object by using their senses.

## 2  TEACH

■ **Safety Consideration:** Choose objects that do not have sharp edges, will not break, and are not too heavy.

■ Use the Teacher Resource Master **Activity Worksheet,** page 95.

## 3  APPLY

■ Record observations made about each object and write them on the chalkboard. Students have observed properties of each object. While it is not necessary that students learn the word *property* at this level, you may wish to introduce it.

### Close

■ Explain to students that they have just carried out a scientific experiment. Introduce the steps of the scientific method. See page 150 under FOCUS for steps to follow.

## PREPLAN

**Lesson Objective**

**3. Observe** and **compare** properties that are opposite.

**Science Background**

■ This lesson focuses on the way we compare and contrast matter by using the senses.

■ Each observable characteristic of a certain piece of matter is a property of that piece. We can observe these properties and use them to compare objects.

## 1 FOCUS

■ Read *Jack and Jake* by Aliki to your students. Ask students to tell you how Jack and Jake are different? How does their big sister feel when people can't tell Jack and Jake apart? How do you think Jack and Jake feel? Have students write a story telling how they are different from everyone else.

## OPTIONS

### YOU CAN . . . DO AN EXPERIMENT

**Process Skill:** Predicting

**Objective: Predict** whether objects will sink or float.

**Setup/Teach**

Gather an assortment of household and schoolroom materials that student pairs can test in a dish pan of water. Examples may include cork, toothpick, clothespin, soap, or a button. Be sure to gather several things that sink and several that float.

■ Show students how to record predictions and results.

# How Are Things Different?

Think about each of these things. [1]Tell how they are different.

1. Have students c
the opposite proper
the objects in the
illustrations.

pleasant odor, unpleasant odor          hot, cold

sweet, sour

128

## TEACHER RESOURCE MASTERS

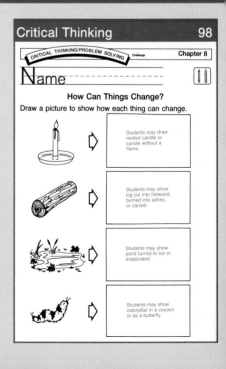

Critical Thinking                98

CRITICAL THINKING/PROBLEM SOLVING  Challenge          Chapter 8

**N**ame

**How Can Things Change?**

Draw a picture to show how each thing can change.

Students may draw melted candle or candle without a flame.

Students may show log cut into firewood, burned into ashes, or carved.

Students may show pond turned to ice or evaporated.

Students may show caterpillar in a cocoon or as a butterfly.

loud, soft

rough, smooth

129

**ACTIVITY**

# You Can...

## Do an Experiment
Get some things to test.
Guess which ones float or sink.
Test to see if you are right.

## TEACHER RESOURCE MASTERS

## 2 TEACH

■ Have students study each grouping pictured on these two pages. Ask them to tell how each pair in a group is opposite to the other pair in the group.
■ Ask students what senses they would have to use to discover the differences that exist within each group.

### Guided Practice
■ Play an opposites game. Have students brainstorm to make a list of words that could be used to describe something (adjectives). Then, have them suggest another list of the opposites.
■ If necessary, use the **reteaching strategy** in OPTIONS.

### Independent Practice
■ Use the Teacher Resource Master **Independent Practice,** page 101.

## 3 APPLY

Use a "feely" bag that contains objects with various textures. As students feel the texture of an object, they should identify the texture, pull the object from the bag, and ask a fellow student to name something in the room that has an opposite texture.

### Close
■ List some properties on the chalkboard. Ask students to write the opposite properties.

## OPTIONS

### Reteaching Strategy
■ Have students keep a list of opposite words. The list might be used to write and illustrate a story book.
■ Refer to page 128 for a teaching strategy for You Can . . . Do an Experiment.

### Resource Options
■ Use Activity Book, pages 27 and 28, "Observing."

## PREPLAN

### Lesson Objectives
**4. Identify** and **classify** some solids, liquids, and gases.

**5. Describe** some properties of solids, liquids, and gases.

### Science Background
■ In this lesson, observation is used to help students discover the main properties that differentiate solids, liquids, and gases.

■ Solid, liquid, and gaseous states of the same matter differ in physical properties such as shape and volume. These differences are due to differences in the motion and spacing of particles. In solids, the particles are locked into a characteristic geometric pattern. Though the particles are in constant motion, they vibrate within their geometric pattern. Thus, solids have a definite size (volume) and shape. Particles in liquids vibrate rapidly enough to overcome some of their mutual attraction so that they tumble over one another. Thus, liquids take the shapes of their containers. Gaseous particles travel rapidly enough to overcome mutual attraction. They have no definite volume or shape.

### Lesson Vocabulary
solid          liquid          gas

**Note:** The activity on student page 134 may be used for guided discovery before you begin this lesson.

## 1  FOCUS

■ Display some common liquids, solids, and objects that are filled with air (gas). Ask students to name some properties of each.

**Career:** Use "I Want To Know About . . . an Ice Sculptor," student page 135, with this lesson.

# Solid, Liquid, or Gas?

Some things are solids.

A **solid** has a shape.

1. Have students name the obvious solid objects.

[1]Can you name some solid things?

130

## TEACHER RESOURCE MASTERS

Some things are liquids.

You can pour a **liquid.**

Liquids do not have a shape of their own.

Use Application Activity on page 223.

131

## 2 TEACH

■ **Problem Solving:** Use several empty clear plastic containers of different shapes that will hold liquid, a solid block that will fit in all the containers, and a pitcher of water that has been colored with food coloring. Then, without comment, place the block in the first container, "pour" the block from the first into the second, and so on. Lay the block aside, pour liquid into the first container, and then into the second, and so on. Have students tell what they observed and ask how the liquid was different from the solid.

Have students blow up a beach ball or balloon and allow them to feel the air pushing out as it expands.

### Guided Practice

■ Prepare a large chart for the class. Have students write answers under: What I Know About . . . Solids/Liquids/Gases.

■ If necessary, use the **reteaching strategy** in OPTIONS.

### Independent Practice

■ Use the Teacher Resource Master **Independent Practice,** page 102.

## 3 APPLY

■ Use Application Activity, "A Drink of Water," on student page 223.

### Close

■ Invite a high school chemistry student to do some exciting but safe experiments with solids, liquids, or gases.

## OPTIONS

### Reteaching Strategy

Ask students to **work cooperatively** and cut out magazine pictures of solids, liquids, and objects to represent gases. Have them classify the pictures and paste them on a poster.

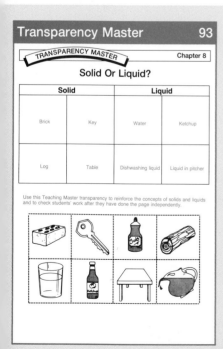

**Transparency Master** 93

TRANSPARENCY MASTER Chapter 8

**Solid Or Liquid?**

| Solid | | Liquid | |
|---|---|---|---|
| Brick | Key | Water | Ketchup |
| Log | Table | Dishwashing liquid | Liquid in pitcher |

Use this Teaching Master transparency to reinforce the concepts of solids and liquids and to check students' work after they have done the page independently.

**Independent Practice 3** 102

INDEPENDENT PRACTICE Lesson 3 Chapter 8

**Name**

Circle the liquids and gases. obj. 4 & 5

Students should circle water at the fountain, milk being poured, water in the pond, and should indicate gases as present in balloon and in the air.

Draw lines to the pictures that go together. obj. 4

# OPTIONS

## LANGUAGE CONNECTION

**Writing:** Have students make up a story about what it would be like if liquids could not be poured or did have their own shape. Once the first draft has been completed, have students look over their stories and add any descriptive words that would make their stories clearer or more effective.

## LANGUAGE CONNECTION

**Writing:** Have students write or dictate on a tape recorder a story entitled "My Life as an Ice Cube." Once the first draft has been completed, students can share their stories with a friend.

● **Enrichment:** Have students name some things they have seen change from solid to liquid or liquid to solid. These might include water, candle wax, and plastic.

▲ **Challenge:** Melt a small amount of paraffin in a small pan on a hot plate and show students the melted wax. Cool the pan in cold water until the wax solidifies. Show the solid wax to students and have them compare the properties of the solid and liquid wax.

## Resource Options

■ Use Big Book, page 32, "Where Does It Go?" and Teacher Resource Master **Language Arts Connection** page 190.
■ Use Activity Book, pages 29 and 30, "Observing."
■ Use Activity Book, pages 49 and 50, "A Drink of Water."

Some things are gases.

A **gas** does not have its own shape.

A gas can fill up a space.

132

# TEACHER RESOURCE MASTERS

Air fills up a space.

What gives this balloon a new shape?   1. air

What is air?   2. gas

133

## TEACHER RESOURCE MASTERS

Critical Thinking                    97

CRITICAL THINKING/PROBLEM SOLVING  Inferring    Chapter 8

Name

**What Does It Need?**

Fill each thing with air.
Draw what it will look like.

Students' drawings should reflect that all objects inflate when filled with air.

## OPTIONS

■ Have students draw and color pictures contrasting a solid object with a liquid and an object filled with a gas. Allow students to decide what to draw. Look for expressions of the ideas that solids maintain a certain shape, that liquids flow and take the shape of their container, and that gases can expand to fill the shape of their container. Have students tell about their drawings. Ask them questions relating to the properties of solids, liquids and gases. Ask: **If the solid object were real, how might you change its shape?** *Possible answers might include heating it, pressing, pounding, or bending.* **What would happen if you poured the liquid into something else?** *It would take the shape of the new container.* **What would your object look like if the gas escaped?** *The object would be deflated.*

■ Have students name foods they have seen changes in at home. While most changes mentioned may represent changes that make the foods inedible, encourage students to tell about other changes observed in cooking, mixing, canning, or freezing foods.

■ Have students name other ways they use or can have fun with air. The students may not be aware of having fun with air when they play with balloons, fly flags or banners, play with pinwheels, fly airplanes, or catch falling leaves.

## PREPLAN

**Time Allotment:** 25 minutes

**Process Skills:** Observing/Communicating

### Objectives

1. **Observe** the effects of air.
2. **Construct** an air spinner.

### Setup

■ The spinners can be made from construction paper. Use a paper clip at the bottom for best results.

■ The Teacher Resource Master **Activity Worksheet,** page 96, has a pattern for an air spinner.

🙌 Have students work in **cooperative pairs** to collect data and record observations.

## 1   FOCUS

■ Ask students for evidence that air exists. If students can't think of any evidence, blow up a paper lunch bag. Ask: **What is this bag filled with?** *air*

## 2   TEACH

🙌 Provide students with a pattern for making an air spinner. Have students construct air spinners like the one shown in the diagram.

## 3   APPLY

■ Lead students to recognize that the air in the room affected the motion of their spinners. Relate this to planes, gliders, birds, and helicopters.

### Close

■ Discuss the results of the activity with students. Challenge students to construct a spinner that moves faster, always turns right, or so on.

**ACTIVITY**

# Is air there?

## What you need

a pattern          construction paper          scissors

paper clip          pencil

## What to do

1. Use the pattern to make a spinner.

2. Hold the spinner high.

3. Watch it fall.

4. What happens to the spinner?

5. What does air do?

134

## ACTIVITY RESPONSES

Accept all reasonable student responses to questions during any activity discussion.

# I WANT TO KNOW ABOUT...

## *An Ice Sculptor*

Jean Pierre Frémont is a sculptor.
He makes sculptures out of ice.
He begins with a huge block of ice.
Then he carves it into a shape.
The sculpture is used for a party.
[1]What happens to it after the party?

1. Discuss how the ice as a solid may change to liquid water.

*Career*

## TEACHER RESOURCE MASTERS

### Feature Background
■ Ice is the solid form of water. A solid has a definite shape and volume. When the temperature of the ice warms to 0°C, the ice melts.
■ Water is a liquid. A liquid has no definite shape, but it does have a definite volume. At normal atmospheric pressure, the melting and freezing point of water is 0°C.
■ Melting is a physical change. A physical change does not alter the chemical composition of the material. During a physical change, only the form of the material changes. Other physical changes are tearing, breaking, cutting, and boiling.

### Feature Vocabulary
sculptor
sculpture
carve

### Teaching Suggestions
■ Ask: **Where must an ice sculptor work in order to keep a sculpture from melting?** *The sculptor must work in a walk-in freezer.*
■ Ask students if they have ever seen an ice sculpture. Have them describe the sculpture. Ask students how the sculpture changed as it melted.
■ Freeze water in a mold. Have students observe the shape and discuss how it changes as it melts. Compare the shape made by the mold to carved shapes.
■ Discuss other materials that can be carved and the skills needed to carve. Invite someone who does carving to your classroom.
■ Involve students in making shapes from clay, sand, or soap flakes molded over cardboard shapes. Discuss how shapes can be changed. Answers may indicate adding heat or a liquid.

pages 136, 137

**Chapter Closure:** Use these pages to review and reinforce chapter concepts.

## What I Learned

Have students read the rebus summary statements aloud to be sure they interpret the pictures correctly. After each sentence, discuss other words that would also make the sentences true.

## Words I Know

Use any or all of the following suggestions to reinforce the chapter vocabulary.

Write each science word or word group on the chalkboard. Ask students to read them. Add the words to the class science list or have students write the words in their individual science word books. Ask students to tell about these words to help you evaluate their comprehension. Have students use each science word or word group in a sentence.

## CHAPTER REVIEW
## 8

# What I Learned

- You find out when you observe.
- You observe with your   ,  ,

  eyes    ears

   ,  , and  .

  nose  tongue    hands

- Things can be different.
- Things can be a [solid], a [liquid], or a [gas].

  solid    liquid    gas

# Words I Know

observe  solid  liquid  gas

136

# TEACHER RESOURCE MASTERS

Test A    104

**TEST A** Recalling Facts Chapter 8

**N**ame _____ Each question is worth 14 points.

Use the words in the box to finish each sentence. obj. 1 & 2

| air | gas | liquid | water |
|-----|-----|--------|-------|

1. You can see ___water___.
2. You cannot see ___air___.
3. Water is a ___liquid___.
4. Air is a ___gas___.
5. Draw lines to tell which is a solid, liquid, or gas. obj. 1 & 2

solid  liquid  gas

## What I Know

*Use the picture to answer the questions.*

1. What sounds might you hear?
2. Which things would taste sweet?
3. Which things would feel cold?
4. Which things are liquids?
5. Which things are solids?

137

## What I Know

Have students refer to the picture to answer the questions and extend concepts.

1. Sounds you might hear include the voices and laughter of people, the crackling of the fire, the wind, and so on.
2. Hot chocolate and marshmellows would taste sweet.
3. The air, the ice, the snow and so on would feel cold.
4. Liquids include the water under the ice and the hot chocolate.
5. Solids include the snow, the ice, skates, firewood, trees, and so on.

## OPTIONS

### Resource Options

Use Color Transparencies #8a and #8b.

## TEACHER RESOURCE MASTERS

Test B                                                105

TEST B          Understanding/          Chapter 8
                Applying Concepts

Name   Each question is worth 11 points.

1. Use red to circle the hot things.   obj. 3
   Use blue to **X** the cold things.

2. Draw a line from each sense to one thing in the picture.   obj. 1 & 2

Answers will vary but should reflect the senses.

3. Circle the thing that can change to a liquid.   obj. 1 & 2

# CHAPTER
## 9

# *What Are Forces?*

## Planning Guide

| Lessons | Objectives | Vocabulary |
|---------|-----------|------------|
| **Chapter Introduction** pp. 138, 139 | | |
| **Lesson 1 Moving Things** pp. 140–143 | 1. **Describe** the relative distance, position, and motion of objects. | move |
| **Lesson 2 Push, Pull, or Lift** pp. 144–147 | 2. **Infer** that people can move objects by pushing, pulling, or lifting. 3. **Explain** that pushing, pulling, and lifting are forces. 4. **Describe** how forces can change the way something moves. 5. **Recognize** gravity as a pulling force. | pull push force gravity |
| **Lesson 3 Doing Work** pp. 148–151 | 6. **Recognize** that people use machines to do work. 7. **Infer** that machines can be simple or complex. | work machine |
| **Chapter Review** pp. 152, 153 | | |

# Planning Guide

| Text Activities | | Teacher Resource Masters | Other Components |
|---|---|---|---|
| **Title/Skill** | **Materials per Group** | | |
| **Have you Ever . . . Played Tug-of-War?** p. 139<br>Inferring<br>Time Allotment: 20 minutes | thick jute yarn | | **Activity Center:** "Push and Pull"; "Can I Play?"; "Crayon Machine"; "Wind Up" |
| **How Do Things Move?** p. 143<br>Classifying/Communicating<br>Time Allotment: 30 minutes | chart<br>graph<br>crayons<br>pencil | Activity Worksheet, p. 109<br>Independent Practice, p. 114<br>Language Arts Connection, p. 191 | Big Book, p. 33 |
| **You Can . . . Observe a Force,** p. 147<br>Observing<br>Time Allotment: 15 minutes | books<br>ramp (board)<br>ball | Activity Worksheet, p. 110<br>Critical Thinking, p. 111<br>▲ Critical Thinking, p. 112<br>Math Connection, p. 113<br>◆ Reteaching Activity, p. 117<br>Independent Practice, p. 115<br>Language Arts Connection, p. 192 | Poster #6<br>Big Book, p. 34 |
| **How Can You Make a Machine?** p. 150<br>Predicting<br>Time Allotment: 2/20 minute periods | 6 heavy books<br>pencil and paper | Transparency Master, p. 107<br>◆ Family Science, p. 108<br>Independent Practice, p. 116<br>Language Arts Connection, pp. 193, 194 | Big Book, p. 35<br>Big Book, p. 36 |
| | | Test A, p. 118<br>Test B, p. 119 | Color Transparencies #9a and #9b<br>Software: "What Will Happen?" |

◆ Basic / ▲ Advanced / All other masters are for use by all students.

# CHAPTER 9

# *What Are Forces?*

## For Exceptional Students

## ESL/LEP

**Chapter 9/Lesson 2, Page 146**
Have each student make word cards with the following words: *push, pull,* and *lift.* Show students different items in your classroom. Ask students to show you the word card that tells how you make the item move. Or have students place their word cards in a bag or bowl. Students then pick a word card and find an item in the classroom that demonstrates the word.

**Chapter 9/Lesson 2, Page 146**
Play a game with vocabulary words. Be sure to include the words *force, gravity,* and *machine.* Choose a word. On the chalkboard draw enough blank lines for each letter of the word. Students take turns choosing letters. If the chosen letter appears in the word, write it in the appropriate blank(s). Students then guess what the word is. When the word is complete, have students read the word aloud.

## Gifted

**Chapter 9/Lesson 2, Page 146**
Talk about the movement of parts of instruments when they are played. Some musicians use pushes while others use pulls to play instruments. For example, a harpist pulls (plucks) the strings of a harp, a pianist pushes the keys of a piano, and a hammer inside the piano hits (pushes) a wire which vibrates to produce a musical note. Ask students to name other instruments that are played by pushes and pulls.

## Mainstreamed

**Chapter 9/Lesson 2, Page 146**

**Developmentally Handicapped:** Show students pictures of machines that push or pull, such as a tractor, snow plow, or tow truck. Ask students to identify the machine and describe the type of work that it does.

---

**Language Arts Connection**    **191**

LANGUAGE ARTS CONNECTION    Composition Rhymes    **Big Book 33**

Name    Use with Chapter 9, Lesson 1.

**Moving Things**

Change each word on the left.
Think of a word that rhymes.
Think of things that move.

goat  ⟶  <u>b</u> oat
tar  ⟶  <u>c</u> ar
hike  ⟶  <u>b</u> ike
grain  ⟶  <u>t</u> <u>r</u> ain
mane  ⟶  <u>p</u> <u>l</u> ane
dragon  ⟶  <u>w</u> agon

# Projects to Do

## Whole Class Science Project

Bring in a collection of simple tools and scrap pieces of wood, nails, screws, nuts and bolts. You may want to have different-sized holes drilled into one short 2″ × 4″ board for students to try using screwdrivers and wrenches. Provide an area of the room where students can work during free play time.

## Science Fair Projects

Individual students could do one of the following projects:

1. Make a collection of magnets of different shapes. Compare the pulling force of each using units of mass such as paper clips.
2. Compare the pulling force of a horseshoe magnet for a large iron nail when various objects are placed between the magnet and the nail. Place objects such as a pane of acrylic, various thicknesses of cardboard, or plywood, between the magnet and the nail.
3. Make a display of machines that use pulls and pushes as they do work.
4. Make a display of mechanical toys that require either a push or a pull in order to operate.

| Language Arts Connection 192 | Language Arts Connection 193 | Language Arts Connection 194 |
|---|---|---|

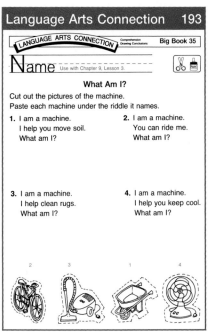

# CHAPTER 9

pages 138–153

## Chapter Concepts
■ Objects can move certain distances at various speeds and in different directions.
■ Pushes and pulls are forces that can cause objects to move.
■ People use machines to exert pushes and pulls to do work.

## Chapter Background
■ This chapter deals, in a general way, with Newton's first and second laws of motion. In one form, these laws state that a force is required to change the motion of an object, and that the greater the mass of the object, the more force needed to change its motion. Most students will easily sense the truth of these ideas intuitively without having them stated formally. Note that change in motion means starting, stopping, or changing direction.

## Looking Ahead
■ You will need a library book that describes how to make a booklet with sequential pages to show an object in motion to **Close**, Lesson 1.
■ To **Close** Lesson 2, ask a collector of antique toys to bring a few toys from his or her collection to display and discuss with the class.

## Look for These Symbols

   —Hands-on activity

   —Cooperative learning

   —Overhead transparency

◆   —Basic/Reinforcement

●   —Average/Enrichment

▲   —Advanced/Challenge

   —Science Center

   —Calculator Practice

SCIENCE
In Your World

138

# CHAPTER 9

# *What Are Forces?*

What things can move?

What things cannot?

What makes things move?

## Have You Ever...

### Played Tug-of-War?

1. Sit across from a friend.

2. Hold one end of a rope.

3. Have a friend hold the other.

4. Pull on the rope.

What happens?

139

## PREPLAN

**Time Allotment:** 20 minutes

### Objectives

1. **Discuss** things that can and cannot move.
2. **Infer** that force is needed to move an object.

### Setup

To conduct the activity, collect the following materials for each student or **cooperative learning** group:
thick jute yarn

## 1   FOCUS

- Discuss the pictures on pages 138, 139.

## 2   TEACH

- Have the title and introductory paragraph read aloud.
- Ask: **Do all things move?** *no* **What are some ways we move things?** *by pushing and pulling them*

### Have You Ever . . .

- Have one student gently pull on one end of the yarn. Then have another student pull harder on the other end. Compare the different movements.

### Student Responses

- When we each pull on an end of the yarn, the yarn gets very tight.

## 3   APPLY

- Help students see that pushing on each end of yarn does not have the same results as pulling.

### Close

- Brainstorm a list to identify instances of pulling and pushing. Demonstrate some. For instance, hold a book between your hands by pushing on either end.

pages 140–143

## PREPLAN

### Lesson Objective
1. **Describe** the relative distance, position, and motion of objects.

### Science Background
■ Motion can be defined as the movement of an object from one location to another.
■ Motion can be described by both direction and speed.

**Note:** The activity on student page 143 may be used for guided discovery before you begin this lesson.

### Lesson Vocabulary
move

## 1  FOCUS

■ Ask students to observe a bulletin board, chalkboard, or wall area. Ask them to close their eyes while you move some object to a different position in the same area. Ask them to open their eyes and observe again. Ask: **What has changed? How has it changed?** Emphasize that the object has moved. Repeat the game several times making it a little more difficult to find the object that moved.

# Moving Things

[1] What has moved?

[2] What did not move?

[3] How can you tell?

1. spider
2. fly
3. can observe change in spider's position

Things that **move** change their place.

140

## TEACHER RESOURCE MASTERS

These kites move in the air.

They move up and down.

They move right or left.

¹Which kite is near the ground?

²Which kite is high above?

³What makes the kite move?

1–2. Have students
identify each kite by
color and position.
3. wind, people

141

## TEACHER RESOURCE MASTERS

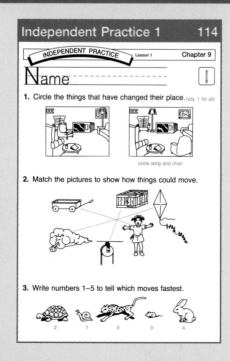

Independent Practice 1     114

INDEPENDENT PRACTICE   Lesson 1   Chapter 9

Name

1. Circle the things that have changed their place. (obj. 1 for all)

circle lamp and chair

2. Match the pictures to show how things could move.

3. Write numbers 1–5 to tell which moves fastest.

2   1   5   3   4

## 2   TEACH

■ Identify objects that move fast and those that move slow. Discuss what makes them move.

⊞ ⊞ Set up relay races. Choose races that ask students to move slowly, to move fast, or to change directions. Students may **work cooperatively** in teams for the races.

### Guided Practice

■ Make a list of things that move and tell someone else how each moves. Include both direction and speed.

■ If necessary, use the **reteaching strategy** in OPTIONS.

### Independent Practice

■ Use the Teacher Resource Master **Independent Practice,** page 114.

## 3   APPLY

■ Have the students look out the window and find a moving object. Ask them to identify the object and tell what direction it is moving, such as up-down, right-left, or toward-away.

### Close

SC ⊞ Have students make small booklets that have sequential pages to show an object in motion when pages are turned rapidly.

## OPTIONS

### Reteaching Strategy

Encourage a volunteer student to pantomime a movement of an animal. Ask students to identify size and the motion of the animal.

### Resource Options

■ Use Big Book, page 33 "The Paper Boat" and Teacher Resource Master **Language Arts Connection,** page 191.

# OPTIONS

### LANGUAGE CONNECTION

**Writing:** Have students think about what kind of machine they would like to be. Would they be a machine that would push, pull, or lift? What kind of work would their machine do? How many parts do they have? Have students write a story. Once the first draft has been completed, students should edit their stories to add any details or corrections that would improve them.

### LANGUAGE CONNECTION

**Reading:** Read *The Mean, Clean, Giant Canoe Machine* by Joseph Slate to your students. Have students describe the machine. Ask students to tell you what the pigs were trying to do to the machine. What happened? Ask students whether this story is fact or fantasy.

SC ♦ **Reinforcement:** Have students fold a sheet of newsprint paper in three parts. Ask students to draw something that moves slowly in part one, something that moves fast in part two, and something that moves very fast in part three.

SC ● **Enrichment:** Have students cut out catalog pictures of machines and paste them on manila paper. Have students write a sentence to tell what each machine does.

SC ▲ **Challenge:** Have students think about how the wheel might have been discovered and draw a cartoon story that tells about the discovery.

Sometimes things move fast.

Sometimes things move slowly.

1. Discuss with students which car and horse are moving fast to cover a distance.

¹Which of these things is moving fast?

²What makes these things move?

2. car's machine parts, horse's muscles and brain that allow it to move

142

# TEACHER RESOURCE MASTERS

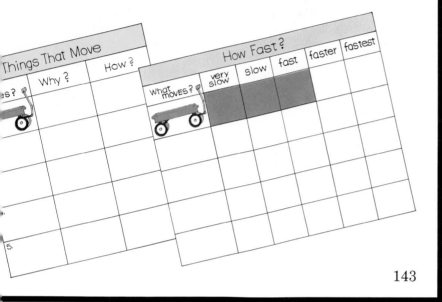

# How do things move?

**ACTIVITY**

## What you need

chart     graph     crayons     pencil

## What to do

1. Make a chart to show things you see move.
2. Tell what makes them move.
3. Do they move fast or slowly?
4. Make a graph to show what moves faster.
5. Why do some things move faster than others?

143

## ACTIVITY RESPONSES

Accept all reasonable student responses to questions during any activity discussion.

## PREPLAN

**Time Allotment:** 30 minutes
**Process Skills:** Classifying/Communicating

### Objectives

1. **Group** objects that move fast and those that move slowly.
2. **Explain** what causes objects to move.
3. **Make** a graph comparing speed of moving objects.

### Setup

■ Duplicate the Teacher Resource Master **Activity Worksheet,** page 109, for this activity.

**Cooperative Grouping:** threes—Assign roles as explained on page T24.

## 1   FOCUS

■ Read the story of the tortoise and the hare. Talk about which animal in the story moved faster.

## 2   TEACH

■ Help students make a list of things they see move. Guide them so they come up with both slow and fast objects.
■ Guide students through the example of the wagon on both the chart and the graph. Ask for one other moving object from the list they made above. Help students record their object on both the chart and the graph. Have groups work independently and describe three more objects.

## 3   APPLY

■ Have each group report their findings for one object.
■ Talk about pushes and pulls and how they affect the speed an object moves.

### Close

■ Look at one graph and compare the recorded speed for different objects.

## PREPLAN

### Lesson Objectives

**2. Infer** that people can move objects by pushing, pulling, or lifting.

**3. Explain** that pushing, pulling, and lifting are forces.

**4. Describe** how forces can change the way something moves.

**5. Recognize** gravity as a pulling force.

### Science Background

■ Pushes and pulls are forces.

■ Forces may cause objects to move.

■ There is a direct relationship between the amount of force applied and the resulting speed of motion of the object.

### Lesson Vocabulary

push     pull     force     gravity

## 1   FOCUS

Try this experiment: have pairs of students sit on the floor facing one another. They should clasp hands at arm's length. While they are at rest, ask: **Why aren't you moving? What will it take to begin to move? What happens when you move?** Have students start moving. Ask: **When do you push? When do you pull? How do you think your muscles are helping?**

# Push, Pull, and Lift

You can move many different things.

You can **push** and **pull** to make things move.

144

## TEACHER RESOURCE MASTERS

Pushing and pulling are forces.

**Forces** make things move.

How can you use forces to move these things?

1. Have students describe how they would push or pull these toys to move them.

145

## 2  TEACH

■ Identify both small and large objects in the classroom. Have students predict which objects require a small force to move and which require a large force. Have them arrange the objects in order from smallest to largest force.

■ Tell which objects on pages 144 and 145 you would push and which you would pull. Tell what would happen to each object when pushed or pulled.

### Guided Practice

■ Exhibit a group of objects (or pictures of objects) and ask students what must be done to move each and classify that action as a push or pull. Have students arrange the objects in order from easiest to hardest to move with a push or pull.

■ If necessary, use the **reteaching strategy** in OPTIONS.

### Independent Practice

■ Use the Teacher Resource Master **Independent Practice,** page 115.

## 3  APPLY

Ask students to bring to class examples of toys that move. Have the class determine together how each toy could be moved. If students do not bring them, include simple toys such as a pinwheel, a top, a gyroscope, and a yo-yo.

### Close

■ Find people in your community who collect antique toys and ask them to bring examples of their collections to school to discuss with the class.

## OPTIONS

### Reteaching Strategy

Collect pictures of objects that move. Make word cards Push and Pull. Ask students to classify the pictures.

### Resource Options

■ Use Poster #6, "Fun Machines."

## TEACHER RESOURCE MASTERS

Critical Thinking                    111

CRITICAL THINKING/PROBLEM SOLVING   Classifying   Chapter 9

Name

**Pushing And Pulling**

Who is using the most energy?
Paste the pictures in order.

Independent Practice 2          115

INDEPENDENT PRACTICE   Lesson 2   Chapter 9

Name

1. Write push, pull, or lift beside each picture.  obj. 2 & 3

push

lift

pull

2. Draw something you could move by pushing.  obj. 4

Students may draw a grocery cart, a wagon, a lawnmower, and so on.

3. Draw an arrow to tell how this will move.  obj. 5

## OPTIONS

### YOU CAN . . . OBSERVE A FORCE

**Process Skill:** Observing
**Setup/Teach**
Provide a board and a ball for each **cooperative learning** group. Lead students to realize that pushes and pulls need not always be supplied by people. Students may conclude that if an object falls or rolls downhill, there must be a force pulling it in that direction. Introduce the word *gravity*.

### LANGUAGE CONNECTION

**Reading:** Read *Machines At Work* by Byron Barton. Ask students to tell you what was happening in the story. What kinds of machines were in the story? Ask students to look at each machine and decide if it pushes, pulls, or lifts. Have students explain their answers.

### MATH CONNECTION

Pose the following problem to your students. Write 10, 20, 30, and 40 on the chalkboard. Have students use estimation to choose the best answer.

**Claire found 13 items in her house that needed a push to move. She found 11 items that needed a pull to move. About how many items did Claire find?**

10
20
30
40

### Resource Options

■ Use Big Book, page 34, "Joey" and Teacher Resource Master **Language Arts Connection,** page 192.

You can lift things.

You push to lift things.

You can pull to lift things, too.

[1] Which shows a pulling force?

[2] Which shows a pushing force?

[3] Which force makes it easier to lift?

1. Child lifting box is pulling.
2. Child lifting box onto shelf is pushing.
3. It is often easier to push than pull.

146

## TEACHER RESOURCE MASTERS

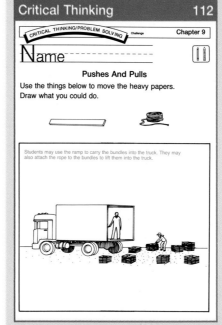

Critical Thinking    112

CRITICAL THINKING/PROBLEM SOLVING    *Challenge*    Chapter 9

Name

**Pushes And Pulls**
Use the things below to move the heavy papers.
Draw what you could do.

Students may use the ramp to carry the bundles into the truck. They may also attach the rope to the bundles to lift them into the truck.

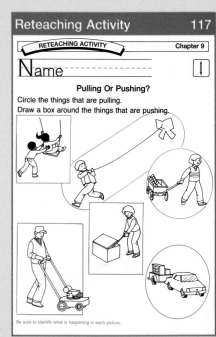

Reteaching Activity    117

RETEACHING ACTIVITY    Chapter 9

Name

**Pulling Or Pushing?**
Circle the things that are pulling.
Draw a box around the things that are pushing.

Be sure to identify what is happening in each picture.

## ACTIVITY

# You Can...

### Observe a Force

Hold a ball at the top of a ramp.
Let the ball go.
Do not push or pull.
In what direction does it move?

**Gravity** is a force.

It pulls on things.

It pulls them toward Earth.

147

## OPTIONS

♦ **Reinforcement:** Have students bring in pictures of objects that need a push or pull in order to operate. Examples might include lawn mowers, non-electric tools, and so on.

● **Enrichment:** Students may enjoy having contests to see whose windup or battery-powered toy can push or pull the greatest number of wooden blocks or other objects.

▲ **Challenge:** Students may be interested in bringing in windup or battery-powered toys that push or pull. Ask students where the toys get the ability to push or pull if no person is providing it. (They get the ability to push or pull from the motor that runs them.) If a toy is a windup toy, some students may be able to deduce that the toy's ability to run came from the person who wound it up.

**SOCIAL STUDIES CONNECTION**
Have students bring in pictures that show pushes and pulls being exerted in times before gasoline powered engines and electricity. Have them work in **cooperative learning groups** and make posters by drawing pictures of these early machines. Books by Eric Sloane will also give students this kind of information.

## TEACHER RESOURCE MASTERS

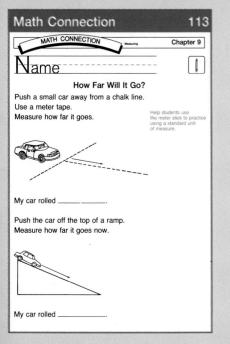

Math Connection                    113

MATH CONNECTION    Measuring    Chapter 9

Name                              1

**How Far Will It Go?**

Push a small car away from a chalk line.
Use a meter tape.
Measure how far it goes.

Help students use the meter stick to practice using a standard unit of measure.

My car rolled _____.

Push the car off the top of a ramp.
Measure how far it goes now.

My car rolled _____.

pages 148–151

## PREPLAN

### Lesson Objectives
6. **Recognize** that people use machines to do work.
7. **Infer** that machines can be simple or complex.

### Science Background
■ A machine is any device that helps us do work. Some machines increase the applied force. Sometimes machines are used only to change the direction of the applied force. Thus we can lift an object more conveniently by using a downward push or pull. Another use of a machine is to increase the speed or range of movement.

■ Work is done whenever a force causes an object to move. Machines help us exert forces to do work. Machines can be as simple as a pry bar or a doorknob.

### Lesson Vocabulary
work    machine

**Note:** The activity on student page 150 may be used for guided discovery before you begin this lesson.

## 1 FOCUS

■ Bring in a group of machines such as a screwdriver, can opener, or bicycle. Ask how each is used. Tell students that each of these machines requires a force to move. Have students tell where you apply the force and if it is a pushing or pulling force. Ask: **How are these machines used?** Accept all reasonable answers.

**Science and Technology:** Use "I WANT TO KNOW ABOUT . . . Robots," student page 151, with this lesson.

## Doing Work

**Machines** can push or pull.

They can move things.

Machines help us do work.

[1]How do people use these machines?

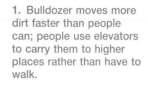

1. Bulldozer moves more dirt faster than people can; people use elevators to carry them to higher places rather than have to walk.

148

## TEACHER RESOURCE MASTERS

Transparency Master 107

TRANSPARENCY MASTER    Chapter 9

**How Do We Use Some Machines?**

Identify kinds of tools and discuss how we use them to help us do work.

Some machines have only a few parts.

Some have many parts.

[1]How do you use these machines?

1. Have students identify these machines with few
parts and describe how they help do work.

149

## TEACHER RESOURCE MASTERS

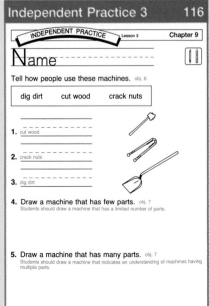

## 2 TEACH

■ Be sure students realize that machines do not produce pushes and pulls by themselves. Machines must have a source of energy such as a person or a motor in order to operate.

■ Ask students to describe the action of some simple tools and tell how they help people. You may need to point out that pushes and pulls can sometimes be in the form of "twists".

### Guided Practice
■ Have students draw and label examples of machines that push and machines that pull.

■ If necessary, use the **reteaching strategy** in OPTIONS.

### Independent Practice
■ Use the Teacher Resource Master **Independent Practice,** page 116.

## 3 APPLY

Conduct a "machines at school" hunt. Have students **work cooperatively** to find three different machines used in the classroom or on the playground.

### Close
Have an "invention" fair. Ask student pairs to create a machine that does something real or imaginary.

## OPTIONS

### Reteaching Strategy
Have students make a catalog of machines. Ask students to cut out or draw machines to paste on pages and write a description of the work they can help do.

### Resource Options
■ Use Big Book, page 35, "Washing Machine, Toaster, Steam Shovel, Train, Rocket" and Teacher Resource Master **Language Arts Connection,** page 193.

pages 148–151

## PREPLAN

**Time Allotment:** two 20-minute periods
**Process Skills:** Inferring/Experimenting

### Objectives
1. **Infer** solutions to a problem.
2. **Experiment** to test proposed solutions.

### Setup
■ Make a chart that lists the steps for solving a problem.

**Cooperative Grouping:** fours—Assign roles as explained on page T24.

## 1 FOCUS

■ Tell students that they are going to be working as a team of scientists to solve a problem. Review with students the following steps scientists use to solve a problem. (1) name the problem (2) predict a way to solve the problem (3) experiment (4) record what happens (5) draw conclusions about what worked best.

## 2 TEACH

■ Form student groups. Guide any group that needs help finding a solution.
■ Remind students to keep a record of their experimental tests.
■ Use the Teacher Resource Master **Activity Worksheet,** page 110.

## 3 APPLY

Have each student group demonstrate the use of their machine in front of the class. Ask students to describe how they arrived at their solutions.

### Close
■ List any problems teams had to overcome while working toward a solution.

---

## ACTIVITY

## How can you make a machine?

### What you need

6 heavy books     machine parts

pencil and paper

### What to do

1. Suppose your team has to move six books.
2. How far do you have to move them?
3. Is your pathway bumpy or smooth?
4. What machine could you make to help you?
5. How did your team do?
6. What problems did you have to fix?

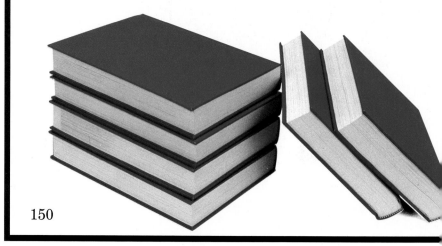

150

## ACTIVITY RESPONSES

Accept all reasonable student responses to questions during any activity discussion.

# I WANT TO KNOW ABOUT...

## Robots

Robots are machines.
There are different kinds of robots.
Robots do different kinds of work.
Some robots put parts on cars.
Some carry heavy things.
Robots help do work for people.

### Science and Technology

151

## TEACHER RESOURCE MASTERS

### Feature Background

■ The term *robot* was introduced by the dramatist Karel Capek in his play *R.U.R.* (*R*ossum's *U*niversal *R*obots). In the play, the robots turn against their human masters and eventually destroy them.

■ Modern robots perform simple manipulative tasks. The form of each robot is based on its function. Most robots are simply mechanical arms controlled by a computer "brain." The robots may contain sensing devices that measure temperature and pressure. Some robots are stationary, while others move.

■ Jobs done by robots include automobile assembly, such as welding, inspecting, and handling parts, die casting, and spray painting; making other robots; inspecting underwater oil platforms; exploring the surfaces of other planets; and handling radioactive materials.

### Feature Vocabulary

robot
machine

### Teaching Suggestions

■ Allow students to describe any robots they have seen in real life, or on television or in a movie. Compare these robots to industrial robots.

■ Mention that robots can be toys or do work.

■ Ask students to think about what kinds of simple chores an industrial robot could do in the home, at school, or in other work environments. Refer to the Feature Background for current uses.

■ Help students write a short play about a world of robots or a time in the future when ordinary people will have robots to help them.

pages 152, 153

**Chapter Closure:** Use these pages to review and reinforce chapter concepts.

## What I Learned

Have students read the rebus summary statements aloud to be sure that students interpret the pictures correctly. After each sentence is read, discuss other words that might make the sentence true.

## Words I Know

Use any or all of the following suggestions to reinforce the chapter vocabulary.

Write each science word or word group on the chalkboard. Ask students to read them. Add the words to the class science list or have students write the words in their individual science word books. Ask students to tell about these words to help you evaluate their comprehension. Have students use each science word or word group in a sentence.

**CHAPTER REVIEW**

**9**

### What I Learned

- Things can be  or  .

  pushed    pulled

- Gravity is a force.
  Gravity pulls things toward 🌎 .

  Earth

- 🚛 help us do work.

  Machines

### Words I Know

move    push    pull    forces

gravity    machines

152

## TEACHER RESOURCE MASTERS

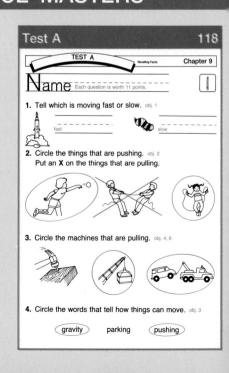

## What I Know

*Use the picture to answer the questions.*

1. Why do things move?
2. How can you move things?
3. How could you move a wagon?
4. How could you move a heavy box?
5. How can machines help you do work?

153

### What I Know

Have students refer to the picture to answer the questions and extend concepts.
1. Things move due to forces, such as pushing or pulling.
2. You can move things by pushing or pulling them.
3. You could pull or push it.
4. You could push, pull, or lift it.
5. Machines can push or pull heavy things.

## OPTIONS

### Resource Options

Use Color Transparencies #9a and #9b.

## TEACHER RESOURCE MASTERS

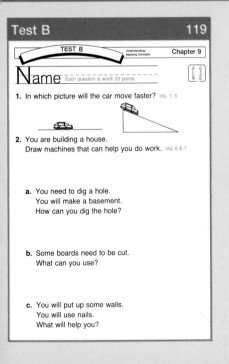

Test B                                    119

TEST B          Understanding/        Chapter 9
                Applying Concepts

Name  Each question is worth 25 points.

1. In which picture will the car move faster? obj. 1, 5

2. You are building a house.
   Draw machines that can help you do work. obj. 6 & 7

   a. You need to dig a hole.
      You will make a basement.
      How can you dig the hole?

   b. Some boards need to be cut.
      What can you use?

   c. You will put up some walls.
      You will use nails.
      What will help you?

# CHAPTER 10

# *Magnets*

## Planning Guide

| Lessons | Objectives | Vocabulary |
|---|---|---|
| **Chapter Introduction** pp. 154, 155 | | |
| **Lesson 1 Magnets Pull** pp. 156–159 | 1. **Recognize** that magnets can attract.<br>2. **Explain** that magnets can attract certain metals.<br>3. **Infer** that magnets can attract through certain materials. | magnets<br>attract |
| **Lesson 2 Magnets Push** pp. 160–163 | 4. **Recognize** that the ends of magnets are different.<br>5. **Observe** and **explain** the activity at the ends of magnets.<br>6. **Identify** the ends of magnets as poles. | repel<br>poles |
| **Lesson 3 Using Magnets** pp. 164–165 | 7. **Tell** how people use magnets. | |
| **Chapter Review** pp. 166, 167 | | |
| **Unit Review** pp. 168, 169 | | |

# Planning Guide

| Text Activities | | Teacher Resource Masters | Other Components |
|---|---|---|---|
| **Title/Skill** | **Materials per Group** | | |
| **Have You Ever . . . Used a Magnet?** p. 155<br>Observing<br>Time Allotment: 30 minutes | paper plates<br>paper clips<br>small magnets<br>crayons or markers<br>glue | | **Activity Center:**<br>"Magnet Magic"; "Go Fishing"; "Magnet Fun" |
| **You Can . . . Keep Your Fingers Dry,** p. 158<br>Observing<br>Time Allotment: 15 minutes<br><br>**Making a Magnet,** p. 224<br>Observing/Inferring<br>Time Allotment: 30 minutes | paper clip<br>clear plastic cup<br>water<br>magnet<br><br>iron nail<br>paper clips<br>magnet<br>pencil<br>paper | Activity Worksheet, p. 123<br>Critical Thinking, p. 125<br>▲ Critical Thinking, p. 126<br>◆ Reteaching Activity, p. 131<br>Independent Practice, p. 128<br>Language Arts Connection, p. 195 | Big Book, p. 37<br>Activity Book, p. 31<br>Activity Book, pp. 51, 52 |
| **What Do Magnets Pull?** p. 159<br>Predicting/Classifying<br>Time Allotment: 20 minutes | magnet<br>objects to test<br>  (examples include<br>plastic tie wire, penny,<br>paper clip, toothpick and<br>so on.)<br>pencil and paper | | |
| **How Do Ends of Magnets Act?** p. 163<br>Observing/Inferring<br>Time Allotment: 20 minutes | 2 magnets that are labelled N and S<br>pencil and paper | Transparency Master, p. 121<br>Activity Worksheet, p. 124<br>Social Studies Connection, p. 127<br>Independent Practice, p. 129<br>Language Arts Connection, p. 196 | Big Book, p. 38 |
| | | ◆ Family Science, p. 122<br>Independent Practice, p. 130 | |
| | | Test A, p. 132<br>Test B, p. 133 | Color Transparencies #10a and #10b |
| | | | Unit Test |

◆ **Basic** / ▲ **Advanced** / All other masters are for use by all students.

# CHAPTER 10

# *Magnets*

## ESL/LEP

**Chapter 10/Lesson 2, Page 162**
Make a bulletin board display or science center about opposites. Include the words *attract* and *repel, North pole* and *South pole*. Divide the bulletin board in half. Place one of the words for each opposite pair on the left side, the other on the right. Do not put the matching words directly across from one another. Attach a piece of yarn to each word on the left and have students identify the pair by attaching the yarn to the opposite words on the right.

## Gifted

**Chapter 10/Lesson 3, Page 165**
Some students may want to make a list of careers that use magnets. Encourage students to tell how the magnets are used in each occupation. For example, a car mechanic may drop a small part onto the engine. The mechanic may use a magnet to pick up the part. Students may also want to use their creative writing skills to make up stories about how magnets could be used in other occupations.

## Mainstreamed

**Chapter 10/Lesson 3, Page 165**

**Learning Disabled:** Place bottle caps or paper clips in a large paper bag. Tie a piece of string to a magnet. Have students take turns lowering the magnet into the bag. Each time have students count aloud the number of caps or paper clips pulled from the bag.

## Whole Class Science Project

Provide students with magnets, steel wool pads, paper, cardboard, aluminum, a shoe box, a drinking glass, sand or dirt, and water. Students can experiment to determine whether a magnet can pick up a piece of steel wool when any of the materials above are placed between the magnet and the steel wool. Students can then record their findings by making a chart.

## Science Fair Projects

Individual students could do one of the following projects:

1. Make a display or bulletin board showing different uses for magnets. Examples might include large magnets used to separate scrap metal from other trash, magnets on toys, or magnets used to attach papers to metal objects.

2. Have students make a compass. Have students find the direction North on the playground using their compass. Students can write a story telling how a compass can help people that are lost.

**Language Arts Connection** 195

LANGUAGE ARTS CONNECTION — Language Study Skills, Finding Details — Big Book 37

Name — Use with Chapter 10, Lesson 1.

**Magnets Pull**

Hidden in the picture are things a magnet can pull.
Circle each thing a magnet can pull.
The words in the box will help you.

| paper clip | nail | chain |
| thumbtack | scissors | safety pin |

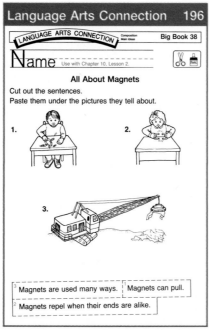

**Language Arts Connection** 196

LANGUAGE ARTS CONNECTION — Composition, Main Ideas — Big Book 38

Name — Use with Chapter 10, Lesson 2.

**All About Magnets**

Cut out the sentences.
Paste them under the pictures they tell about.

1.   2.

3.

³ Magnets are used many ways. | ¹ Magnets can pull.

² Magnets repel when their ends are alike.

pages 154–167

## Chapter Concepts

■ Magnets can pull or attract some metals such as iron.

■ Magnets can push or repel when the ends or poles are alike.

■ Magnets can have different shapes and sizes and are used in many ways because of their ability to attract and repel.

## Chapter Background

■ Magnets are made from materials that are *ferromagnetic*. This word means that these materials are magnetic in the same way as iron. Nickel and cobalt are ferromagnetic. Other materials will also respond to magnetic fields.

■ It is easy to cause a magnet to become nonmagnetic. Just heat a magnet on the stove for about five minutes. The heating destroys the alignment of magnetic domains. Another way to cause a magnet to become nonmagnetic is to hit it several times with a hammer.

## Look Ahead

■ Get a package of iron filings to use in the **Close** activity for Lesson 2.

■ To teach this lesson most successfully you can gather a variety of magnets and magnetic tools and toys. Refer to the Lesson Background and APPLY sections of Lesson 3 for more information.

## Look for These Symbols

- —Hands-on activity
- —Cooperative learning
- —Overhead transparency
- ◆ —Basic/Reinforcement
- ● —Average/Enrichment
- ▲ —Advanced/Challenge
- SC —Science Center
- —Calculator Practice

# CHAPTER 10

# *Magnets*

Magnets stick to some things.

Magnets stick to refrigerators.

What other things will magnets stick to?

## Have You Ever...

### Used a Magnet?

1. Draw a maze on a paper plate.

2. Put a paper clip on "Start."

3. Hold a magnet under the plate.

4. Pull the paper clip with the magnet.

What makes the paper clip move?

155

## PREPLAN

**Time Allotment:** 30 minutes

### Objectives
1. **Observe** how magnets work.
2. **Observe** the attraction of a magnet to a paper clip through paper.

### Setup
To conduct the activity, collect the following materials for each student or **cooperative learning** group:

| | |
|---|---|
| paper plate | small magnets |
| paper clip | crayons or markers |

## 1  FOCUS

■ Display magnets similar to the ones in the picture. Have students use a clip magnet and discover surfaces in the classroom that are magnetic.

## 2  TEACH

■ Have the title and introductory paragraph read aloud.
■ Ask: **How could you find what magnets stick to?** *experiment with a magnet*

**Have You Ever . . .**
■ Duplicate copies of a maze and have students paste it on paper plates.

**Student Responses**
■ The magnet moves the paper clip.

## 3  APPLY

■ Ask students to decide if magnets push or pull or do both. Make a bar graph to show students' opinions. Keep the graph until you have finished the chapter.

### Close
■ Start a class experience chart that lists "What We Know About Magnets." As you move through the chapter, have students add ideas to the list.

## PREPLAN

### Lesson Objectives

1. **Recognize** that magnets can attract.
2. **Explain** that magnets can attract certain metals.
3. **Infer** that magnets can attract through certain materials.

### Science Background

■ Magnets have a magnetic field in the space around them. When certain metals, such as iron or steel (an alloy of iron and other substances) are introduced into this field, forces of attraction occur between the magnet and the object.

■ Strong magnets have more intense fields that result in greater forces.

■ The magnets discussed here are permanent magnets. Passing an electric current through a coil of wire also produces a magnetic field. This type of magnet is called an electromagnet. The advantage of an electromagnet is that the magnetism can be shut off by switching off the current. The scrapyard crane pictured on page 157 uses an electromagnet.

### Lesson Vocabulary

magnets attract

**Note:** The activity on student page 159 may be used for guided discovery before you begin this lesson.

## 1 FOCUS

Obtain several different kinds of magnets. Select volunteers to hold up the objects and demonstrate their attraction for paper clips or other objects. The volunteers should be encouraged to describe the feeling of attraction. **CAUTION:** *Put all tape cassettes and computer diskettes away while students are using magnets.*

# Magnets Pull

**Magnets** can pull.

You can feel them pull.

When magnets pull, they **attract.**

Magnets attract some metals.

Iron is one metal magnets attract.

156

## TEACHER RESOURCE MASTERS

Critical Thinking    125

CRITICAL THINKING/PROBLEM SOLVING   Predicting/Classifying    Chapter 10

Name

### What Do Magnets Attract?

Think about your house.
Draw what magnets could attract in the kitchen.
Draw what they could attract in a garage.

| In The Kitchen | In A Garage |
|---|---|
| Answers may include<br>can opener<br>bottle opener<br>knife<br>refrigerator<br>pots and pans<br>dishwasher | Answers may include<br>screwdriver<br>hammer<br>wrench<br>nails<br>screws<br>bolts<br>washers<br>metal tool box |

Some magnets have a strong pull.

Some do not.

Strong magnets pull heavy things.

What could this magnet pull?

1. Answers may include cars, heavy metal boxes, and so on.

Use Application Activity on page 224.

157

## TEACHER RESOURCE MASTERS

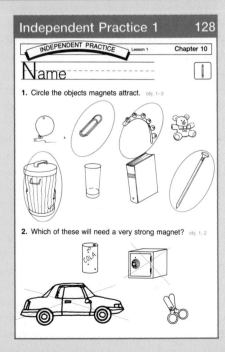

Independent Practice 1     128

INDEPENDENT PRACTICE   Lesson 1    Chapter 10

Name

1. Circle the objects magnets attract. obj. 1–3

2. Which of these will need a very strong magnet? obj. 1, 2

## 2   TEACH

■ Have students classify several objects as metals or nonmetals. Work with students until they can differentiate metal and nonmetal objects with good accuracy.

### Guided Practice

Write the word *magnet* on the chalkboard. If you have steel chalkboards, use bits of adhesive magnetic tape to attach pictures of iron or steel objects to the ends of the word to reinforce the idea that a magnet attracts some metal objects. As an alternative, have students **work cooperatively** in pairs and do the same on paper attaching cut out pictures with paste or tape.

■ If necessary, use the **reteaching strategy** in OPTIONS.

### Independent Practice

■ Use the Teacher Resource Master **Independent Practice,** page 128.

## 3   APPLY

■ Use Application Activity, "Making a Magnet," on student page 224.

### Close

Bring an aluminum soda can and a can that is made of steel to class. Have students predict which will be attracted to the magnet. Explain that not all metals are magnetic.

## OPTIONS

### Reteaching Strategy

■ Review the meaning of the word *attract*. Have students make up sentences using the word in contexts other than that of magnets.

### Resource Options

■ Use Big Book, page 37 "Needle in the Haystack" and Teacher Resource Master **Language Arts Connection,** page 195.

# OPTIONS

## YOU CAN . . . KEEP YOUR FINGERS DRY

**Process Skill:** Observing

**Objective: Observe** how a magnet can pull through some materials.

**Setup/Teach**

SC Gather clear plastic cups, paper clips, magnets, and water. Set up the experiment in a science center. Students can use the science log found on page 205 of the Teacher Resource Book to communicate their findings.

## LANGUAGE CONNECTION

**Reading:** Read *Mickey's Magnet* by Franklyn Branley to your students. Make up three different summaries for the story. Ask students to choose the one that best summarizes the story.

## 🖩 MATH CONNECTION

Draw or show the following sets of magnets.

a) 2 sets of 3 magnets

b) 3 sets of 2 magnets

c) 1 set of 6 magnets

Pose the following problem to your students.

**Mr. Tilton has 6 magnets. He wants to share them equally among 3 students. How many magnets will each student get?** Ask students to choose the drawing that solves the problem.

## Resource Options

■ Use Activity Book, page 31, "Observing."

■ Use Activity Book, pages 51 and 52, "Making a Magnet."

---

ACTIVITY

# You Can...

## Keep Your Fingers Dry

Place a paper clip in a clear cup.

Pour water into the cup.

Use a magnet to remove the clip.

Do not get the magnet wet.

Magnets can even pull through some things.

They can attract through paper.

[1]What else do you think they can pull through?

1. cloth, thin plastic, and other materials depending on the strength of the magnet

158

---

# TEACHER RESOURCE MASTERS

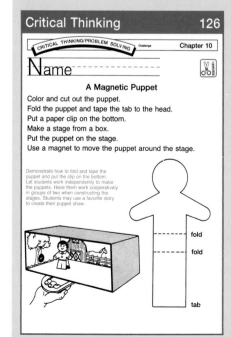

**Critical Thinking** 126

CRITICAL THINKING/PROBLEM SOLVING Challenge    Chapter 10

Name

**A Magnetic Puppet**

Color and cut out the puppet.
Fold the puppet and tape the tab to the head.
Put a paper clip on the bottom.
Make a stage from a box.
Put the puppet on the stage.
Use a magnet to move the puppet around the stage.

Demonstrate how to fold and tape the puppet and put the clip on the bottom. Let students work independently to make the puppets. Have them work cooperatively in groups of two when constructing the stages. Students may use a favorite story to create their puppet show.

fold
fold
tab

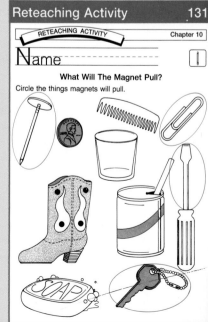

**Reaching Activity** 131

RETEACHING ACTIVITY    Chapter 10

Name

**What Will The Magnet Pull?**

Circle the things magnets will pull.

## What do magnets pull?

### What you need

magnet    things to test    pencil and paper

### What to do

1. Guess what things magnets will pull.
2. Make a group with these things.
3. Use a magnet.
4. Try each thing in your group.
5. What did you find out?

## ACTIVITY RESPONSES

Accept all reasonable student responses to questions during any activity discussion.

## PREPLAN

**Time Allotment:** 20 minutes
**Process Skills:** Classifying/Predicting

### Objectives

1. **Predict** magnetic properties of some objects.
2. **Classify** objects according to magnetic properties.

### Setup

Obtain an assortment of objects for each group. Include the objects shown and any other objects that could be handled safely by students.

**Cooperative Grouping:** twos—Assign roles as explained on page T24.

## 1  FOCUS

■ Use two or three objects different from those students will test. Ask students to predict whether objects will be attracted by a magnet. Test the predictions.

## 2  TEACH

■ Distribute magnets after students have grouped the objects based on their predictions.
■ Use the Teacher Resource Master **Activity Worksheet,** page 123, with this activity.

## 3  APPLY

■ Be sure students realize that the magnetic materials contain iron (or possibly nickel, which is also magnetic). Many children hold the misconception that all metals are magnetic. Introduce the words magnetic and non-magnetic when speaking about the two groups of objects.

### Close

■ Make a class graph or chart that indicates what objects in the classroom are magnetic and what objects are not.

## PREPLAN

### Lesson Objectives
**4. Recognize** that the ends of magnets are different.
**5. Observe** and **explain** the activity at the ends of magnets.
**6. Identify** the ends of magnets as poles.

### Science Background
■ The ends of magnets have opposite magnetic characteristics. These ends are called magnetic poles. Earth also has a magnetic field and magnetic poles. When a magnet is allowed to turn freely on Earth, it becomes aligned with Earth's field. One end is attracted toward the north magnetic pole of Earth while the other end is attracted toward the south magnetic pole. (These poles are not in the same places as the true North and South Poles.) The end that points north is called the north-seeking pole of the magnet and is labeled N. The opposite pole is labeled S for the south-seeking pole.
■ Opposite magnetic poles attract each other, but like magnetic poles exert a repelling force on each other.

### Lesson Vocabulary
repel     poles

**Note:** The activity on student page 163 may be used for guided discovery before you begin this lesson.

## 1  FOCUS

■ Display a variety of magnets to the class. Point out the ends of the magnets. Ask students to speculate why the ends are painted different colors or marked with different letters.

# Magnets Push

Magnets can push.

Magnets can push each other.

When magnets push, they **repel.**

Have you ever felt magnets repel?

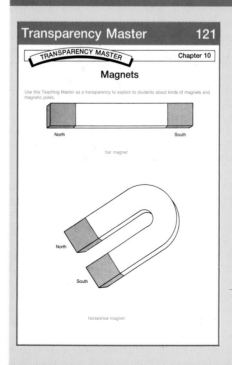

160

## TEACHER RESOURCE MASTERS

Transparency Master        121

TRANSPARENCY MASTER        Chapter 10

Magnets

Use this Teaching Master as a transparency to explain to students about kinds of magnets and magnetic poles.

North        South

bar magnet

North

South

horseshoe magnet

Magnets repel if their ends are alike.

The ends of magnets are called **poles.**

Each magnet has two poles.

One pole is N, and the other is S.   1. repelling force

What would you feel if you touched N to N?

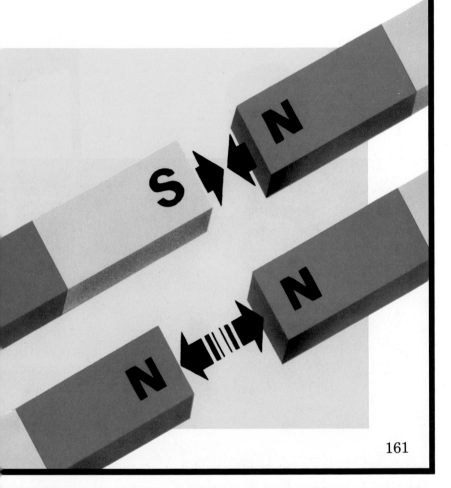

161

## TEACHER RESOURCE MASTERS

## 2   TEACH

■ Write the word *repel* on the chalkboard and discuss its meaning. Ask students to make up sentences using the word repel.

### Guided Practice
Ask student pairs to tell about when magnets attract and when they repel.
■ If necessary, use the **reteaching strategy** in OPTIONS.

### Independent Practice
■ Use the Teacher Resource Master **Independent Practice,** page 129.

## 3   APPLY

Bring some round magnets to class. Ask: **Where are the poles on these magnets?** Students can experiment to feel the repelling force with two round magnets.

### Close
Show the magnetic field of a magnet by using an overhead projector, a piece of acetate, a magnet, and iron filings. Place the magnet on the glass plate while the projector is lit. Place the acetate over the magnet and sprinkle on iron filings. Tap the acetate lightly to allow the filings to align along the magnetic field. Experiment with both poles of the magnet for students to observe how the filings react to magnetic poles. Remember to wear safety goggles.

## OPTIONS

### Reteaching Strategy
Look up the picture on page 162. Set up the same scenario for students to sense the feeling of repelling.

### Resource Options
■ Use Big Book, page 38, "Magnets" and Teacher Resource Book **Language Arts Connection,** page 196.

## TEACHER RESOURCE MASTERS

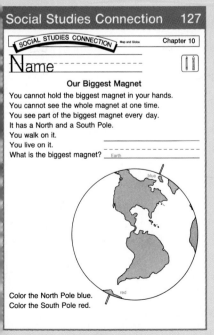

Social Studies Connection   127

SOCIAL STUDIES CONNECTION   Map and Globe   Chapter 10

Name

**Our Biggest Magnet**
You cannot hold the biggest magnet in your hands.
You cannot see the whole magnet at one time.
You see part of the biggest magnet every day.
It has a North and a South Pole.
You walk on it.
You live on it.
What is the biggest magnet?   Earth

Color the North Pole blue.
Color the South Pole red.

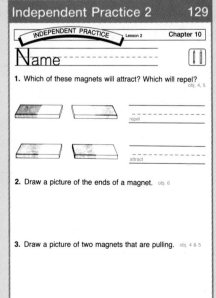

Independent Practice 2   129

INDEPENDENT PRACTICE   Lesson 2   Chapter 10

Name

1. Which of these magnets will attract? Which will repel?   obj. 4, 5

repel

attract

2. Draw a picture of the ends of a magnet.   obj. 6

3. Draw a picture of two magnets that are pulling.   obj. 4 & 5

# OPTIONS

### LANGUAGE CONNECTION

**Writing:** Write the following story on the chalkboard. Explain to students the difference between a complete and incomplete sentence. Have students read the story and decide whether the underlined part is a complete or incomplete sentence.

Jason and Mike were playing with magnets. They found out magnets could pull lots of things. <u>made from iron</u>. They even found out that their magnets could repel.

### MATH CONNECTION

Pose the following problem to your students.

**I have some magnets behind my back. The number of magnets is between 0 and 10. The number is 2 more than 6. How many magnets do I have?** *8*

♦ **Reinforcement:** Place a magnet, paper clips, pieces of cloth, food wrap, waxed paper, steel washers, brass fasteners, and other objects in a shoe box for students to test. Put the test kit in the science center or allow children to check it out for use at home. Encourage students to add items to the box.

● **Enrichment:** Draw a large maze on a sheet of paper. Put a small magnet at the beginning of the maze. Allow students to use a second magnet to move the first one through the maze. Students should use the correct pole to repel the magnet in order to make it move through the maze.

Look at this picture.

These poles are the same.

[1]What will he feel?

1. He will feel a push.
2. He will feel a pull.

[2]What will he feel if he touches N to S?

162

## TEACHER RESOURCE MASTERS

# How do ends of magnets act?

## What you need

2 magnets    pencil and paper

## What to do

1. Use two magnets.
2. Put one end of each magnet together.
3. When do you feel a push?
4. When do you feel a pull?
5. Tell about what happens.

163

## ACTIVITY RESPONSES

Accept all reasonable student answers to questions during any activity discussion.

## PREPLAN

**Time Allotment:** 20 minutes
**Process Skills:** Observing/Inferring

### Objectives

1. **Construct** an arrangement of two magnets that will cause attraction or repulsion.
2. **Infer** how a magnet behaves toward another magnet.

### Setup

Sort out your strongest pairs of bar magnets. If the magnets are too weak, the effects will be too subtle for students of this age.

**Cooperative Grouping:** twos—Assign roles as explained on page T24.

## 1  FOCUS

■ Have students predict the results of the various combinations of ends.

## 2  TEACH

■ **Troubleshooting:** If one magnet is significantly stronger than the other, the weaker one will tend to act as an unmagnetized iron object and be attracted by both ends of the stronger magnet.
■ Be sure each student has the opportunity to feel magnetic effects individually.
■ Use the Teacher Resource Master **Activity Worksheet,** page 124, with this activity.

## 3  APPLY

■ As students complete the activity, ask them to show you an arrangement of magnets that causes them to repel (or attract). Encourage students to use the words attract and repel to describe the results of the experiment.

### Close

■ Help students develop a general conclusion regarding how all magnets behave toward each other.

## PREPLAN

### Lesson Objective
**7. Tell** how people use magnets.

### Science Background
■ Many auto and home stereo speakers have impressively strong magnets. Stereo installation and repair shops or auto junkyards are a source of worn-out speakers whose magnets can be salvaged. Test the rear end of the speaker with an iron object to see if it has a strong magnet. These can be used for vivid attraction and repulsion demonstrations as well as to strengthen classroom bar magnets temporarily. **CAUTION:** *The attraction between two strong magnets can cause them to come together with a force that can injure fingers.* Use caution and do not allow students to handle them. Do not get them near tape cassettes or computer disks. You can demonstrate their strength by picking up large quantities of nails or similar objects.

## 1   FOCUS

■ Display all the kinds of magnets your class has used in this chapter. Ask students how they imagine magnets might be useful to help people to do work.

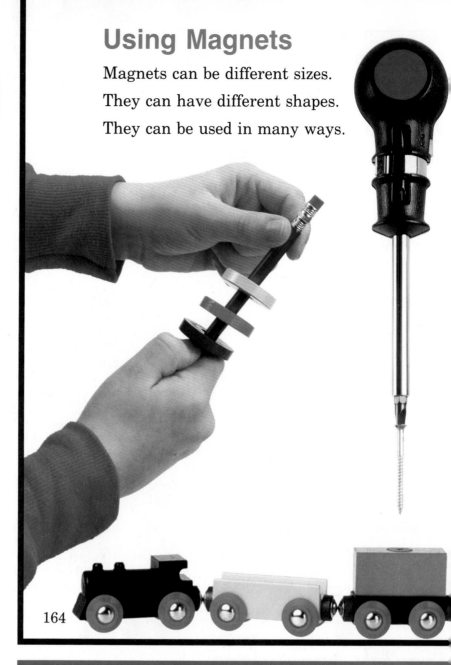

# Using Magnets

Magnets can be different sizes.

They can have different shapes.

They can be used in many ways.

164

## TEACHER RESOURCE MASTERS

Some people use magnets at work.

Some children use them for play.

¹How do you use magnets?

1. Encourage students to identify the illustrations and relate experiences they have had with toys or tools that are magnetic.

165

## 2 TEACH

■ Ask students to suggest other ways that magnets are used in their home or school.

### Guided Practice
■ List all the words students can tell you to describe what they know about magnets. Ask students to write sentences about using magnets. Review the students' sentences to be sure students understand chapter concepts.
■ If necessary, use the **reteaching strategy** in OPTIONS.

### Independent Practice
■ Use the Teacher Resource Master **Independent Practice, page 130.**

## 3 APPLY

Display a collection of household items or tools that are magnetic. Allow students to demonstrate how useful they are. Items might include a magnetic screwdriver, tack hammer, mechanics tool, can opener, stud finder, children's travel games, and so on.

### Close
■ Ask students to relate what they learned about moving things and forces in Chapter 9 to magnets. Lead them to describe magnetism as a force.

## OPTIONS

### Reteaching Strategy
■ Review with students ways people can use magnets to do work. Ask students to write a story about someone who has a problem that could be solved if they used a magnetic tool.

## TEACHER RESOURCE MASTERS

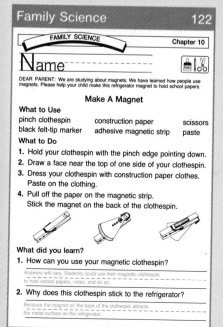

Family Science                    122

FAMILY SCIENCE          Chapter 10

Name

DEAR PARENT: We are studying about magnets. We have learned how people use magnets. Please help your child make this refrigerator magnet to hold school papers.

**Make A Magnet**

**What to Use**
pinch clothespin       construction paper       scissors
black felt-tip marker   adhesive magnetic strip   paste

**What to Do**
1. Hold your clothespin with the pinch edge pointing down.
2. Draw a face near the top of one side of your clothespin.
3. Dress your clothespin with construction paper clothes. Paste on the clothing.
4. Pull off the paper on the magnetic strip. Stick the magnet on the back of the clothespin.

**What did you learn?**
1. How can you use your magnetic clothespin?

Answers will vary. Students could use their magnetic clothespin to hold school papers, notes, and so on.

2. Why does this clothespin stick to the refrigerator?

Because the magnet on the back of the clothespin attracts the metal surface on the refrigerator.

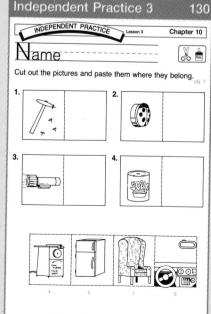

Independent Practice 3          130

INDEPENDENT PRACTICE   Lesson 3   Chapter 10

Name

Cut out the pictures and paste them where they belong.

1.                    2.

3.                    4.

**Chapter Closure:** Use these pages to review and reinforce chapter concepts.

## What I Learned

Have students read the rebus summary statements aloud to be sure that students interpret the pictures correctly. After each sentence is read, discuss other words that might make the sentence true.

## Words I Know

Use any or all of the following suggestions to reinforce the chapter vocabulary.

Write each science word or word group on the chalkboard. Ask students to read them. Add the words to the class science list or have students write the words in their individual science word books. Ask students to tell about these words to help you evaluate their comprehension. Have students use each science word or word group in a sentence.

**CHAPTER REVIEW 10**

## What I Learned

• Magnets can attract some 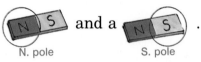 .

metals

• Every magnet has a  and a  .

N. pole    S. pole

• Magnets can repel each other.

• Magnets repel when their  are alike.

poles

## Words I Know

**magnets  attract  repel  poles**

166

## TEACHER RESOURCE MASTERS

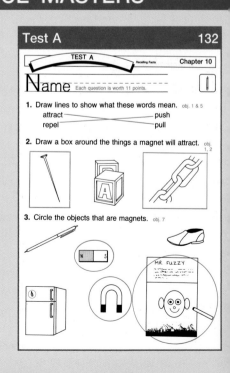

Test A  132

TEST A  Recalling Facts  Chapter 10

Name Each question is worth 11 points.

**1.** Draw lines to show what these words mean. obj. 1 & 5
attract —————— push
repel —————— pull

**2.** Draw a box around the things a magnet will attract. obj. 1, 2

**3.** Circle the objects that are magnets. obj. 7

MR. FUZZY

## What I Learned

*Use the picture to answer the questions.*

1. What can magnets pull?
2. When do magnets push?
3. How can magnets be used for work?
4. How can magnets be used for play?

167

### What I Know

Have students refer to the picture to answer the questions and extend concepts.

1. Magnets can pull, or attract, some metals, such as things made of iron.
2. Magnets push, or repel, when their poles are alike.
3. Some tools such as certain hammers, screwdrivers, and can openers are magnetic and they make it easier to do some jobs.
4. Some toys such as certain train sets, marbles, "drawing" toys with iron filings and so on are magnetic.

## OPTIONS

### Resource Options

Use Color Transparencies #10a and #10b.

## TEACHER RESOURCE MASTERS

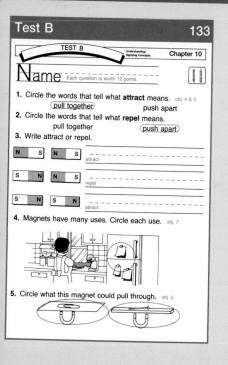

### The Writing Connection

Remind students of the different types of machines they learned about in the unit. Students should include whether their machine is one that pushes or pulls. They should also describe the parts of the machine. They may also enjoy inventing a homework machine.

### Other Ideas

Share *Look Closer!* by Peter Ziebel with your class. You may want to show students one page a day to figure out what they are seeing. Have students write what they think the object is and why. See who can figure out the most objects.

Ask students to write a story describing their favorite smell. Why did they choose it? As another activity, students can write a story describing their least favorite smell. If students wish, the story could compare and contrast the two smells.

Have students choose a familiar liquid or solid. Students can write clues describing the object. Have them exchange papers and see if other students can guess what has been described.

Students can write a story about the feeling they have when in an elevator, on an airplane, or on a slide. Are they being pushed or pulled? Is the feeling a good one? Why or why not?

Have students finish writing a story that begins, "If I had a robot . . . ." Have students cut a piece of construction paper in the shape of their robot and copy their story onto the robot shape.

Have students pretend their bodies have become like a magnet and they have become attached to another person. Students can write a story about what their life is like while they are attached to someone else.

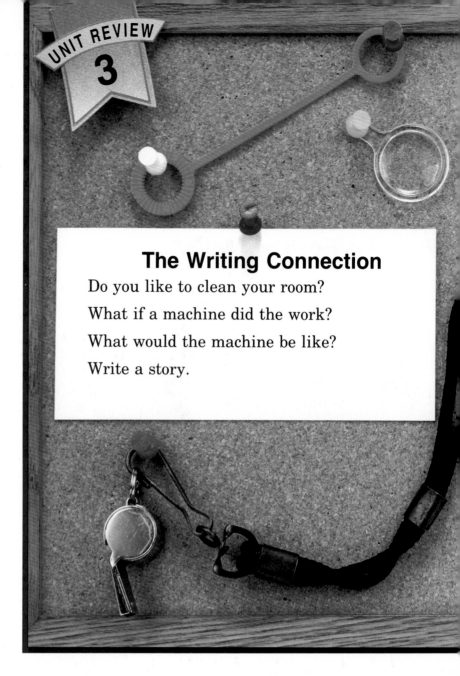

## The Writing Connection

Do you like to clean your room?

What if a machine did the work?

What would the machine be like?

Write a story.

## Something To Do

Use a tape recorder.

Record different sounds.

Ask a friend to guess the sounds.

## Would You Believe?

A hummingbird can move backward when it flies.

## Books To Read

**Look at Magnets** by Rena K. Kirkpatrick

**Machines** by Fred Wilkin

**Take Another Look** by Tana Hoban

## Something to Do

Students may need help using the tape recorder. Have students **work in cooperative groups** to record a short story using sound effects. The sound effects may be actual sounds, or students may choose to make their own sounds.

## Would You Believe?

The hummingbird is the only bird that can fly backward. It can also take off straight upward and fly sideways. Because its wings can beat so fast, the hummingbird can even stay in one place in the air. The sound of its wings moving gives the hummingbird its name.

## Books to Read

♦ **Take Another Look** by Tana Hoban, New York: Greenwillow Books, 1981. Grades K–3. This pictures book uses a die-cut circle to look at a portion of a black and white photograph before viewing the whole picture. The paired photographs show that things are not always what they seem.

● **Machines** by Fred Wilkin, Chicago: Children's Press, 1986. Grades 1–3. This book describes jobs machines perform and how they work.

▲ **Look at Magnets** by Rena K. Kirkpatrick, Milwaukee: Raintree Publishers, Inc., 1985. Grades 2–4. Magnets and their uses are covered in this book.

# Human Body

## Bulletin Board

**Goals:** Students should develop the concept that they are special individuals who need to practice good health habits because they deserve to keep themselves well.

**Materials:** label cards     toothbrush
photographs of students    magazine
soap wrapper     photographs
washcloth

**Procedure:** This bulletin board may be set up initially or as you proceed through the unit lessons. Surround the concepts with photographs of students taken in class or brought from home.

## SC Science Center

**Goals:** The purpose of this science center is to reinforce and extend knowledge of the basic food groups and how to eat for good health. You may find other suggestions in the margin material suitable for additional science center activities.

**Materials:** memory matching cards    crayons
sweet potatoes    paper
cups    pencils
toothpicks
construction paper

**Procedure:** Assemble materials and print instructions for the suggested activities. Suggested concepts: (1) foods come in more than one form, such as milk—cheese, yogurt; (2) choices need to be made—green light, red light; (3) counting—count the number of servings; (4) planning menus; and (5) growing food—a sweet potato. Have students complete a science center worksheet when they have finished these activities. A science center worksheet can be found on page 205 in the Teacher Resource Package.

## Places to Go, People to See

### Field Trip Ideas

Visit a gymnasium where children are training for gymnastic competitions or attend a gymnastic competition.

### Speakers and Visitors

Ask a police officer or firefighter to speak to students about safety.

## Audiovisuals for the Students

 ### Films and Filmstrips

*Busy Bodies,* 16 mm, 10 min., color, Stanton Films.
*Health,* 16 mm, 11 min., color, Counselor Films, Inc.
*In Touch With the World,* 16 mm, 13 min., color, National Geographic Society.

 ### Videotapes

*All About You,* thirty 15 min., color, Agency for Instructional Technology.
*Leaps and Bounds,* sixteen 15 min., color, Hawaii State Department of Education.
*Slim Goodbody's Daily Desk'ercises,* 30 min., color, Society for Visual Education.

 ### Computer Software

*Body Awareness* A three-part program teaches about parts of the body. No reading or keyboard skills necessary.
Type: Games
Hardware: Apple II+, IIe, IIc
Supplier: Learning Well
*Nutrition Series* A three-program series includes Food for Thought; You Are What You Eat; and Food Group Puzzles. Teaches nutrition and the five basic food groups. Can be bought separately.
Type: Games
Hardware: Apple II+, IIe, IIc
Supplier: Marshware

## Resources for the Teacher

 ### Materials at Little/No Cost

National Dairy Council
6300 N. River Road
Rosemont, IL 60018

Food Nutrition Information Center
National Agriculture Library
Room 304
Beltsville, MD 20705

Write to these two organizations for a variety of information about nutrition.

 ### Resource Books

Bates, Ira J. and Alvin E. Winder. *Introduction to Health Education.* Palo Alto, CA: Mayfield Publishing Company, 1984.
Brandreth, Gyles. *Your Vital Statistics.* Secaucus, NJ: Citadel Press, 1986.

## UNIT 4

### Human Body

#### UNIT CONCEPTS

**Chapter 11**
- Body parts are used for movement and to sense the world around us.
- People eat healthful food, exercise, rest, and practice cleanliness to stay healthy and strong.

**Chapter 12**
- Each person is special because he/she has different physical characteristics and has different interests and abilities.
- Following safety rules helps to protect our bodies.

# Human Body

170

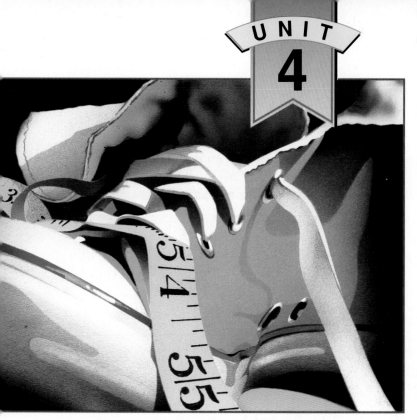

There's something about me
That I'm knowing.
There's something about me
That isn't showing.
I'm growing!

"Something About Me"
Anonymous

171

# ACTIVITY CENTER

For fun, hands-on, independent activities that integrate reading, writing, math, and technology with the chapters in this unit, have students complete some or all of the Activity Center Activities below. Look for specific chapter references in the Lesson Planning Guides.

**Reading: 11** Label Fun, **12** Name Game
**Writing: 11** Healthy Me, **12** I'm Growing
**Math: 11** Exercise Plus, **12** Your Number Book
**Technology: 11** Jackets for Food, **12** Buckle Up

## CONNECTING LITERATURE TO SCIENCE

### Understanding the Selection

■ Ask students to tell one thing about themselves that they like or think is special.

■ Read the poem aloud. Then have students read the poem aloud with you.

■ Ask: **What is happening to the poet?** *The poet is growing.*

■ Draw a cluster diagram on the board and ask students to tell ways they know they are growing. See the example below.

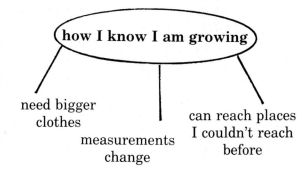

### Relating the Selection to Unit Concepts

■ Ask students how their bodies change when they grow. Ask how they look different. Possible answers: *They get taller; their arms and legs get longer; their feet get bigger; their teeth change.*

■ Discuss with students what helps their bodies to grow. Ask: **What do you need to help make sure your body grows strong and healthy?** *food* Ask: **Do all foods help you grow strong and healthy?** *No. Some foods help you grow strong and healthy, but others don't.*

### Relating the Selection to the Student's World

■ Have students look at the photograph and help them read what is written on the button.

■ Have students make a list or draw pictures showing what makes them special. Allow volunteers to share their list or drawings.

# *You and Your Body*

## Planning Guide

| Lessons | Objectives | Vocabulary |
|---|---|---|
| **Chapter Introduction** pp. 172, 173 | | |
| **Lesson 1 Your Body** pp. 174–177 | 1. **Identify** parts of the body. <br> 2. **Discuss** how body parts inside and outside work together. | body <br> heart |
| **Lesson 2 Keep It Working** pp. 178–185 | 3. **Identify** healthful foods. <br> 4. **Communicate** ways the body maintains good health. | energy <br> healthful |
| **Chapter Review** pp. 186, 187 | | |

# Planning Guide

| Text Activities | | Teacher Resource Masters | Other Components |
|---|---|---|---|
| **Title/Skill** | **Materials per Group** | | |
| **Have You Ever . . . Run a Three-legged Race?** p. 173 Observing Time Allotment: 30 minutes | scarves or strips of cloth | | **Activity Center:** "Label Fun"; "Healthy Me"; "I'm Growing"; "Exercise Plus"; "Jackets for Food" |
| **What Body Parts Move?** p. 177 Observing/Communicating Time Allotment: 30 minutes | jump rope pencil and paper | Transparency Master, p. 135 Activity Worksheet, p. 137 ▲ Critical Thinking, p. 140 ◆ Reteaching Activity, p. 144 Independent Practice, p. 142 Language Arts Connection, p. 197 | Activity Book, p. 32 Poster #5 Big Book, p. 39 |
| **You Can . . . Keep a Record,** p. 183 Communicating Time Allotment: 10 minutes a day | drawing paper toothbrush toothpaste pencil | ◆ Family Science, p. 136 Activity Worksheet, p. 138 Critical Thinking, p. 139 Math Connection, p. 141 Independent Practice, p. 143 Language Arts Connection, pp. 198, 199 | Big Book, p. 40 Big Book, p. 41 |
| **What Foods Are Good for You?** p. 184 Inferring/Classifying Time Allotment: 30 minutes | magazines scissors 2 paper plates glue pencil 2 lunch bags | | |
| | | Test A, p. 145 Test B, p. 146 | Color Transparencies |

◆ Basic / ▲ Advanced / All other masters are for use by all students.

# *You and Your Body*

## For Exceptional Students

## ESL/LEP

**Chapter 11/Lesson 1, Page 176**
Have students learn about different body parts by showing them pictures of people. Provide students with word cards to match the body parts they see.

**Chapter 11/Lesson 2, Page 183**
Write the vocabulary words *body, heart, energy, healthful,* and *exercise* on the chalkboard. Pronounce each word and discuss its meaning. Have students use each vocabulary word in a sentence or story.

## Gifted

**Chapter 11/Lesson 1, Page 176**
Experiment with heart rates. Bring in a stethoscope for student use. Prepare a simple chart. Example:

| Student Name | Heartbeat | Faster |
|---|---|---|
|  |  |  |

Working in pairs, have each student listen to a partner's heartbeat using a stethoscope. One by one, have each student run in place for approximately 50 counts. Listen again for the heartbeat and record what is heard on the chart. Ask the following questions: **Did the heartbeat change? When did it sound slow? When did it sound fast? Why is it good for the heart to beat faster during exercise?**

## Mainstreamed

**Chapter 11/Lesson 1, Page 176**

**Learning Disabled:** Help students to learn body parts by singing the song "Head, Shoulders, Knees, and Toes." Have students touch the body part as the song is sung. Change the song to include different body parts.

# Projects to Do

## Whole Class Science Project

Have students plan and prepare a meal in the classroom. Have each student request parents to send an ingredient. **CAUTION:** *Give supervision with sharp implements, crockpots, or ovens.* Parents or another class may be invited by written invitation. Have students learn how to set a table and serve their guests. A menu could be designed as a favor. The menu should reflect that the food choices were selected from the healthful food groups.

## Science Fair Projects

Individual students could do one of the following projects:

1. Draw a picture of a sense organ, label it, and write a sentence about how to protect the sense organ.
2. Using the panels from ten different boxes of cereal, read and list the grains found in the cereals.

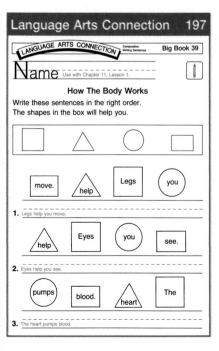

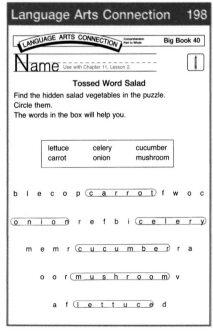

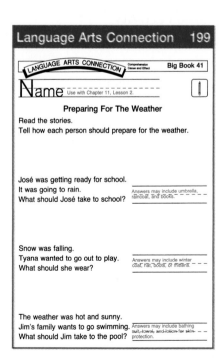

# CHAPTER 11

pages 172–187

## Chapter Concepts
■ Body parts are used for movement and for sensing the world around us.
■ People eat healthful food, exercise, rest, and practice cleanliness to stay healthy and strong.

## Chapter Background
■ Good health is a composite of your physical, social, and mental well-being. Physical health is the physical condition of your body. Social health is the quality of your relationships with others. Mental health is the condition of your mind, self-concept, and the expression of your feelings.
■ Wellness is the highest level of health you can achieve. Practicing healthful behaviors can increase the level of health for you and others.

## Looking Ahead
■ Arrange to reserve a videotape or film on the human body and how its parts move and work together to **Close** Lesson 1.

## Look for These Symbols

- —Hands-on activity
- —Cooperative learning
- —Overhead transparency
- ◆ —Basic/Reinforcement
- ● —Average/Enrichment
- ▲ —Advanced/Challenge
- SC —Science Center
- —Calculator Practice

SCIENCE
In Your World

172

# CHAPTER 11

# *You and Your Body*

Think about the games that you play.

What games do you play outdoors?

What games do you play indoors?

Some games are good exercise.

## Have You Ever...

### Run a Three-Legged Race?

**1.** Work with a friend.

**2.** Stand side by side.

**3.** Tie a scarf around your knees.

**4.** Walk fast!

What parts of your body move?

173

---

## PREPLAN

**Time Allotment:** 30 minutes

**Objective**
1. **Communicate** what body parts are involved in a three-legged race.

**Setup**
To conduct the activity collect the following materials for each **cooperative learning group:**
scarves or strips of cloth

## 1  FOCUS

■ Discuss the pictures on pages 172, 173.
■ Discuss games students may like to play. Ask which games need a large area to play and why.

## 2  TEACH

■ Read the title and introductory paragraph aloud.

**Have You Ever . . .**
Model the position for a three-legged race. As needed, assist teams in tying their legs together.
■ Guide students to run short three-legged races. Have students note how they use parts of their body.
■ **Safety Consideration:** Stage this activity outdoors or in a large indoor area.

**Student Responses**
■ We use almost every part of our body to run a race.

## 3  APPLY

■ Discuss with students the differences between running three-legged races and running unimpeded, without partners. Record their observations.

**Close**
■ Have students compare activities and list which body parts are used for each.

pages 174–177

## PREPLAN

### Lesson Objectives
1. **Identify** parts of the body.
2. **Discuss** how body parts inside and outside work together.

### Science Background
■ Nerve cells for smell are in the upper part of the nose. The senses of smell and taste are connected. Odors that pass from the mouth to the nose contribute to a food's flavor.
■ The semicircular canals of the inner ear are important in maintaining balance.
■ Skin contains nerve endings that are sensitive to pressure, pain, and temperature. Impulses from nerve cells in the skin travel to the spinal cord and on to the brain where the impulses are interpreted.

### Lesson Vocabulary
body    heart

**Note:** The activity on student page 177 may be used for guided discovery before you begin this lesson.

## 1   FOCUS

Trace an outline of one student's body and cut it out. Ask: **What are the names of the body parts you can see?** *arms, legs, head, hands, feet*. Using the body outline, have students name parts inside the body. They may include heart, bones, lungs, and stomach. Have students draw and cut out these parts inside the body and paste them on the outline. Discuss what these parts do.

**Science and Technology:** Use "I WANT TO KNOW ABOUT . . . X Rays, student page 185, with this lesson.

# Your Body

Your **body** has many parts.

You can see some parts.

174

## TEACHER RESOURCE MASTERS

<sup>1</sup>What body parts do you use to sense your world?
<sup>2</sup>What parts do you use to move?

1. eyes, ears, nose, tongue, and hands
2. muscles in arms, legs, hands, and feet

175

## TEACHER RESOURCE MASTERS

Critical Thinking     140

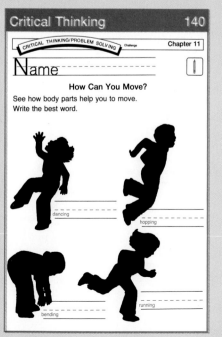

CRITICAL THINKING/PROBLEM SOLVING   Challenge    Chapter 11

### Name

**How Can You Move?**
See how body parts help you to move.
Write the best word.

dancing       hopping

bending       running

Independent Practice 1     142

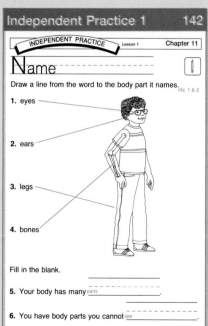

INDEPENDENT PRACTICE   Lesson 1    Chapter 11

### Name

Draw a line from the word to the body part it names. <sub>obj. 1 & 2</sub>

1. eyes

2. ears

3. legs

4. bones

Fill in the blank.

5. Your body has many parts _____.

6. You have body parts you cannot see _____.

## 2   TEACH

Discuss body parts that are senses. To test sense of touch, blindfold five students. Have them stand in a row. Give the student at one end of the row an object. The student feels the object and passes it to the next person, and so on. Have students decide what the item was. Have them give reasons for their responses.

Borrow a *stethoscope* from a physician so that students will be able to listen to heart valve sounds and air moving in and out of their lungs.

### Guided Practice

■ Give each student a piece of newsprint paper. Name a body part. Ask students to draw that part and then draw a picture of something the body part helps them do.
■ If necessary, use the **reteaching strategy** in OPTIONS.

### Independent Practice

■ Use the Teacher Resource Master **Independent Practice,** page 142.

## 3   APPLY

■ Have students look at the body outline used in **FOCUS.** Have students find out about other parts of the body that were left out.

### Close

■ Show students a film or videotape that describes the body and how its parts work together.

## OPTIONS

### Reteaching Strategy

Cut out body-part illustrations from an old high school textbook. Make word cards to match the illustrations. Have students match the pictures to the word cards.

### Resource Options

■ Use Activity Book, page 32, "Measuring."

# OPTIONS

## LANGUAGE CONNECTION

**Writing:** Write the following story on the chalkboard. Have students read the story and choose the word or group of words that makes the sentence correct.

Cam's heart __(1)__ very fast. He had just finished __(2)__ a race. Cam's team had won first place!

(1) was beating     (2) run
    beating            ran
    beated          running
    were beating    runned

◆ **Reinforcement:** Involve students in singing games using body parts. Students at this level enjoy "Hokey Pokey," "If You're Happy and You Know It, Clap Your Hands," "Simon Says," and "Did You Ever See a Lassie?"

● **Enrichment:** On separate cards, mount enough cutout drawings of ears, eyes, hands, mouths, and noses to give each student in the room a card. On a table, place several objects, such as a glass of water, a flower, a piece of cotton, or a nickel. Hold up one object. Have some students identify the picture on his or her card and tell something that could be found out about the object using the part of the body shown on the card.

## Resource Options

■ Use Poster #5, "The Birthday Piñata."
■ Use Big Book, page 39, "One-Two-Three-Four" and Teacher Resource Master **Language Arts Connection,** page 197.

You have body parts you cannot see.

You can hear your **heart.**

You can feel your bones.

1. Discuss with students other body organs they may name such as lungs, stomach, brain, and so on.

[1] What other parts are inside your body?

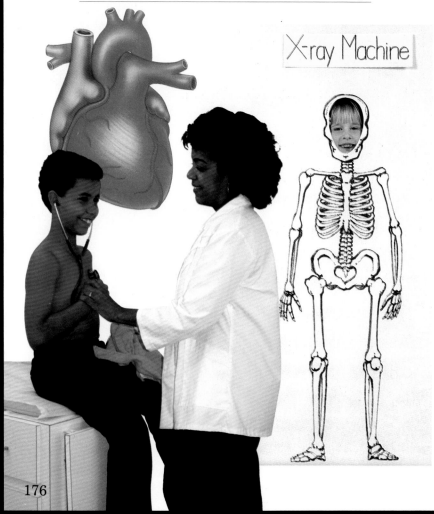

176

# TEACHER RESOURCE MASTERS

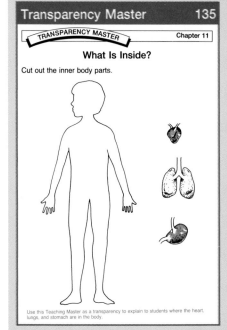

Transparency Master     135

TRANSPARENCY MASTER    Chapter 11

**What Is Inside?**

Cut out the inner body parts.

Use this Teaching Master as a transparency to explain to students where the heart, lungs, and stomach are in the body.

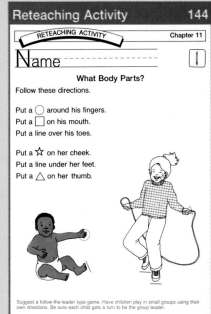

Reteaching Activity     144

RETEACHING ACTIVITY    Chapter 11

Name

**What Body Parts?**

Follow these directions.

Put a ◯ around his fingers.
Put a ☐ on his mouth.
Put a line over his toes.

Put a ☆ on her cheek.
Put a line under her feet.
Put a △ on her thumb.

Suggest a follow-the-leader type game. Have children play in small groups using their own directions. Be sure each child gets a turn to be the group leader.

## What body parts move?

### What you need

jump rope      pencil and paper

### What to do

1. Choose a friend to work with you.

2. Use a jump rope.

3. What body parts move when you jump rope?

4. Ask your friend to list those parts.

5. Trade jobs and make a list for your friend.

6. Do all body parts move?

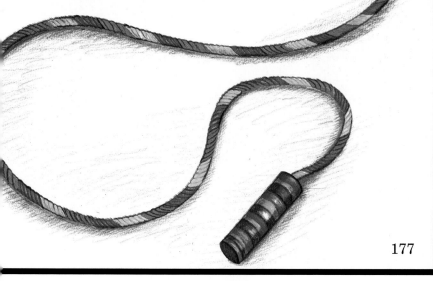

177

## ACTIVITY RESPONSES

Accept all reasonable student responses to questions during any activity discussion.

## PREPLAN

**Time Allotment:** 30 minutes

**Process Skills:** Observing/Communicating

### Objective

1. **Recognize** that internal and external body parts work together to allow us to move.

### Setup

Arrange for the activity to be done in a gymnasium or other appropriate space. Have jump ropes available.

■ Ask a parent volunteer to videotape the activity.

**Cooperative Grouping:** twos—Assign roles as explained on page T24.

## 1  FOCUS

■ Discuss activities that require using more than one body part at a time. Show the students a jump rope and use the directions in the book to preview the task.

## 2  TEACH

■ Move around the gym area to be sure students are recording data.
■ Use the Teacher Resource Master **Activity Worksheet,** page 137.

## 3  APPLY

■ Make a class chart and list the body parts students name that they have recorded. Classify the parts listed as inner and outer parts. Ask students to tell if they noticed that their hearts moved faster when they were jumping. Ask them to infer why this might happen when they are exercising.

### Close

■ Show the videotape of the activity. Ask students to relate what new information they learned about exercise or how body parts work together to help us move.

## PREPLAN

### Lesson Objectives
3. **Identify** healthful foods.
4. **Communicate** ways the body maintains good health.

### Science Background
■ The four healthful food groups are the milk group, meat group, fruit/vegetable group, and grain group. A fifth group, the combination group, includes servings or partial servings from the four basic food groups when combined, such as pizza.
■ Diets high in fats, sodium, and sugar contribute to health problems.
■ Mental, physical, and social benefits gained from physical fitness include: more energy, better muscle tone, increased lung capacity, a strong heart muscle, and feeling better about yourself.
■ During sleep, heart rate slows, blood pressure decreases, muscles relax, and growth hormone is released into the blood.
■ Soap breaks down the oil on the skin and removes dirt that may clog pores. Fingernails can collect dirt and bacteria and need to be kept trimmed.

### Lesson Vocabulary
energy    healthful

**Note:** The activity on student page 184 may be used for guided discovery before you begin this lesson.

## 1    FOCUS

■ Discuss what we must do to keep body parts working well. Answers may include exercise, eat healthful food, and get plenty of rest. List these answers on a chart to be displayed in the room.

## Keep It Working

1. healthful foods such as fruits, vegetables, meats, dairy products, breads, and grains
2. water

Your body does work.

It needs **energy** to work.

It needs healthful food for energy.

[1]What should you eat each day?

[2]What should you drink?

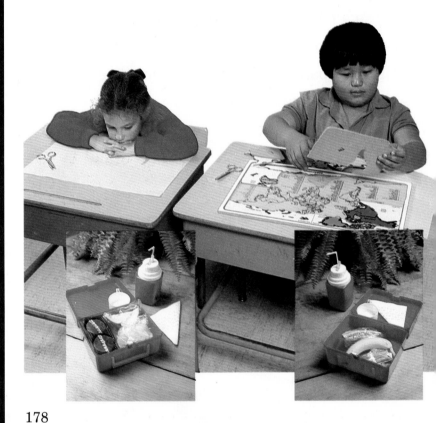

178

## TEACHER RESOURCE MASTERS

Some foods are not healthful.

These foods may taste good.

But they are not good for you.

You do not need them to grow.

What foods are not healthful?

◄ high sugar and salt content foods

179

## 2 TEACH

■ Discuss the meaning of the word *energy*. Talk about athletes who eat carefully in order to have energy. Additional strategies can be found on p. 183.
■ Make a chart where students list healthful and unhealthful foods.

### Guided Practice

■ Provide each student with a paper divided into four squares with each square labeled with one of the ways to keep body parts working well. Have students draw illustrations for each label.
■ If necessary, use the **reteaching strategy** in OPTIONS.

### Independent Practice

■ Use the Teacher Resource Master **Independent Practice,** page 143.

## 3 APPLY

■ Have the school dietician visit the classroom and discuss with students how their school lunches are planned. Have students prepared to offer healthful suggestions for lunches they would like as a part of the school lunch program.

### Close

■ Have students write a letter to themselves naming one new way they will work to stay healthy.

## OPTIONS

### Reteaching Strategy

■ Have students role-play the following: A child complains to a parent about never having anything good to eat/parent explains why choosing healthful foods is best.

### Resource Options

■ Use Big Book, page 40, "Sarah's Salad" and Teacher Resource Master **Language Arts Connection,** page 198.

# TEACHER RESOURCE MASTERS

**Critical Thinking**    139

CRITICAL THINKING/PROBLEM SOLVING    Communicating    Chapter 11

# Name

**What Is Best For Me?**

Cut out the food that is healthful.
Paste a healthful dinner on the place mat.
Students should include everything but the soft drink can and lollipop.

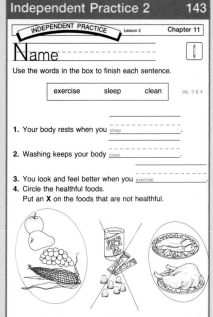

**Independent Practice 2**    143

INDEPENDENT PRACTICE    Lesson 2    Chapter 11

# Name

Use the words in the box to finish each sentence.

| exercise | sleep | clean |    obj. 3 & 4

1. Your body rests when you _sleep_ .

2. Washing keeps your body _clean_ .

3. You look and feel better when you _exercise_ .

4. Circle the healthful foods.
   Put an **X** on the foods that are not healthful.

# OPTIONS

### LANGUAGE CONNECTION

**Writing:** Write the following story on the chalkboard. Have students read the story and choose the word or group of words that makes the sentence correct.

Link likes to eat food that is good for him. Yesterday he __(1)__ an apple and some greenbeans. Tomorrow he __(2)__ a banana and some carrots.

(1) eat     (2) will eat
     eats        is eating
     ate         will ate
     ates        ate

◆ **Reinforcement:** Have students stand with their arms at their sides. Demonstrate how to rotate the shoulders forward and then backward. Have students rotate their shoulders forward while you count to 10. Then have them relax to the count of 5. Students should then rotate their shoulders backward to the count of 10 and then relax again. Play some appropriate music or establish a rhythm for the students to perform the exercise.

◆ **Reinforcement:** Ask students to bring in pictures of food or people doing exercises. Collect these pictures and pass a picture to each student. Ask questions like these: "Who has a picture of a food in the milk group?" "Who has a picture of someone using arm muscles?" Students who have the appropriate pictures can show their pictures and respond by giving the answer to the question.

**Resource Options**
■ Use Big Book, page 41, "Weather Changes" and Teacher Resource Master **Language Arts Connection,** page 199.

Your body needs **exercise.**

Your heart beats faster when you exercise.

Exercise can make your heart strong.

180

## TEACHER RESOURCE MASTERS

Exercise keeps your body in good shape.
[1] What do you like to do for exercise?

1. Discuss with students how certain sports, games, and exercise develop and strengthen muscles.

181

TEACHER RESOURCE MASTERS

## OPTIONS

▲ **Challenge:** Have students plan a healthful meal that incorporates a balance of foods from the four food groups. Discuss combination foods. Have each student bring in food to contribute to the meal and share a nutritious lunch that students have planned together.

### PHYSICAL EDUCATION CONNECTION

On the floor, make two 18-inch circles using masking tape or chalk. Have students stand in the center of each circle. On signal from you, have students jump left out of the circle and then jump right into the center again. In like manner, have them jump right out of the circle and jump left back into the circle. Establish a rhythm for the activity by chanting "jump 1, jump 2, jump 3, jump 4." Encourage students to feel their heart both before and after jumping to discover the faster beating due to exercise.

Have the students use body movements to demonstrate how to grow like a plant, jump like a frog, swing like a monkey, swim like a tadpole, or walk like a person. Lively, entertaining exercises often make students feel good about themselves and improve posture.

# OPTIONS

## YOU CAN . . . KEEP A RECORD

**Process Skill:** Communicating

**Objective: Collect** data and **keep** a record of their tooth brushing habits.

**Setup/Teach**

■ Show students how to make a chart to record their tooth brushing habits. Prepare a letter to send home to parents to explain the activity. Students could use checkmarks or stickers to denote when they have brushed their teeth. Have students bring their records back to class after an allotted time. Discuss how students have kept track of their tooth brushing activity. Ask students if keeping a record improved their tooth brushing habit.

■ Ask students to relate how they feel after they have been playing. What happens to their breathing? What happens to their heartbeat? How does their skin feel?

■ Have students cut pictures from magazines showing people involved in physical fitness activities. Use these pictures to make a class collage.

■ You may wish to show pictures from Olympic events and describe what the Olympic games are all about. Point out the different events that are beneficial for the heart and skeletal muscles.

■ Have a volunteer place a pedometer on his or her leg and demonstrate by walking around the room several times how this instrument measures the distance traveled (walked or jogged).

How do you feel at the end of the day?

You may be tired.

Your body needs rest.

[1]How does sleep help your body?

1. Sleep allows body organs a time to slow down.

182

# TEACHER RESOURCE MASTERS

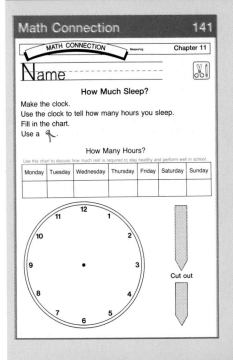

Math Connection | 141

MATH CONNECTION — Measuring — Chapter 11

**Name**

### How Much Sleep?

Make the clock.
Use the clock to tell how many hours you sleep.
Fill in the chart.
Use a ✂.

### How Many Hours?

Use this chart to discuss how much rest is required to stay healthy and perform well in school.

| Monday | Tuesday | Wednesday | Thursday | Friday | Saturday | Sunday |
|--------|---------|-----------|----------|--------|----------|--------|
|        |         |           |          |        |          |        |

Cut out

You need to keep your body clean.
A clean body helps you stay healthy.
How do you keep your body clean?

## OPTIONS

- **Problem Solving:** Have students share their daily physical activities each day for one week. Examples might include baseball, watching TV, or chores. Ask students to describe the way they felt after each activity. Encourage them to relate physical activity with having good feelings about themselves.
- Have students learn *refusal skills* by role playing how to say *no* to foods and behaviors that are not healthful.
- Ask: **Why do adults ask students not to snack on junk food?** *not good for teeth; put on weight; may curb appetite for a healthful meal*
- Draw students attention to healthful snacks. Provide healthful finger foods such as celery, carrots, popcorn, and so on. Ask students what sounds they hear when eating these. Answers will include *crunch, munch,* and *snap.*
- Introduce the four food groups: meat, grain, dairy, and fruit/vegetables. Make a separate label for each group. Using a wire coat hanger, attach each label to the hanger with a string. Have a picture representing each food group that can be attached by a string under the correct food group. Have students help you place the food pictures with the correct food group. Display the food mobile in the room. Discuss the idea that it takes food from all four food groups to keep people healthy and strong.
- SC Have students make a drawing showing foods they like to eat. Try to encourage the choice of healthful foods over nonhealthful foods.

### ACTIVITY

# You Can...

## Keep a Record

Brush your teeth.
Keep a record to tell how often.
Give yourself a reward.

183

## TEACHER RESOURCE MASTERS

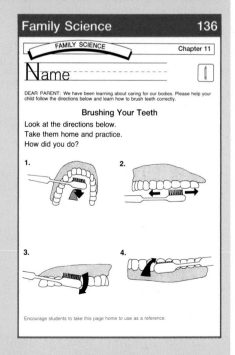

Family Science                    136

FAMILY SCIENCE               Chapter 11

Name

DEAR PARENT: We have been learning about caring for our bodies. Please help your child follow the directions below and learn how to brush teeth correctly.

**Brushing Your Teeth**

Look at the directions below.
Take them home and practice.
How did you do?

1.    2.

3.    4.

Encourage students to take this page home to use as a reference.

## PREPLAN

**Time Allotment:** 30 minutes

**Process Skills:** Inferring/Classifying

### Objective
1. **Recognize** foods that are healthful and foods that are not healthful.

### Setup
■ Gather magazines, paper plates, and brown lunch bags.

 **Cooperative Grouping:** twos—Assign roles as explained on page T24.

## 1  FOCUS

■ Using pictures or charts, review the names of the four food groups and what foods are included in each of these groups.

## 2  TEACH

■ Have students mark one lunch bag with a smiling face and mark the other bag with a frowning face. Have students place pictures of healthful foods in the bag with the smiling face and the pictures of foods that are not healthful in the bag with the frowning face. Have students paste food choices from each bag on paper plates.

■ Use the Teacher Resource Master **Activity Worksheet,** page 138.

## 3  APPLY

■ Discuss possible food choices they might make from the healthful food groups to enjoy a healthful lunch.

### Close
■ Students should explain why they placed a specific food in a healthful or not healthful category.

---

**ACTIVITY**

# What foods are good for you?

### What you need

| magazines | paper bags | scissors |
|---|---|---|
| 2 paper plates | glue | pencil |

### What to do

1. Cut out some pictures of foods.

2. Find foods that are good for you.

3. Find foods that are not.

4. Glue your pictures in two groups.

5. Tell about your work.

184

## ACTIVITY RESPONSES

Accept all reasonable student responses to questions during any activity discussions.

# I WANT TO KNOW ABOUT...

## X Rays

What do your bones look like?
X-ray pictures show bones.
An X ray can show where a bone is broken.
It can also show when a bone is mended.
Or if a bone isn't broken at all!
Have you ever had an X ray?

*Science and Technology*

185

## TEACHER RESOURCE MASTERS

### Feature Background

■ X rays were discovered by Wilhelm Roentgen in 1895.

■ X rays are a form of electromagnetic radiation. Visible light, microwaves, and radio waves are also part of the electromagnetic spectrum.

■ X rays are used in medicine and dentistry. X rays may be used in industry to reveal cracks in metals. For example, airplane parts may be x-rayed to reveal cracks that would otherwise go undetected.

■ Scanners at airports use X rays to check for weapons.

### Feature Vocabulary

X ray

### Teaching Suggestions

■ Ask if any student has had an X ray. Allow students to share their experiences with the class. Have students describe why they needed an X ray.

■ Borrow an X ray of a leg, arm, and chest from a local physician. Borrow X rays of teeth from a local dentist. Show the X rays to your class.

■ Explain to students about the dangers of overexposure to X rays and how people who take X rays protect themselves.

■ Discuss how X rays are used in industry to detect cracks in metals and at airports for safety. Have students imagine other ways X-ray machines could be used. Invite creative answers. Have students draw their X-ray machines.

■ Have an X-ray technician visit your classroom and describe their job.

**Chapter Closure:** Use these pages to review and reinforce chapter concepts.

## What I Learned

Have students read the rebus summary statements aloud to be sure they interpret the picture correctly. After each sentence, discuss other possible words that would also make the statement true.

## Words I Know

Use any or all of the following suggestions to reinforce the chapter vocabulary.

Write each science word or word group on the chalkboard. Ask students to read them. Add the words to the class science list or have students write the words in their individual science word books. Ask students to tell about these words to help you evaluate their comprehension. Have students use each science word or word group in a sentence.

---

# CHAPTER REVIEW 11

### ▬ What I Learned ▬

- Your  has many parts.

  body

- Your body needs healthful  .

  foods

- Your body needs  and  .

  exercise          rest

- You need to keep your body  .

  clean

### ▬ Words I Know ▬

**body    heart    energy    exercise**

186

---

# TEACHER RESOURCE MASTERS

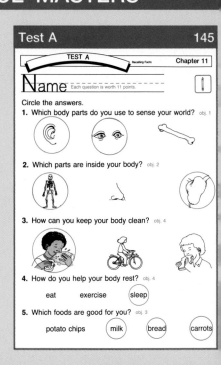

Test A                                    145

---

## What I Know

*Use the picture to answer the questions.*

1. What do some body parts help you do?

2. How does your body get energy to work?

3. Why do you need to exercise and rest?

4. How can you keep your body clean?

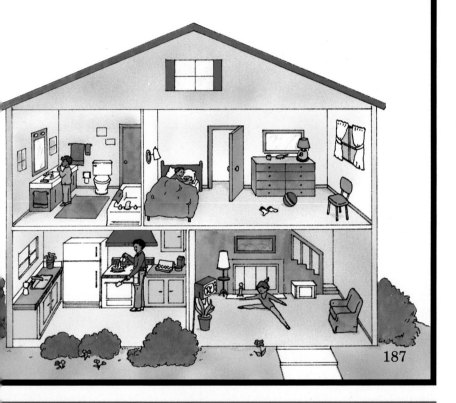

187

## What I Know

Have students refer to the picture to answer the questions and extend concepts.

**1.** Body parts help you to sense your world. These include eyes, ears, nose, tongue, hands, and skin. Arms, legs, fingers, and toes are used to move.

**2.** Healthful food provides your body with the energy it needs.

**3.** Your body needs exercise and rest to help body parts work at their best and to stay healthy.

**4.** Taking baths or showers, washing your hands frequently, shampooing your hair, helps to keep your body clean.

## OPTIONS

### Resource Options

Use Color Transparencies #11a and #11b.

## TEACHER RESOURCE MASTERS

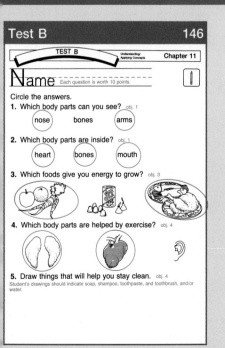

Test B     146

# *You Are Important*

## Planning Guide

| Lessons | Objectives | Vocabulary |
|---|---|---|
| **Chapter Introduction** pp. 188, 189 | | |
| **Lesson 1 You Are Special** pp. 190–193 | 1. **Communicate** that individuals are unique.<br>2. **Identify** characteristics that make individuals special. | special |
| **Lesson 2 Staying Safe** pp. 194–199 | 3. **Identify** areas for safety awareness.<br>4. **Discuss** safety rules for getting to and from school.<br>5. **Communicate** safe practices at home and at play.<br>6. **Recognize** a need for safety awareness around animals, plants, and in inclement weather. | safety rules |
| **Chapter Review** pp. 200, 201 | | |
| **Unit Review** pp. 202, 203 | | |

# Planning Guide

| Text Activities | | Teacher Resource Masters | Other Components |
|---|---|---|---|
| **Title/Skill** | **Materials per Group** | | |
| **Have You Ever . . . Made a Drawing of Yourself?** p. 189 Communicating Time Allotment: 30 minutes | large drawing paper crayons or markers | | Activity Center: "Name Game"; "I'm Growing"; "Your Number Book"; "Buckle Up" |
| **How Are You Special?** p. 193 Inferring/Communicating Time Allotment: 30 minutes | large piece of kraft paper scissors markers pencil and paper | ◆ Family Science, p. 148 Activity Worksheet, p. 149 Math Connection, p. 153 | Big Book, p. 42 Big Book, p. 43 Activity Book, p. 33 Activity Book, p. 53 |
| **Whose Shoes?** p. 225 Observing/Classifying/ Communicating Time Allotment: 30 minutes | shoes | Independent Practice, p. 154 Language Arts Connection, pp. 200, 201 | |
| **You Can . . . Write Safety Tips,** p. 196 Classifying/Communicating Time Allotment: 30 minutes | drawing paper assorted construction paper scraps glue scissors markers crayons | Transparency Master, p. 147 Activity Worksheet, p. 150 Critical Thinking, p. 151 ▲ Critical Thinking, p. 152 | Big Book, p. 44 |
| **How Can You Stay Safe?** p. 198 Communicating Time Allotment: 30 minutes | large drawing paper crayons pencil | ◆ Reteaching Activity, p. 156 Independent Practice, p. 155 Language Arts Connection, p. 202 | |
| | | Test A, p. 157 Test B, p. 158 | Color Transparencies #12a and #12b |
| | | | Unit Test |

◆ Basic / ▲ Advanced / All other masters are for use by all students.

# *You Are Important*

## For Exceptional Students

## ESL/LEP

**Chapter 12/Lesson 1, Page 192**
To help students understand the word *special* have them write the word vertically down the side of a piece of paper. Students then write descriptive words about themselves that begin with each letter in the word *special*. Encourage students to name unique features or characteristics that make them special.

**Chapter 12/Lesson 2, Page 197**
Have each student draw a picture and label it to show a safety rule they have learned. These pictures can be bound together and shared with another first grade class or with a kindergarten class. Ask students to share what is happening in their picture.

## Gifted

**Chapter 12/Lesson 2, Page 198**
Have students find out what can happen to people involved in car accidents when they do not use seat belts. Students can go to the library or interview adults. Have students find out what the seat belt or car seat laws are in their state and how these rules became laws.

## Mainstreamed

**Chapter 12/Lesson 2, Page 198**
**Hearing Impaired:** Show the student a set of dichotomous pictures (child riding bike in street/riding on sidewalk; child using hand signals/child turning without signaling; crossing with bike between cars/crossing away from cars). Ask student to identify the correct riding behavior in each pair. Have students give reasons for their choices.

# Projects to Do

## Whole Class Science Project

Have each student write and illustrate a page just about himself or herself. Students can include details about their families, friends, or favorite things to do. Include a picture of each student or family if possible. Put the pages together to make a class scrapbook. This may be duplicated so that each student has his/her own copy. Or the scrapbook may be checked out by students to share with their families. The scrapbook can be updated throughout the year. New students could use the scrapbook to get to know their new classmates.

## Science Fair Projects

Individual students could do one of the following projects:

1. Make an *I Am Special* poster. The poster is to show several favorite possessions that are all in the student's favorite color.
2. Have students discuss a cultural difference with the class. Students can share food, costumes, or pictures that identify the culture.

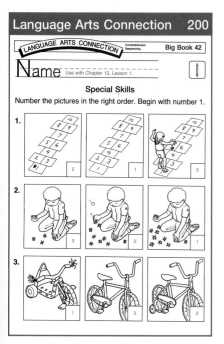

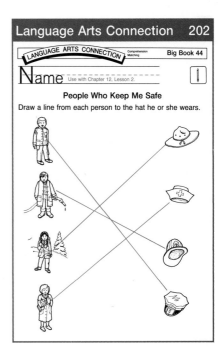

# CHAPTER 12

pages 188–201

## Chapter Concepts
■ Each person is special because he/she has different physical characteristics and different interests and abilities.
■ Following safety rules helps to protect our bodies.

## Chapter Background
■ Your health and happiness depend on your ability to fulfill your basic needs. Basic needs are requirements for sustaining life and promoting physical and mental growth. Abraham Maslow identified a hierarchy of basic needs. The first level includes physiological needs such as food, water, and sleep. The second level involves safety and security—feeling free from bodily harm. The third level is a need for love and affection. The fourth level focuses on a need for self-esteem. And, the fifth level is self-actualization— realizing your talents and developing your capabilities.

## Looking Ahead
■ Ask a police officer or firefighter to speak to students about safety.
■ You will need a full-length mirror for the activity on page 192.

## Look for These Symbols
■ —Hands-on activity
■ —Cooperative learning
■ —Overhead transparency
◆ —Basic/Reinforcement
● —Average/Enrichment
▲ —Advanced/Challenge
SC —Science Center
▱ —Calculator Practice

## SCIENCE
In Your World

188

# CHAPTER 12

## *You Are Important*

Does everyone have the same hair color?

Are everyone's eyes the same color?

Is everyone the same size?

How are you different from your friend?

**ACTIVITY**

### Have You Ever...

### Made a Drawing of Yourself?

Draw a picture of yourself.

Do you look like your mother?

Do you look like your father?

Do you look like a brother?

Do you look like a sister?

Is there anyone exactly like you?

189

## PREPLAN

**Time Allotment:** 30 minutes

**Objectives**
1. **Identify** characteristics that make individuals different.
2. **Communicate** through drawing that everyone is unique.

**Setup**
To conduct the activity, collect the following materials for each student or **cooperative learning group:**
large drawing paper
crayons or markers

## 1 FOCUS

■ Discuss the pictures on pages 188, 189.
■ Display a class photograph or individual pictures of different people. Have students point out the similarities and differences among the people pictured.

## 2 TEACH

■ Read the title and introductory paragraph.

### Have You Ever . . .
■ Use this activity as an introduction to every individual's uniqueness.

**Student Responses**
■ There is no one exactly like me. I am different because of the way I look, and the things that I do.

## 3 APPLY

■ Describe a student in the classroom by naming unique characteristics about him or her. Then have students guess the name of the student you described.

**Close**
■ Ask students to swap pictures and write a story about the person whose drawing they have.

## PREPLAN

### Lesson Objectives
**1. Communicate** that individuals are unique.

**2. Identify** characteristics that make individuals special.

### Science Background
■ The way students feel about themselves and their relationships with others determines their ability to adjust and grow in any environment.

■ Personality is a person's special blend of characteristics. These characteristics are influenced by heredity, environment, culture, and self-concept.

■ Heredity is the process of passing traits from one generation to the next.

■ Environment includes everything around you and its influence on you.

■ Culture is a blend of the influence of the people in your home, city, state, and nation.

■ Self-concept includes all the beliefs you have about yourself including your strengths and weaknesses.

### Lesson Vocabulary
special

**Note:** The activity on student page 193 may be used for guided discovery before you begin this lesson.

## 1 FOCUS

■ Ask a student to find someone in the room who is like him or her in one way. Have that person come and stand in the front of the room and tell one way he or she is different from the first student. This person then picks someone who is like him or her, and so on. At the end of the game, help the students infer that no two people are alike in every way.

# You Are Special

You are different from everyone else.

You may look like your mother or father.

But there is no one just like you.

You are **special.**

190

## TEACHER RESOURCE MASTERS

People can be different sizes.

They can think in different ways.

They can like to do different things.

These things make each person special.

Use Application Activity on page 225.

191

## TEACHER RESOURCE MASTERS

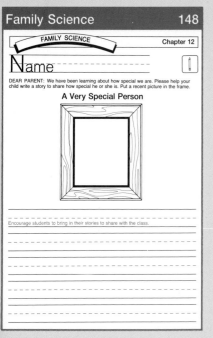

**Family Science** 148

FAMILY SCIENCE | Chapter 12

**Name**

DEAR PARENT: We have been learning about how special we are. Please help your child write a story to share how special he or she is. Put a recent picture in the frame.

**A Very Special Person**

Encourage students to bring in their stories to share with the class.

**Independent Practice 1** 154

INDEPENDENT PRACTICE | Lesson 1 | Chapter 12

**Name**

Draw a happy face on the head if the sentence is right.
Draw a sad face on the head if the sentence is not right.

1. You are different from everyone else.

2. Everyone likes to play the same games.

3. Feelings are special.

4. Everyone can do something special.

5. You are the only person just like you.

pages 190–193

## 2 TEACH

■ Make a bar graph to have students find others with similar likes or favorite activities.

■ Discuss how feelings are special too. There are positive feelings and negative feelings. Discuss some ways to handle negative feelings.

### Guided Practice

Divide the class into small groups. Give each group a picture of a person or a family. Ask each group to think about the physical characteristics, possible feelings, and likes or dislikes they can infer about the people in the picture. Have each group talk about their picture in front of the class.

■ If necessary, use the **reteaching strategy** in OPTIONS.

### Independent Practice

■ Use the Teacher Resource Master **Independent Practice,** page 154.

## 3 APPLY

■ Use Application Activity, "Whose Shoes?", on student page 225.

### Close

■ Read *Emma* by Wendy Kesselman. Discuss how Emma is special.

## OPTIONS

### Reteaching Strategy

List on note cards some words that describe several people. Include words that name physical traits, hobbies or interests, favorite colors, and so on. Ask students to choose one card and draw what that person might look like and what that person might be doing.

### Resource Options

■ Use Big Book, page 42, "Anthony I Can't" and Teacher Resource Master **Language Arts Connection,** page 200.

Chapter 12 **191**

# OPTIONS

## LANGUAGE CONNECTION

**Writing:** Write the following story on the chalkboard. Have students look at the underlined parts. Students should decide which type of mistake has been made by choosing either Spelling, Capitalization, Punctuation, or No Mistake.

Winter is my favorite time of the year.
            (1)                         (2)
<u>In january it is</u> my <u>birthday. It snows</u> where I live. I love to go sledding in the snow. I can't wait for winter this year!

| 1 Spelling | 2 Spelling |
|---|---|
| Punctuation | Punctuation |
| <u>Capitalization</u> | Capitalization |
| No Mistake | <u>No Mistake</u> |

## LANGUAGE CONNECTION

**Reading:** Read *Spence Is Small* by Christa Chevalier to your students. Stop when Spence climbs the chair. Have students predict what will happen. Ask students how they think Spence feels about being so small. Does Spence feel the same at the end of the story? Why or why not?

▲ **Challenge:** Have students cut out magazine pictures that show ways to keep the body fit and healthy. Glue these pictures to a large sheet of construction paper to make a collage.

## Resource Options

■ Use Big Book, page 43, "The Toymaker" and Teacher Resource Master **Language Arts Connection,** page 201.

■ Use Activity Book, page 33, "Communicating."

■ Use Activity Book, page 53, "Whose Shoes?"

Some things make you special.

Think about what you can do.

Think about what you like to do.

[1] What is special about you?

1. Explain to students how a combination of being able to do certain skills and having certain hobbies makes them unique.

192

# TEACHER RESOURCE MASTERS

Math Connection                    153

MATH CONNECTION        Measuring        Chapter 12

Name

Explain to students how to measure using minutes. Discuss how practicing can help develop a skill.

**What Can You Do?**

You can learn to do something well.
You can practice.
Count the minutes you practice.
How do you feel about yourself?

| I can practice | How long? | | | | |
|---|---|---|---|---|---|
| | Monday | Tuesday | Wednesday | Thursday | Friday |
| 1. tying my shoe | | | | | |
| 2. catching a ball | | | | | |
| 3. jumping rope | | | | | |
| 4. | | | | | |
| 5. | | | | | |

## How are you special?

### What you need

large piece of paper  scissors

markers     pencil and paper

### What to do

1. Lie on the floor on the paper.

2. Have a friend trace around you.

3. Cut out your body outline.

4. Think about what makes you special.

5. Write those things on your outline.

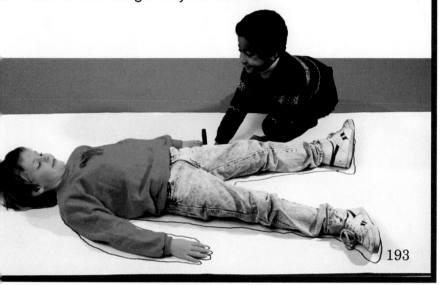

193

## ACTIVITY RESPONSES

Accept all reasonable student responses to questions during any activity discussion.

## PREPLAN

**Time Allotment:** 30 minutes

**Process Skills:** Inferring/Communicating

### Objectives

1. **Communicate** that individuals are unique.

2. **Identify** characteristics that make individuals special.

### Setup

Have the brown kraft paper cut into appropriate lengths.

**Cooperative Grouping:** twos—Assign roles as explained on page T24.

## 1 FOCUS

■ Introduce this activity by talking with students about things that make the teacher special. Examples: nice, enjoys riddles, bike rider, loves chocolate. Have a student draw around the teacher's perimeter. Glue "special labels" for teacher on the teacher's outline.

## 2 TEACH

■ Students can add a new "special card" to their body shape daily.

■ Use the Teacher Resource Master **Activity Worksheet,** page 149, with this activity.

## 3 APPLY

■ Play "Guess Who's Special." Copy some "special" information from a few body outlines each day. Read them to the class and ask the class to guess who is being described.

### Close

■ Review what it means to be special. Emphasize the importance of differences and similarities. Encourage students to verbalize that everyone is unique and special.

## PREPLAN

### Lesson Objectives
3. **Identify** areas for safety awareness.
4. **Discuss** safety rules for getting to and from school.
5. **Communicate** safe practices at home and at play.
6. **Recognize** a need for safety awareness around animals, plants and in inclement weather.

### Science Background
■ The National Safety Council lists falls, fires, burns, and poisonings as the leading causes of accidental deaths in the home for persons of all ages.
■ Medicines and pesticides are the most common substances associated with poisoning.
■ Many states have mandatory seat belt laws. Parents with children under a certain weight (usually 40 pounds) and a certain age must use a child restraint system.

### Lesson Vocabulary
safety rules

**Note:** The activity on student page 198 may be used for guided discovery before you begin this lesson.

## 1   FOCUS

Have students make a smiling face circle and a frowning face circle mounted on craft sticks. Give examples of students engaged in a variety of activities. Have students use the smile and frown faces to indicate whether each example is a practice that is safe or unsafe. Examples may include: climbing on the furniture to reach an object, finding matches and bringing them to an adult, taking someone else's medicine, buckling seat belts, saying *no* to a stranger, or not sitting in their seats on a school bus.

## Staying Safe

Do you know how to stay safe?   1. certain safety rules

Knowing how to stay safe is important.

Staying safe keeps you healthy.

[1]What do you need to learn to stay safe?

## TEACHER RESOURCE MASTERS

There are **safety rules** to follow at school.

There are rules to follow going to school.

There are also some to follow going home.

How do you get to and from school?

What rules do you follow?

. walk, ride in a car, ride a bus, or bicycle
. Discuss with students safety rules for traveling in each of these modes.      195

## TEACHER RESOURCE MASTERS

| Critical Thinking | 152 |
|---|---|

CRITICAL THINKING/PROBLEM SOLVING Challenge      Chapter 12

Name      ✏

**Practice Safety**

Do the puzzle.

**Across**
1. Always wear a _____ when you ride in a car.
4. Walk in the _____ when you go across a street.
5. You may start a _____ if you play with matches.

**Down**
1. Sit down when you ride on a _____.
2. Use hand signals when you ride a _____.
3. You can take medicine when your _____ gives it to you.

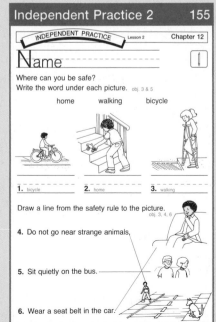

| Independent Practice 2 | 155 |
|---|---|

INDEPENDENT PRACTICE    Lesson 2      Chapter 12

Name      ✏

Where can you be safe?
Write the word under each picture. obj. 3 & 5

home      walking      bicycle

1. bicycle      2. home      3. walking

Draw a line from the safety rule to the picture. obj. 3, 4, 6

4. Do not go near strange animals.

5. Sit quietly on the bus.

6. Wear a seat belt in the car.

## 2  TEACH

■ Discuss various ways to avoid accidents at home.

### Guided Practice

Assign **cooperative groups** the job of making up safety rules for different situations. Give each group a piece of chart paper with a labeled situation. Examples of situations may include:
• two friends are riding bicycles
• some small children find some matches
• a family is at a swimming pool
■ If necessary, use the **reteaching strategy** in OPTIONS.

### Independent Practice

■ Use the Teacher Resource Master **Independent Practice,** page 155.

## 3  APPLY

Have students take out their smiling and frowning faces. Let volunteers give safety statements and have students use their circle faces to indicate whether the volunteers' statements are correct.

### Close

■ Ask a policeman, a school bus driver, and a fireman to serve on a panel. Have students prepare questions to ask.

## OPTIONS

### Reteaching Strategy

SC Put safety rules on sentence strips. Make labels that include: At Home, In The Car, On A Bike, and so on. Ask students to put safety strips under the correct headings.

### Resource Options

■ Use Big Book, page 44, "The Safety Song" and Teacher Resource Master **Language Arts Connection** page 202.

# OPTIONS

## YOU CAN . . . WRITE SAFETY TIPS

**Process Skills:** Inferring/Communication

**Objective: Communicate** some safety rules inferring how to help them be more memorable.

**Setup/Teach**

Show students some advertising pages from a magazine. Have them relate catchy phrases they have heard on TV. Ask students why they remember certain phrases. Discuss how clever advertising helps people remember things better. Ask students to think of clever ways to illustrate safety rules to help people remember them.

## LANGUAGE CONNECTION

**Writing:** Write the following story on the chalkboard. Have students look at the underlined parts. Students should decide which type of mistake has been made by choosing either Spelling, Capitalization, Punctuation, or No Mistake.

(1)
Nancy walks to school She makes sure to follow the safety rules. When Nancy
(2)
gets to main Street she waits for the crossing guard.

| 1 Spelling | 2 Spelling |
|---|---|
| Punctuation | Punctuation |
| Capitalization | Capitalization |
| No Mistake | No Mistake |

♦ **Reinforcement:** Ask students to observe places at home or in the classroom that could be potential safety hazards. Examples could include toys left on stairs or books and lunchboxes left in classroom aisles. Make a class list and discuss how to become safety conscious.

[1]How can you stay safe when you play?

[2]How can you stay safe at home?

1.–2. Discuss rules bicycle riding, running playing on playgrou equipment, climbing trees, and so on.

ACTIVITY

# You Can...

## Write Safety Tips

Think of some safety tips.

Write them in a clever way.

Put them where people can see.

196

# TEACHER RESOURCE MASTERS

**Reteaching Activity**   156

RETEACHING ACTIVITY   Chapter 12

Name

**Playing Safely**

Tell who is playing in safe places.
Put an **X** in the boxes.

1–4. Discuss with students safety concerns pertinent to your area.

What rules might you need to know for summer?

Do you know how to be safe near animals?

Do you know how to be safe near plants?

What do you practice to stay safe in a storm?

## TEACHER RESOURCE MASTERS

**Transparency Master**    147

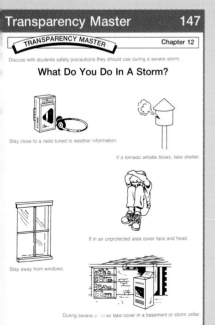

TRANSPARENCY MASTER    Chapter 12

Discuss with students safety precautions they should use during a severe storm.

**What Do You Do In A Storm?**

Stay close to a radio tuned to weather information.

If a tornado whistle blows, take shelter.

If in an unprotected area cover face and head.

Stay away from windows.

During severe weather take cover in a basement or storm cellar.

**Critical Thinking**    151

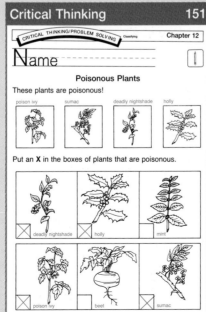

CRITICAL THINKING/PROBLEM SOLVING   Classifying    Chapter 12

# Name

**Poisonous Plants**

These plants are poisonous!

poison ivy    sumac    deadly nightshade    holly

Put an **X** in the boxes of plants that are poisonous.

⊠ deadly nightshade    ⊠ holly    mint

⊠ poison ivy    beet    ⊠ sumac

## OPTIONS

▲**Challenge:** Mount and display pictures of traffic signs and other informational signs (such as danger, quiet, beware of dog, or watch your step). Help students identify the signs and discuss them. Then describe or name a place and ask, "Which sign might we find here?" Guide students in discussing why the sign would or would not be found at that given place.

### SOCIAL STUDIES CONNECTION

Arrange a field trip to a fire station. Ask a firefighter to discuss how to call the fire station when there is a fire and what other steps the students should take. After returning to class, have students draw a map of the escape route they would take in case of a fire in their home. Have them write the telephone number of the fire department on the map.

■ Bring in pictures of plants and animals that are indigenous to your area that could be a safety hazard.

■ Have some students dress up as a lifeguard, a weather forecaster, an animal or plant caretaker and give a talk to other students about summer safety.

●**Enrichment:** Set up a safety community in your classroom. Use tape to make crosswalks and have students make traffic signs. Allow students to pretend that they are travelling around the community and practice using safety rules. Students can pretend to be riding bicycles or be pedestrians.

**Career:** Use "I WANT TO KNOW ABOUT . . . A Fire Chief, student page 199, with this lesson.

## PREPLAN

**Time Allotment:** 30 minutes

**Process Skill:** Communicating

### Objectives
1. **Relate** a bicycle safety rule.
2. **Relate** a car safety rule.
3. **List** other rules to follow to stay safe.

### Setup
■ Assemble the materials needed for each student.

 **Cooperative Learning:** twos—Assign roles as explained on T24.

## 1 FOCUS

■ Name some safety rules. Ask students to relate where they might need to remember each rule.

## 2 TEACH

Have students write and illustrate safety rules on their posters.

■ Discuss how symbols and drawings, as well as words, can be used to give warnings.

■ Use the Teacher Resource Master **Activity Worksheet,** page 150, with this activity.

## 3 APPLY

■ Allow time for students to share their posters with the class. The posters could also be shared with a younger class of students (kindergarten) or the principal might allow the students to display their posters in an area of the school.

### Close
■ Have students share incidents when they didn't follow safety rules. Explain how their actions will be different now.

## ACTIVITY

### How can you stay safe?

#### What you need
poster     crayons     pencil

#### What to do
1. Make a poster about being safe.
2. Tell about a safe bicycle rule.
3. Tell about a safe rule to use in a car.
4. What other rules do you follow to stay safe?

198

## ACTIVITY RESPONSES

Accept all reasonable student responses to questions during any activity discussion.

# I WANT TO KNOW ABOUT...

## A Fire Chief

Christina Gonzales is a fire chief.

She has many important jobs.

She checks schools to see if alarms work.

She reminds schools to practice fire drills.

She makes sure children learn fire safety rules.

[1]Can you guess what she does at a real fire?

1. directs fire fighters in fighting the fire, watches for the safety of people at the fire, may organize traffic control

*Career*

199

## TEACHER RESOURCE MASTERS

### Feature Background

■ Firefighters can be either male or female. Recruits must be at least 18 years of age, have a high school diploma, and pass a Civil Service Examination.

■ Training to become a firefighter begins with 16 weeks at a training academy and 2 weeks of medical training. The firefighters are then assigned to a fire station where they complete a 3-year apprenticeship. During this 3-year stay, the firefighters are periodically tested.

■ Promotion Examinations are given periodically. A firefighter must have been on the force at least five years to take the exam. The order of progression is firefighter, lieutenant, captain, battalion chief, and assistant chief. The fire chief is generally a politically chosen position.

### Feature Vocabulary

fire chief

### Teaching Suggestions

■ Ask: **Why do we practice fire drills at school?** *We practice so that in a real emergency everyone will know what to do.*

■ Review with students safety rules such as: feeling a door before opening it, staying low to the floor, and stop, drop, and roll.

■ Have students draw a fire escape plan for their home or school. Ask students to review their plan with their family.

■ Discuss with students what they think a person would learn at the firefighters' training school.

**Chapter Closure:** Use these pages to review and reinforce chapter concepts.

## What I Learned

Have students read the rebus summary statements aloud to be sure they interpret the pictures correctly. After each sentence, discuss other possible words that would also make the statement true.

## Words I Know

Use any or all of the following suggestions to reinforce the chapter vocabulary.

Write each science word or word group on the chalkboard. Ask students to read them. Add the words to the class science list or have students write the words in their individual science word books. Ask students to tell about these words to help you evaluate their comprehension. Have students use each science word or word group in a sentence.

**CHAPTER REVIEW**
**12**

=== **What I Learned** ===

- You are special.
- It is important for you to stay  .

  safe

- Follow safety rules at  and at  .

  school          home

- Your body needs to stay safe when you ride in

  a  , on a  , or on a  .

  car          bike          bus

=== **Words I Know** ===
**special          safety rules**

200

# TEACHER RESOURCE MASTERS

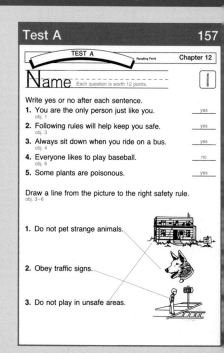

Test A                                         157

TEST A          Recalling Facts          Chapter 12

**N**ame ___ Each question is worth 12 points.

Write yes or no after each sentence.
1. You are the only person just like you.          yes
   obj. 1
2. Following rules will help keep you safe.          yes
   obj. 3
3. Always sit down when you ride on a bus.          yes
   obj. 4
4. Everyone likes to play baseball.          no
   obj. 6
5. Some plants are poisonous.          yes

Draw a line from the picture to the right safety rule.
obj. 3-6

1. Do not pet strange animals.

2. Obey traffic signs.

3. Do not play in unsafe areas.

## What I Know

*Use the picture to answer the questions.*

1. What makes you special?

2. What things do you like to do?

3. How can you keep your body safe?

4. What safety rules should you follow?

201

## What I Know

Have students refer to the pictures to answer the questions and extend concepts.

**1.** The things you can do and the things you like to do make you special.

**2.** Swimming, playing baseball, going on trips, visiting with friends may be some things students like to do.

**3.** You can keep your body safe by following safety rules at home, school, riding in a car, riding on a bus, riding a bicycle, or handling animals and plants.

**4.** Safety rules may include:
Do not play with matches.
Walk your bicycle across the street.
Always wear a safety belt in a car.
Do not tease animals.

## OPTIONS

### Resource Options
Use Color Transparencies #12a and #12b.

## TEACHER RESOURCE MASTERS

Test B                    158

| TEST B | Understanding/Applying Concepts | Chapter 12 |

**Name** Each question is worth 20 points.

Fill in the right word.

| alone | toys | crosswalk | matches |

**1.** Do not play with matches .
obj. 3 & 5

**2.** Do not swim alone .
obj. 3 & 5

**3.** Walk in the crosswalk .
obj. 3 & 4

**4.** Do not leave toys on stairs.
obj. 3 & 5

Write a safety rule for the picture.
obj. 3 & 4

Answers may include obey crossing guards, walk your bike across the street, look both ways before crossing the street, and so on.

**The Writing Connection**

When writing their names, students should write their names vertically on a piece of paper. Stress that each person is special. Encourage students to use words that describe what is special about them. When students have finished, they can write a story that explains why they chose the words they did.

**Other Ideas:**

Have students think of someone they know. What do they like about the person? What things make the person special? Students can make a book about this special person.

Have students write a letter to a parent or relative thanking them for something they have done for them.

Have students write recipes for healthy snacks. Make a class recipe book for students to take home.

Have students keep a journal for one month. Provide time each day for students to record their thoughts and feelings.

Students can write a story that predicts their future. What will they be doing? Where will they be living? You may want to pick specific ages for students to write about.

Have students write a story about how it feels to be scared. Students should include their own personal experiences.

Have students write a story about something they have done that has made them proud.

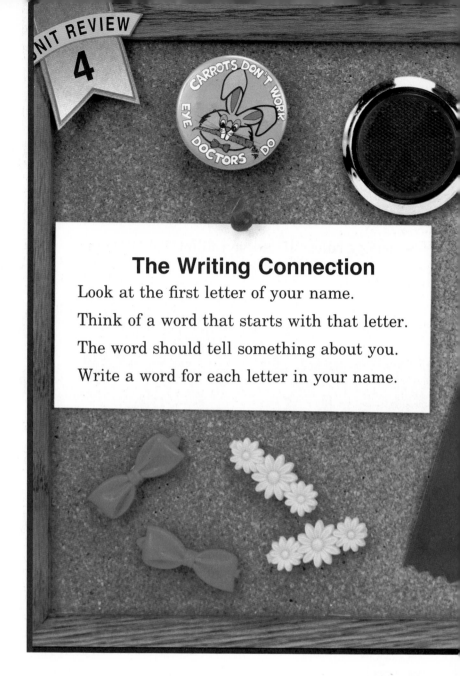

## The Writing Connection

Look at the first letter of your name.

Think of a word that starts with that letter.

The word should tell something about you.

Write a word for each letter in your name.

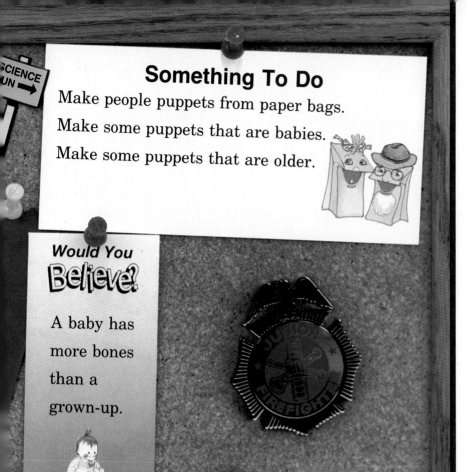

# Something To Do

Make people puppets from paper bags.

Make some puppets that are babies.

Make some puppets that are older.

## Would You Believe?

A baby has more bones than a grown-up.

## Books To Read

**Feelings** by Richard L. Allington

**Jack and Jake** by Aliki

**Much Bigger Than Martin** by Steven Kellogg

### Something to Do

Have students work in **cooperative learning groups** to complete this activity. Have them take an idea from one of the lessons to make their puppets. Have each group use its puppets to perform a play for the class.

### Would You Believe?

A baby has 270 to 300 bones, while an adult has 206. As we grow, some of our bones fuse, or grow together.

### Books to Read

♦ **Feelings** by Richard L. Allington, Milwaukee, WI: Raintree Publishers, Inc., 1985. Grades K–2. This book describes events that arouse common emotions in children.

● **Jack and Jake** by Aliki, New York: Greenwillow Books, 1986. Grades K–3. The only person who can tell the identical twins apart is their older sister.

▲ **Much Bigger Than Martin** by Steven Kellogg, New York: Dial Books for Young Readers, 1976. Grades K–2. A little brother imagines he becomes much bigger than his older brother after being tired of being the smallest.

**To the Teacher**

An appreciation for the nature of science involves an understanding of and experience with a variety of critical thinking process skills because science is not simply an accumulation of scientific facts but is a way of learning how to process information. The Application Activities on the following pages were designed and written specifically to enhance the critical thinking process that is inherent to teaching science and learning in general.

**Application Activities**

Process & Problem Solving Activities

How can you think like a scientist?

You can learn certain skills.

You can learn how to observe and infer.

You can learn to use numbers and measure.

This will help you think as scientists do.

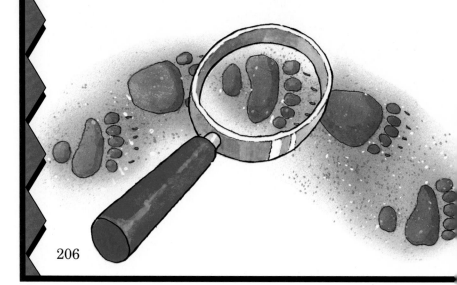

206

# Table of Contents

207

## Process Skill Models

The Process Skill Model activities are designed to introduce students to the process skills that are appropriate to the developmental cognitive stage of students within this grade level. The formal activities within the student text further provide students with practice in utilizing these process skills.

## Problem Solving Activities

The Problem Solving Activities allow students the opportunity to be creative, imaginative, and innovative in finding solutions to problems. Students apply the thinking skills they have learned and are encouraged to have fun proposing, testing, and evaluating their solutions.

## PREPLAN

**Time Allotment:** 30 minutes
**Process Skill:** Observing

### Objectives
1. **Observe** objects and events by using the senses.
2. **Make** and **record** observations of the day's weather.

### Setup
■ Obtain paper and crayons or paints for students to make weather pictures.

▨ **Cooperative Grouping:** twos—Assign roles as explained on T24.

## 1  FOCUS

■ Bring a live animal or a picture of an animal into the class. Ask students to describe the animal using their senses.

## 2  TEACH

■ Discuss with students that careful observing requires using all of the senses. For example, weather observations might include hearing thunder, feeling heat or humidity (stickiness), and smelling or tasting rain.
■ When weather permits, take the students outside to complete this activity.

## 3  APPLY

■ Discuss students' weather observations as a group. Write key observation words on the chalkboard as they are given to you by the students: blue sky, puffy clouds, rainy, and so on.

### Close
■ Discuss the list of observation words. Review what specific sense was used to provide each observation on the list.

---

# Observing

### Skill Meaning

Observing is using your senses. You use your senses to learn about things around you. You observe by seeing, hearing, tasting, touching, and smelling.

### Sample

Ms. Lee's class is observing the weather. Mary drew what she observed.

What do you think Mary observed?

### Practice

1. Go outside. Use your senses.

2. Draw a picture to show what you observe.

208

## ACTIVITY RESPONSES

**What do you think Mary observed?**
Mary observed a sunny day with puffy white clouds in the sky. Since the child in the drawing is wearing long sleeves it is probably not a very warm day.

**Practice**
1–2. Check student drawings to see what observations students included in their drawings.

# Classifying

## Skill Meaning

Classifying is putting objects into groups.

All the objects in a group are alike in some way.

## Sample

Kevin put his crayons in two groups.

How did Kevin classify his crayons?

## Practice

1. Get some crayons.

   Put your crayons in two groups.

2. How did you classify your crayons?

3. What other ways can you classify them?

209

---

## ACTIVITY RESPONSES

**How did Kevin classify his crayons?**
Kevin sorted his crayons as broken or whole groups.

**Practice**
2–3. Answers will vary. Possible ways students may group crayons include color, size, name, broken or unbroken, used or unused, favorite colors, and so on.

---

## PREPLAN

**Time Allotment:** 30 minutes
**Process Skill:** Classifying

### Objectives
1. **Classify** objects based on similarities.
2. **Identify** the properties used to classify objects.

### Setup
■ Obtain 10–15 buttons, some of which are identical in some way.

 **Cooperative Grouping:** individual— No roles assigned.

## 1   FOCUS

■ Demonstrate how buttons can be grouped according to color or size. Ask students to explain classifying. Let the students participate in deciding which buttons should go in each group.

## 2   TEACH

 You may need to help students decide other ways to classify their crayons. These may include classifying by size, by the first letter of the name of the color, or by whether they are broken or unbroken, used or unused.

## 3   APPLY

■ Group a set of objects. Show the group to students. Have students figure out how you have classified the objects.

### Close
■ Have students explain the properties they used to classify each group.

pages 210, 211

# PREPLAN

**Time Allotment:** 30 minutes
**Process Skill:** Inferring

## Objective
1. **Make** an inference using a set of observed clues.

## Setup
■ Obtain a set of animal track cards or a book that illustrates animal tracks. An encyclopedia is a good source. This can be used as a reference by students.
■ Before the lesson begins, prepare a set of "mysterious" footprints somewhere in the classroom. Use construction paper, white powder, or some other material that is easy to clean up.

**Cooperative Grouping:** individual—No roles assigned.

# 1  FOCUS

Show the students the footprints that "mysteriously" appeared in the room. Have them piece together clues concerning who or what made the footprints. Tell students that they are using inferences to explain their observations. Be sure students understand that inferring is based on observations.

# 2  TEACH

■ Ask students if they can infer what may have happened in the illustration on student page 210. After students have made several responses point out that the larger animal tracks were made by a bear. Ask students to infer how they know that the smaller animal was frightened away. Lead students to discover how the tracks have marks that indicate that the smaller animal ran away.

---

# Inferring

## Skill Meaning

Inferring is using what you observe to explain what has happened.

## Sample

Bobby and Linda went for a walk.

They saw these animal tracks.

Linda observed the tracks.

Bobby inferred what might have happened.

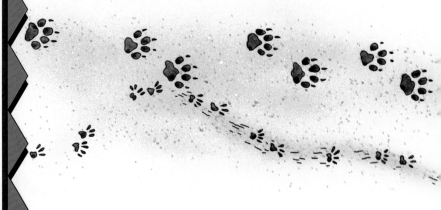

"Two animals made these tracks," Linda said.

"One was big and one was small."

"The small animal was scared away," said Bobby.

210

---

## Practice

**1.** Look at the tracks below.

Write what you think happened.

**2.** Look at these tracks.

Write what you think happened.

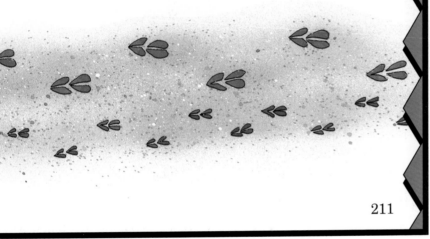

211

## 3 APPLY

■ Give students time to think about the tracks on page 211. Ask them to make inferences about these tracks.

**Close**
■ Discuss how police officers might use footprints or fingerprints to solve crimes.

# ACTIVITY RESPONSES

**Practice**
**1.** A bear and a raccoon were both walking in the area but at different times of the day.
**2.** An adult deer and a younger deer walked through the area probably together.

page 212

# PREPLAN

**Time Allotment:** 30 minutes

**Process Skill:** Communicating

## Objective

1. **Communicate** about an object by means of writing and drawing.

## Setup

■ Obtain a large sheet of paper to write a group poem.

■ Obtain a surprise pet or natural object such as a seashell or a bird's nest.

**Cooperative Grouping:** individual— No roles assigned.

# 1  FOCUS

■ Ask: **In what ways might I communicate, or tell you about a surprise?** *Write on the chalkboard, draw a picture, write a poem, or sing a song.* Tell about your surprise using one suggestion.

# 2  TEACH

■ Read the poem with students. Brainstorm with them other natural objects about which they can write a poem.

# 3  APPLY

SC Have students write their names down the side of a piece of paper. Have them write a poem about themselves.

## Close

■ Ask students to discuss the ways they used the skill of communicating in this activity.

---

# Communicating

**Skill Meaning**

Communicating is telling what you know by speaking, writing, or drawing pictures.

**Sample**

Doug's class was learning about stars.

He wrote a poem about what he learned.

**S**ilvery

**T**winkling

**A**t night

**R**eal far away

**S**hining bright

**Practice**

1. Think about an object you like in nature. Write a poem about it.

2. Read your poem to the class.

3. Draw a picture of your object.

212

## ACTIVITY RESPONSES

**Practice**

1. Encourage students to express themselves thoughtfully in their poems. Students may write about a favorite animal, something in the sky, the ocean, or a forest.

# Measuring

## Skill Meaning

Measuring is finding out how large an object is, how much an object holds, or how long an object is. The object is compared to a unit of measure such as a centimeter.

## Sample

Mr. Smith's students measured some objects. Here is what they measured.

Book  20 cm          Crayon  10 cm          Blackboard eraser  15 cm

## Practice

1. Measure your ✏️ and your 👞 Use a metric ruler.

2. How long is your pencil?

3. How long is your shoe?

213

## ACTIVITY RESPONSES

**Practice**
1. Answers will vary. Check students' work.

## PREPLAN

**Time Allotment:** 30 minutes
**Process Skill:** Measuring

### Objectives
1. **Measure** objects with a centimeter ruler.
2. **Recognize** the centimeter as a standard unit of measurement.

### Setup
■ Obtain centimeter rulers.

🔲 **Cooperative Grouping:** twos—Assign roles as explained on page T24.

## 1   FOCUS

🔲 Have three students use a metric ruler to measure the same pencil. Compare their measurements. Point out that the measurements should be the same because the students are using the same standard unit, the centimeter, and the same pencil.

## 2   TEACH

■ Ask: **Why might you expect to get different measurements for the shoes and pencils, even though the same unit of measurement is being used?** *People's shoe size and the pencils they use may be different.*

## 3   APPLY

■ Have students predict how many centimeters wide their desks are. Then have them measure to check their predictions.

### Close
■ Discuss what else is measured besides length such as weight, temperature, ingredients of a recipe, and so on.

## PREPLAN

**Time Allotment:** 20 minutes
**Process Skill:** Using Numbers

### Objectives
1. **Count** and **record** the number of objects in a given quantity of objects.
2. **Add** the total number of objects in a given quantity of objects.

### Setup
■ Obtain buttons, blocks, beans, or other sets of objects suitable for counting.

▨ **Cooperative Grouping:** twos—Assign roles as explained on page T24.

## 1   FOCUS

▨ Provide students with objects to count. Have them demonstrate counting, adding, and subtracting with objects such as buttons, blocks, or beans. Discuss the definition of using numbers.

## 2   TEACH

■ Have students add and subtract some combinations of legs shown in the pictures. When all the legs are added together, the total is *24*.

## 3   APPLY

■ Direct students to count the two-legged, four-legged, and six-legged animals separately and then add the totals all together.

---

# Using Numbers

### Skill Meaning

Using numbers includes ordering, counting, adding, subtracting, multiplying, and dividing numbers.

### Sample

Ms. Carson's class visited the farm.

The students counted the legs on each animal.

How many legs did they count?

214

## Practice

1. Pretend you visited the jungle.

   How many animals have 2 legs?

   How many animals have 4 legs?

   How many legs are there in all?

2. Draw your favorite animal.

   How many legs does it have?

215

**Close**

■ Focus on the class members themselves to practice using numbers. Ask: **How many boys are in our room? How many girls? How many noses are there in the room? How many ears? How many girls have short hair? How many boys are wearing sneakers?** Make sure students understand that the answer to each of these involves the use of numbers.

## ACTIVITY RESPONSES

**Practice**

1. . . . animals with 2 legs? ___2___
   . . . animals with 4 legs? ___6___
   . . . in all? ___40___
2. Check student answers.

## PREPLAN

**Time Allotment:** 20 minutes
**Process Skills:** Observing/Inferring

### Objectives
1. **Identify** pictorial clues.
2. **Draw** a conclusion from the clues.

### Setup
■ Obtain several postcards with location photographs on the front.

Cooperative Grouping: individual— No roles assigned.

## 1  FOCUS

■ Tell the students that people often send postcards from a place they are visiting. On the postcard they write a short message. Ask if anyone has ever sent or received a postcard. Have students share their experiences.

## 2  TEACH

■ Have students silently read The Scene as you read it aloud. Then have students read Find Out. Allow the students to offer suggestions on how to find out about Emily.

## 3  APPLY

■ Allow students to tell from where they think Emily sent her card. Discuss the clues used to make their conclusions. Display several postcards. Have students tell where they think each card came from. Have students discuss the clues they used to draw their conclusions.

### Close
Have students design their own postcards for a place they would like to visit.

---

# Do You Have a Clue?

Use after page 8.

### You Will Need

paper • pencil • crayons

### The Scene

The mail came.

You got a postcard.

It was from Emily.

She wrote "I wish you were here."

She didn't tell you where she was.

### Find Out

Where is Emily?

How can you find out?

### Solve

Tell where Emily went.

How do you know?

216

## ACTIVITY RESPONSES

**Find Out**
Emily is on vacation at the beach. Use inferences and observations.

**Solve**
1.–2. By using the clues on the postcard, the palm trees, ocean waves, sand pail and shovel, students can infer where Emily is.

# Feed the Birds

Use after page 44.

## You Will Need

empty grapefruit half • yarn or string

bird food • pencil

## The Scene

Snow is on the ground.

You see two birds.

They might be hungry.

## Find Out

How can you help the birds get food?

## Solve

Tell what birds eat.

Find out what they like best.

Draw the place where you put your bird feeder.

Draw the tree, the feeder, and the birds.

217

## ACTIVITY RESPONSES

**Find Out**
Make a bird feeder.

**Solve**
Check students drawings to see how students have observed birds and food for feeders.

## PREPLAN

**Time Allotment:** 30 minutes

**Process Skills:** Observing/Inferring

### Objectives
1. **Identify** foods for birds.
2. **Construct** a bird feeder.

### Setup
■ Ask each student to bring in an empty grapefruit half. Make four holes opposite each other through the side of each grapefruit. Obtain a ball of yarn.

🏠 **Cooperative Grouping:** individual— No roles assigned.

## 1 FOCUS

■ Have students read the section The Scene. Ask: **Why do you think the birds might be hungry?** *Food is hard to find when the ground is covered with snow.*

## 2 TEACH

✂️ Direct students to string the ends of each piece of yarn through opposite holes in the grapefruit and tie a knot at each end.

■ Students may fill the feeders with seeds, cereal, or bread crumbs.

## 3 APPLY

■ Ask students to tell what kind of food they put in their feeders. Ask them if birds liked the food and what kinds of birds they saw.

### Close
■ Explain that when food is hard to find birds depend on people to provide food.

page 218

# PREPLAN

**Time Allotment:** 45 minutes

**Process Skills:** Observing/Communicating

## Objectives
1. **List** features of the school grounds.
2. **Make** a drawing of these features.

## Setup
■ Prepare chart-sized paper that has a sample letter from a child who attends school in a different environment.

**Cooperative Grouping:** individual— No roles assigned.

## 1 FOCUS

■ Have students read The Scene. Read the sample letter you prepared that describes the writer's school and grounds.

## 2 TEACH

Have a student read Find Out. Take students on a walk around the school grounds. When you return to the classroom, have students list some features they saw during the walk. Then, students can draw pictures of the school grounds.

## 3 APPLY

■ Prepare a class letter to the student who wrote the letter. Use it on a bulletin board and display the class pictures.

## Close
■ Compare and contrast class pictures to find similarities and differences in the features illustrated and their placement.

---

# Outdoor Spaces

Use after page 59.

## You Will Need

paper • pencil • crayons

## The Scene

You take the mail out of the box.

Today there is a letter for you.

Your friend wrote about his school.

## Find Out

How can you show what is around your school?

## Solve

Make a list of what you see.

Make a drawing of your school.

218

## ACTIVITY RESPONSES

**Find Out**
Make a drawing, a list, or a map.

**Solve**
Students can write a letter to a relative or friend and mail their drawings.

# Making a Land Map

Use after page 97.

## You Will Need

pencil • crayons

## The Scene

You have a secret hideout.

Your friend wants to see it.

Your friend needs a map.

## Find Out

How can you make a map?

## Solve

Use symbols to draw your map.

Here are some symbols you can use.

Mark your hideout with an X.

219

---

# ACTIVITY RESPONSES

**Find Out**
Think about what features are located in any area. Use symbols to represent the features. Place the symbols in an appropriate proximity to represent their location to one another.

**Solve**
Check student maps and ask them to identify their symbols.

---

## PREPLAN

**Time Allotment:** 30 minutes
**Process Skill:** Communicating

### Objectives
1. **Communicate** what land features might be found on a map.
2. **Construct** a map using symbols.

### Setup
**Cooperative Grouping:** individual—No roles assigned.

## 1  FOCUS

■ Prepare a map of the classroom. Use symbols to identify certain recognizable areas. Give each student a copy of the map and ask them to interpret the symbols. Ask them to suggest other symbols you could have used.

## 2  TEACH

■ Have students read The Scene and Find Out.
■ Explain what a legend is and how it explains what the symbols represent.
■ Have students pretend that they have a hideout in their neighborhood. Ask them to make a map and a legend.

## 3  APPLY

■ Ask students about other symbols they could use in identifying land features such as fields, volcanoes, islands, and so on. Use these symbols to make a class map of an imaginary place.

**Close**
■ Ask students to compare their maps with each other.

## PREPLAN

**Time Allotment:** 3 ten-minute periods
**Process Skills:** Observing/Using Numbers/Predicting/Inferring

### Objectives

1. **Observe** the recorded time that the sun rises.
2. **Infer** that the time of sunrise changes.

### Setup

■ Obtain a copy of a local daily newspaper for four days.

⊞**Cooperative Grouping:** individual—No roles assigned.

## 1  FOCUS

■ Have student read The Scene. Ask: **What does the word sunrise mean?**

## 2  TEACH

■ Have students read Find Out. Help students locate in a newspaper and read the sunrise time for that morning. Have students record the time. Help students find and record sunrise times for the next two days. Discuss the change in time. Help students predict what time the sun will rise on Saturday.

## 3  APPLY

■ Check the time of Saturday's sunrise. Have students check their predictions.

### Close

SC Continue checking sunrise times as a class project to observe how it changes.

# Sun's Up! Get Up!

Use after page 110.

### You Will Need

pencil • newspaper

### The Scene

You are going fishing on Saturday.

You must get up at sunrise.

### Find Out

How will you know what time to get up?

### Solve

Find the time the sun rises.

### Sunrise Time

| | | |
|---|---|---|
| Thursday | | A.M. |
| Friday | | A.M. |
| Saturday | | A.M. |

220

## ACTIVITY RESPONSES

### Find Out
The local newspaper or an almanac.

### Solve
Check students' papers to see if they have recorded the time correctly.

# Space Kids

Use after page 114.

## You Will Need

paper • pencil

## The Scene

You are to be the first child in space.

You will travel to the moon.

On the moon you will do many things.

## Find Out

What do you need to travel in space?

## Solve

Make a list.

Tell about each item on your list.

221

## ACTIVITY RESPONSES

### Find Out
Items might include spacesuit, air supply, food, water, tools for digging, containers or bags, medicine, or camera.

### Solve
Encourage student groups to think about a camping trip their family may have taken to help them determine what kinds of supplies they might need.

---

## PREPLAN

**Time Allotment:** 40 minutes

**Process Skills:** Communicating/Inferring

### Objectives
1. **List** items needed for space travel.
2. **Communicate** why these items are needed.

### Setup
■ Obtain photos that show the lunar surface.

🖾 **Cooperative Grouping:** threes—Assign roles as explained on page T24.

## 1  FOCUS

■ Have the students read The Scene. Then tell students the following information: On the moon, you will collect moon rocks and soil and take pictures of what you see.

## 2  TEACH

■ Display photos of the lunar surface. Have a student read Find Out. Direct each group of three students to list the items they think are needed for their mission to the moon.

## 3  APPLY

🖾 Have student groups choose a way to tell others about their trip into space. Suggest a skit, a mural, or a short story as ways to communicate to others about their adventure.

### Close
■ Have students put together a training program for their space trip.

## PREPLAN

**Time Allotment:** 20 minutes

**Process Skills:** Observing/Classifying/
Communicating

### Objectives
1. **Locate** objects using observation skills.
2. **Identify** the sense used in finding each item.

### Setup
■ Be prepared to provide any items difficult to find in the area searched.
■ Obtain some paper bags.
■ **Cooperative Grouping:** fours—Assign roles as explained on page T24.

## 1  FOCUS

■ Ask the students if anyone has been on a treasure or scavenger hunt. Allow students to describe their experiences.

## 2  TEACH

■ Have students read The Scene aloud. Review the five senses. Ask a student to read the list of items to be found.
■ Allow the groups to move about the room or school grounds. Give each group a paper bag to store the items found.

## 3  APPLY

■ Have each group make books to share what they found.

### Close
■ Choose an item. Have students use each of their five senses to describe it.

---

# What's the Sense?

Use after page 126.

### You Will Need

paper bag • paper • crayons • yarn

### The Scene

You are going on a hunt.

Your senses will help you.

### Find Out

Find something you can smell.

Find something that makes noise.

Find something blue.

Find something sweet.

Find something smooth.

### Solve

Draw what you found.

Make a book.

222

## ACTIVITY RESPONSES

**Find Out**
Discuss what senses students used to find each object.

**Solve**
Check student booklets to be sure they have matched up the word with a drawing that depicts its meaning.

# A Drink of Water

Use after page 131.

## You Will Need

drinking cup • pencil

## The Scene

You are thirsty.

You want a drink of water.

You go to the sink.

No water!

## Find Out

Where can you find a safe drink of water?

## Solve

Tell how you made water to drink.

Draw what you put in the empty glass.

Draw what happened.

223

---

## ACTIVITY RESPONSES

**Find Out**
Accept all reasonable suggestions for ways to get water.

**Solve**
Check student suggestions in their drawings.

---

page 223

## PREPLAN

**Time Allotment:** 30 minutes

**Process Skills:** Observing/Communicating/Inferring

### Objectives
1. **Observe** that an ice cube changes into water when it melts.
2. **Infer** why an ice cube melts.

### Setup
■ Obtain 2–3 ice cubes and 1 drinking cup per student.

⬚ **Cooperative Grouping:** individual—No roles assigned.

## 1   FOCUS

■ Have students read the section labeled The Scene. Discuss why there may be no water.

## 2   TEACH

⬚ Have a student read Find Out. Allow students to suggest ways of finding water to drink. When a student suggests melting ice cubes, distribute a drinking cup and ice cubes to each. Have students explain what happens.

## 3   APPLY

■ Ask students how they could speed up the melting process of the ice cubes. Possible answers include: placing the cup in the sunshine, rubbing the cup with your hands, and so on.

### Close
■ Ask students why they thought of using an ice cube. Discuss why water from a pond or river would probably not be suitable to drink.

page 224

## PREPLAN

**Time Allotment:** 30 minutes

**Process Skills:** Observing/Inferring

### Objectives
1. **Magnetize** an iron nail.
2. **Write** about how the nail was magnetized.

### Setup
■ Magnetize an iron nail before class by stroking the nail in one direction against a strong magnet.

⬛ **Cooperative Grouping:** twos—Assign roles as explained on page T24.

## 1 FOCUS

■ Display the iron nail and pile of clips. Ask students if they think that this ordinary nail will pick up paper clips. Pick up clips with the magnetized nail. Ask students why they think this nail can work as a magnet.

## 2 TEACH

⬛ ⬛ Ask a student to read aloud The Scene and Find Out. Distribute a magnet, paper clip, and an iron nail to each group. Direct students to use these items to make a magnet.

## 3 APPLY

■ Have student groups demonstrate how their new magnet works.

### Close
■ Have students review what directions they used to make a magnet.

---

# Making a Magnet

Use after page 157.

## You Will Need

iron nail • paper clips • magnet • pencil

## The Scene

Some people use magnets when they work.

You are a scientist.

Sometimes you use a magnet.

## Find Out

How can you make a magnet?

## Solve

Rub the nail to make a magnet.

Use the nail to pick up the clips.

Write notes about your work.

1. What did I use?
2. What did I do?
3. What happened?

224

## ACTIVITY RESPONSES

**Find Out**
By rubbing an iron or steel object with a magnet.

**Solve**
1. A magnet and an iron nail.
2. Rub the magnet in one direction against the nail.
3. The nail became magnetized.

# Whose Shoes?

Use after page 191.

## You Will Need

your shoes

## The Scene

A moonwalk is fun.

You take off your shoes.

You jump around.

Soon you stop and get out.

## Find Out

You cannot find your shoes.

Your friend helps you look.

How will he know which shoes are yours?

## Solve

Tell about your shoes.

Draw and color your shoes.

225

## ACTIVITY RESPONSES

**Find Out**
Answers will vary. Possible answers may include size, color, style, laces or no laces, old, new, rubber soles, and so on.

**Solve**
Check student's work to see that they are being specific about style, color, size, material, and so on in describing their shoes.

## PREPLAN

**Time Allotment:** 30 minutes

**Process Skills:** Observing/Classifying/ Communicating

### Objectives
1. **Observe** characteristics of an object.
2. **Identify** and communicate the characteristics of a pair of shoes.

### Setup
**Cooperative Grouping:** twos—Assign roles as explained on page T24.

## 1   FOCUS

■ Ask students if they have been in a moonwalk. Discuss their experiences.

## 2   TEACH

■ Have a student read The Scene. Ask: **What are some ways you can describe your shoes?** *size, shape, color, laces or no laces, type of material, and so on.*
Have students place their shoes in a row on the floor under the chalkboard tray. Ask each student to carefully describe his or her shoes. Choose another student to find the shoes.

## 3   APPLY

■ Discuss how shoes are similar and different. List categories on the chalkboard. Make a graph using the categories. Talk about the results of the graph.

### Close
■ Explain to students the importance of being specific when communicating to help people understand you better.

## USING THE GLOSSARY

This picture glossary provides context sentences for key science words presented in the text. These words are also listed in the *Words I Know* at the end of each chapter. Page references for the science words appear after each entry.

You may use this glossary to reinforce the vocabulary for the science text and teach beginning dictionary skills.

# Glossary

## A

**animals,** page 20

There are many kinds of *animals*.

**astronaut,** page 112

An *astronaut* works in space.

**attract,** page 156

Magnets *attract* some metal things.

## B

**body,** page 174

The parts of your *body* work together.

**body coverings,** page 23

Scales are *body coverings* for fish.

**body parts,** page 21

Fins are *body parts* that fish use to move.

226

**D**

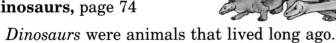

**dinosaurs,** page 74

*Dinosaurs* were animals that lived long ago.

**E**

**Earth,** page 73

We live on *Earth.*

**energy,** page 178

We need healthful food for *energy.*

**exercise,** page 180

*Exercise* can make your body strong.

**F**

**flowers,** page 40

*Flowers* make seeds in their fruit.

**forces,** page 145

You can use *forces* to move things.

227

# G

**gas,** page 132

A *gas* does not have its own shape.

**gravity,** page 147

*Gravity* pulls things toward Earth.

# H

**habitat,** page 26

A fox lives in a forest *habitat*.

**heart,** page 176

Your *heart* pumps blood.

# L

**leaves,** page 37

Most plants have *leaves*.

228

**liquid,** page 131

You can pour a *liquid*.

**litter,** page 61

Please put *litter* in the basket.

**living things,** page 8

Plants and animals are *living things*.

# M

**machines,** page 148

*Machines* help people do work.

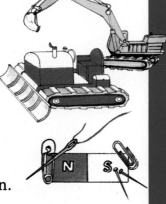

**magnets,** page 156

*Magnets* pull things made of iron.

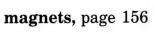

229

**minerals,** page 90

*Minerals* can make rocks shiny or dull.

**move,** page 140

You can *move* from one place to another.

## N

**nonliving things,** page 7

*Nonliving things* do not need food, water, or air.

## O

**observe,** page 125

We *observe* things with our senses.

**P**

**park,** page 58

A *park* is a place for people to rest or have fun.

**plants,** page 36

Trees, grass, and flowers are *plants*.

**poles,** page 161

The ends of magnets are called *poles*.

**pollen,** page 43

Bees carry *pollen* from one flower to another.

**prints,** page 81

We can use *prints* to learn about animals of long ago.

231

**pull,** page 144

You can *pull* a wagon to move it.

**push,** page 144

You can *push* a wagon to move it.

## R

**repel,** page 160

Magnets *repel* when their ends are the same.

**rocks,** page 88

*Rocks* can be made of different

kinds of minerals.

**roots,** page 39

Plants get water through their *roots*.

## S

**safety rules,** page 195

The fire chief told our class about fire *safety rules*.

**shadows,** page 106

We can see *shadows* on a sunny day.

**soil,** page 94

*Soil* is made from rocks and minerals.

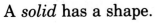

**solid,** page 130

A *solid* has a shape.

**space,** page 52

The sun and the other stars are out in *space*.

233

Your *space* is what is around you.

**special,** page 190

You are *special* because you are different from everyone else.

**stems,** page 38

*Stems* are part of a plant.

234

**sun,** page 105

The *sun* is much bigger than Earth.

# W

**world,** page 60

We should take care of our *world*.

235

## USING THE INDEX

The index is an alphabetical listing of the topics and science words in the text. A boldface capital letter appears before the first entry of each new letter section. Page references for the topics and science words appear after each entry.

Explain the purpose of an index. Help students learn how to use an index as a reference to information.

# Index

236

237

# Photo Credits

Cover: J. Carmichael Jr./The Image Bank **v,** (t) Latent Image, (b) John Gerlach/Tom Stack & Associates; **x,** Latent Image; **xi,** Studiohio; **xii,** Alan Carey; **xiii,** Doug Martin; **xiv,** Cezus/FPG; **xv,** George Anderson; **xvi,** Eddie Hironaka/The Image Bank; **1,** (tl) Tim Courlas, (tr) Steve Lissau, (c) Doug Martin, (b) J. Taposchaner/FPG; **2,** Animals Animals/A. Shaw; **4,** Andy Sacks/TSW-CLICK/Chi-ago; **5,** Karne Philips/TSW-CLICK/Chicago; **6–7,** E. Hanumantha Rao/Photo Researchers; **6,** (t) John Shaw/ Tom Stack & Associates, (c, b) Latent Image; **8,** (t) Latent Image, (b) file photo; **12,** Bob Daemmrich; **13,** (t) Alvin Staffan, (b) Leonard Lee Rue III/Monkeyer Press; **15,** Mark Burnett/Merrill photo; **18,** Tim Fitzharris/Allstock; **19,** Jeff Divine/FPG; **20,** Lynn M. Stone; **21–22,** Joe McDonald/Tom Stack & Associates; **21,** (l) Alan Benoit, (r) Roger K. Burnard; **22,** (l) Steve Lissau, (r) Stephen J. Krasemann/DRK Photo; **24,** (tl) Alvin Staffan, (tr) Wayne Lankimer, (b) Grant Heilman Photography; **25,** John Gerlach/ Tom Stack & Associates, (b) Cobalt Productions; **26–27,** Renee Lynn/Davis-Lynn; **26,** Mark Conlin; **27,** Photri; **29,** Renee Lynn/Davis-Lynn; **30,** Cobalt Productions; **31,** Doug Martin; **34,** Carr Clifton/Allstock; **35,** Michael P. Gadomski/Bruce Coleman, Inc.; **41,** Latent Image; **42,** (tl) Pictures Unlimited, (tc) Rich Brommer, (tr) Roger K. Burnard, (bl) Latent Image, (br) Brian Parker/Tom Stack & Associates; **43,** file photo; **44,** Joe McDonald/Tom Stack & Associates; **45,** Grant Heilman Photography, (inset) Robert C. Simpson/Tom Stack & Associates; **46,** Latent Image; **47,** Kevin Vandivier/Viesta Associates; **50,** Bob Daemmrich; **51,** Ron Sherman/Uniphoto; **52,** (t) Pictures Unlimited, (b) Tim Courlas; **53, 54, 55,** Tim Courlas; **56,** (l) Studiohio, (r) William Weber; **57,** (t) John Gerlach/ Tom Stack & Associates, (b) Lynn M. Stone; **58,** Joe Viesti/Viesti Associates; **59,** Bob Daemmrich/The Image Works; **60,** (t) NASA, (b) Richard Martin; **61,** Michael Collier, (inset) James Westwater; **63,** Frans Lanting/Minden Pictures; **66–67,** Aaron Haupt/Merrill photo; **68,** Diane Graham-Henry and Kathleen Culert-Aguilar; **70,** Earth Scenes/Mickey Gibson; **71,** Earth Scenes/Breck P. Kent; **80,** (t) Photri, (b) Michael Collier; **81,** Photri; **83,** (t) Studiohio, (b) Doug Martin; **86,** Geoff Dore/TSW-CLICK/ Chicago; **88,** Tim Courlas; **89, 90, 91,** Doug Martin; **92,** (t) Steve Lissau, (b) Latent Image; **93,** Tim Courlas; **95,** Cobalt Productions, (insets t) William D. Popejoy, (bl) USDA, (br) David M. Dennis; **96,** David L. Perry; **98, 99,** Latent Image; **102,** NASA; **103,** Comstock; **104,** (t) Tim Courlas, (b) NASA; **105,** (t) Brian Heston, (b) Cobalt Productions; **106,** Latent Image; **107,** Cobalt Productions; **108,** Max Mackenzie/TSW; **109,** Photri; **112,** (t) NASA, (b) Tim Courlas; **113, 114, 115,** NASA; **118–119,** Aaron Haupt/ Merrill photo; **120, 122,** Kenji Kerins; **123,** Animals Animals/Pat Murray; **124–125,** Tim Courlas; **124,** (t) Tony Stone Worldwide, (b) Aaron Haupt/Merrill photo; **125,** (t) B. Kulik/ Photri, (b) Animals Animals/Z. Lesczynski; **126,** Tim Courlas; **127,** Ted Rice; **129,** Studiohio; **130, 131,** Tim Courlas; **132–133,** Grant Heilman Photography, (inset) Linda Dufurrena from Grant Heilman; **134,** Studiohio; **135,** William S. Nawrocki/Nawrocki Stock Photo, Inc.; **138,** Earl Kogler; **141,** (l) Bob Daemmrich, (r) Greg Vaughn/Tom Stack & Associates; **142,** (tl) Latent Image, (tr) Alan Benoit, (bl) Photri, (br) Photo Library Interat'l. Ltd./Stock Imagery; **146,** Ted Rice; **147,** Richard Hutchings/ Photo Researchers; **148,** (l) Larry Lefever from Grant Heilman, (r) Doug Martin; **149,** (t, br) Studiohio, (bl) Bob Daemmrich; **150,** Aaron Haupt/Merrill photo; **151,** Tom Tracy; **154, 155,** Kenji Kerins; **156,** Cobalt Productions; **157,** Frank Cezus; **158,** Studiohio; **159, 160, 162, 163,** Cobalt Productions; **164–165,** Studiohio; **164,** (l) Aaron Haupt/Merrill photo, (r) Studiohio; **165,** Studiohio; **168–169,** Aaron Haupt/ Merrill photo; **170,** Diane Graham-Henry and Kathleen Culbert-Aguilar; **172,** Earl Kogler; **173,** Dan Rest; **176,** (l) Albert Ramos, (r) Red Rice; **178,** (t) Ted Rice, (b) Gerard Photography; **179, 182,** Studiohio; **183,** Tim Courlas; **184,** Stu-

239

240